ALGEBRAIC THEORY OF MEASURE AND INTEGRATION

BY

C. CARATHÉODORY

CHELSEA PUBLISHING COMPANY
NEW YORK, N. Y.

THE PRESENT WORK IS A TRANSLATION INTO ENGLISH OF THE GERMAN-LANGUAGE BOOK MASS UND INTEGRAL UND IHRE ALGEBRAISIERUNG, WRITTEN BY CONSTANTIN CARATHÉODORY

EDITED BY

P. FINSLER
A. ROSENTHAL, AND
R. STEUERWALD

PUBLISHED IN 1956 BY
BIRKHÄUSER VERLAG,
BASEL AND STUTTGART

THE TRANSLATION HAS BEEN MADE BY
F. E. J. LINTON
AND WAS FIRST PUBLISHED, IN 1963, BY
CHELSEA PUBLISHING COMPANY
NEW YORK
UNDER THE TITLE ALGEBRAIC THEORY OF
MEASURE AND INTEGRATION

LIBRARY OF CONGRESS CATALOGUE CARD NUMBER 63-13094

PRINTED IN THE UNITED STATES OF AMERICA

PREFACE[1]

GEORGE BOOLE (1815-1862), in his famous book on logic, *Laws of Thought,* published in 1854, developed a symbolism that today is called Boolean algebra. The simplest example of such an algebra is that obtained by applying to sets the operations of forming unions, intersections, and differences (or passage from a set to its complement).

It is clear from this that the theory of measure, which can be developed even for sets of arbitrary elements, need not lose its significance even for rings of elements of a Boolean algebra.

Some ten years ago, I noticed that it is also possible to construct the analogue, on Boolean rings, of ordinary point functions, which makes possible the algebraization of the integral.

The execution of this program is not of theoretical interest alone. The theorems and the methods of proof that one is led to develop upon closer examination of the new situation are not mere museum pieces. In fact, they reveal relations that would otherwise have remained unnoticed between results found long ago by more pedestrian means. They are conducive, moreover, to an organic, highly elementary, and unified development of the theory.

One could, to be sure, start out with the Borel-Lebesgue measure in the classical manner and, taking advantage of this knowledge, derive the properties of measure and integral in a way not essentially different from that offered in this book. Such a procedure would be unnatural in more than one respect, however, and for this reason it seemed to me more advantageous to develop the theory in its fullest generality.

In the beginning, therefore, the symbolism of Boolean algebra is explained, but not in its original form. Rather, we use the set of axioms discovered by M. H. Stone, which is conceptually the simplest. An equivalent set of axioms is discussed in an appendix at the end of the book.

Now, when the basic material with which one deals in a book are elements of a Boolean algebra and when one is obliged to consider certain sets of such elements as themselves elements of a set, it is important that these elements have a special name, to serve the same purpose as the word "point" in the theory of abstract spaces. This is my only excuse for introducing the word "soma," a word that I have used in earlier publications as well.

C. CARATHÉODORY

[1] From among the papers left by the Author.

EDITORS' PREFACE

THE PRESENT WORK gives a systematic and unified exposition of a very general theory that Constantin Carathéodory began in 1938 and subsequently developed in a series of papers. A list of these papers is to be found at the end of this book.

It is evident from the preface to his book *Reelle Funktionen,* I (Leipzig and Berlin, 1939; reprinted, New York, 1946) that two further volumes had been planned. After the disruption of these plans by the war and its consequences, the author decided on making a complete, self-contained book by judicious selection from, and extensive revision of the material already prepared for these two volumes. In so doing, he was at the same time enabled to make many simplifications and to bring to the fore many new aspects of the theory. It is thus that the present work, destined to be the final one from the pen of this great scholar, came into existence; he was able to complete the manuscript itself before he died. For correction of the proof he had already enlisted the aid of two of the undersigned. After his death, with the consent of his heirs and his publisher, they and the first of the undersigned undertook to prepare the manuscript for publication.

The text is put together from somewhat modified selections of older drafts and later, newly written, parts. It was unavoidable that occasional inconsistencies should arise from the welding together of these heterogeneous components by deletions, rearrangements, revisions, and insertions; and it was impossible to find and relentlessly eradicate them all in the first draft. To track them down, to pursue every ramification of the least inconsistency, to correct every one, all this made the job of proofreading much more extensive and time-consuming than had been anticipated. The editors found some decisions hard to make: piety bade them change not too much; their mathematical conscience, not too little. In any case, they always endeavored to do everything possible both to fulfill the author's intentions and to satisfy the reader's needs.

Professor G. Aumann of Munich was so kind as to help with the proofreading; for this and for many valuable suggestions, we extend him our thanks. Thanks are due also to Professor B. L. van der Waerden of Zurich for many valuable suggestions.

It is greatly to the credit of the Birkhäuser Verlag that this book was published at all. Not only did it decide, in the critical postwar years, to undertake the risk of publication, but it also met with great understanding

MEASURE AND INTEGRATION

the increased difficulties with which the undersigned found themselves confronted after the death of the author and, finally, it issued the book in the attractive format that one has come to expect of this fine publishing house. For all of this, we express our heartiest thanks.

ZURICH, SWITZERLAND — PAUL FINSLER
LAFAYETTE, INDIANA, U.S.A. — ARTHUR ROSENTHAL
MUNICH, GERMANY — RUDOLF STEUERWALD

October, 1955

TRANSLATOR'S PREFACE

THIS BOOK PRESENTS an exposition of the theory of measure and integration in a non-atomic setting, in terms of the algebraic properties of Boolean σ-rings and formal "resolutions of the identity" without recourse (except in the chapter on euclidean space) to any assumption that the σ-rings are fields of sets. The significance of §§ 309-312 is that a proper generalization of the "classical" theory is obtained. On the other hand, the representation theorem of Loomis (cf. the footnote in § 312) indicates that this added generality is not so great as might first be supposed. The value of the present book, however, lies not so much in the extent to which it can claim to generalize "classical" measure theory as in the additional insight its algebraic treatment implicitly affords into the various phenomena, occurring repeatedly in mathematical analysis, generically called "spectral theory."

A cursory glance at the table of contents reveals that two standard topics of measure theory, viz., L_p-L_q duality and the Fubini theorem, are not dealt with. These lacunae can be filled in a variety of ways, however. It may also be pointed out that an enlightening treatment of ergodic theory is included; perhaps this serves as compensation.

The translation itself is rather more strict than free, in keeping with the desire of the editors of the German edition to hew as close as possible to Carathéodory's manuscript. In a few places, however, I felt compelled to alter the mathematical sense of the text; I should like to thank Professor T. H. Hildebrandt of the University of Michigan, who reviewed the German edition of this book for *Mathematical Reviews*, for his kind advice regarding these changes, as well as for his criticism of a partial list of candidates for English terminological equivalents. I extend my thanks also to Chelsea Publishing Company for introducing me to this book and thus launching my doctoral dissertation.

F. E. J. LINTON
New York, Jan. 14, 1963

CONTENTS

CHAPTER ONE

SOMAS

§§ 1-2. The Axiomatic Method

1. The theories that constitute the science of mathematics treat of objects of the most widely varied kind: not only are the real and complex numbers, the points, figures, and subsets of finite-dimensional or infinite-dimensional spaces of arbitrary topological structure, and functions of various kinds, examples of such objects, but so also are the very operations that can be applied to all of these things.

Despite this great diversity of material, there are widely separate branches of mathematics between which there is a striking formal similarity. This is due to the fact that most of the statements that are of interest in any given situation do not depend in the least on the particular choice of objects one is dealing with, but rather depend only on certain properties that these objects have in common.

What immediately suggests itself, then, is that these characteristic properties themselves be treated as the main object of investigation, by defining and dealing with abstract objects which need satisfy no other conditions than those required by the very theory to be developed.

This procedure has been made use of—more or less consciously—by mathematicians of every era. The geometry of Euclid and the literal algebra of the sixteenth and seventeenth centuries arose in this way. But only in more recent times has this method, called the *axiomatic* method, been consistently developed and carried through to its logical conclusion.

2. It is our intention to treat the theories of measure and integration by means of the axiomatic method just described.

In the course of the nineteenth century, largely owing to the influence of the work of Hermann Grassmann (1809-1877), the theory of multidimensional spaces was developed. In addition, George Cantor (1845-1918) created the general theory of sets, as well as the theory of point sets. By use of these two theories, it has been possible to create a very complete theory of measure and integration, susceptible of generalization to an extraordinary extent and, to a like extent, of application. The objects whose measure we wish to find are, in all these generalizations, *sets of irreducible entities,* which we call *abstract spaces,* inasmuch as we call their elements *points*— in deference to the definition of Euclid: **σημεῖόν ἐστιν, οὗ μέρος οὐθέν** (a point is that which is indivisible).

In sharp contrast, the oldest measure theory known to mathematics, which is contained in the first, second, and twelfth books of Euclid, is based on entirely different principles. For example, a parallelogram is there divided into two congruent triangles by the construction of one of its diagonals (Fig. 1) and it is in this way that Euclid proves (Book I, Theorem 34) that the area of the parallelogram is twice the area of each of these triangles.

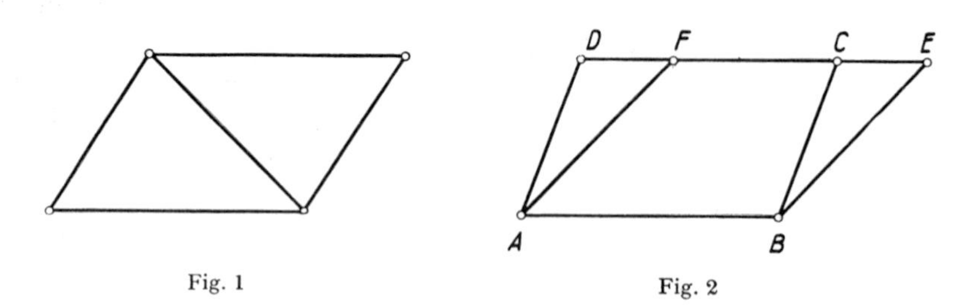

Fig. 1 Fig. 2

Or similarly, by the use of Fig. 2 it is shown (Theorem 35) that two parallelograms $ABCD$ and $ABEF$ having equal base and equal altitude are equal in area.

Now, it is impossible to view geometric figures, which are to be cut apart in this way, or put together in this way, as sets of points. For if one wanted to do so, one would first have to decide whether the points on the sides of a triangle are to be considered as belonging to the triangle or whether one prefers to consider the triangle as the totality of its interior points only; and every choice of this kind leads to a contradiction: for example, in the construction of a parallelogram by joining together two triangles (Fig. 1), one of the diagonals of the parallelogram will either be counted twice, or it will be missing altogether, according to the choice that is made.

Nevertheless, it can be *verified* that Euclid's results and those of modern measure theory *agree,* if we use the fact that the set of interior points of an elementary geometric figure in the sense of Euclid always has the same measure as the sets formed by adding to the interior points the points on the boundary of the figure. But this tiresome procedure does not indicate the common source from which both theories arise.

On the other hand, the notions which we discuss in the next section are tailor-made for the establishment of a general theory of measure, one which contains as special cases not only Euclid's theory but also the most general theory of measure developed in this century.

§§ 3-7. Elementary Theory of Somas

3. In view of the foregoing, we must thus invent abstract entities that have properties enjoyed by, on the one hand, subsets of a fixed, arbitrary set of elements, and on the other hand, the figures of elementary geometry. We shall call these objects *somas* (*τὸ σῶμα* = the body) and shall denote them by capital italic letters, $A, B, \ldots$. The totality of somas occurring in any given investigation shall always constitute a set, which we will usually denote by $\mathfrak{M}_0$. This means that the axioms of set theory—and, in particular, the axiom of choice—are applicable to the subsets of $\mathfrak{M}_0$.

In elementary geometry, one distinguishes clearly between the case in which two given figures overlap and the case in which they do not; in the latter case, the figures are said to be "disjoint." Two subsets of a fixed set can also be called "disjoint," namely, in the case that they contain no element in common.

For every two somas A, B, of $\mathfrak{M}_0$, let it now always be decidable whether they are *disjoint* or not. While in the two cases just mentioned the word "disjoint" has a meaning given to it by the senses of sight or touch, this word will have no such associations for us in the present context. We consider disjointness as a purely formal relation between somas that has the properties indicated below.

If two somas A and B are disjoint, we write

$$A \circ B \tag{3.1}$$

and require that this relation be *symmetric*, i.e., that the formulas $A \circ B$ and $B \circ A$ represent the *same* relation.

We now consider at-most-countable sets of pairwise disjoint somas $A_1, A_2, \ldots$. With each such set of somas let there be associated a unique soma A, which we shall call the *sum* of the somas A_j.[1] The sum of pairwise disjoint sets and the sum of pairwise disjoint elementary geometric figures are, again, notions with visual or tactile associations. What we have said above concerning the word "disjoint" is to hold equally for the word "sum."

We have deliberately restricted the operation of forming sums to sets of *at most countably many* somas. In set theory, of course, an analogous operation is defined for an uncountable number of sets as well. But it turns out

[1] The domain of figures of elementary euclidean geometry can be extended by adjunction of more general figures in such a way that it also satisfies this condition.

that in the theory which we are about to develop, the sums of uncountably many somas need not in general exist (compare § 13, p. 27).

On the other hand, it is essential to establish from the outset the notion of sums of infinitely many somas, because even the circle in elementary geometry cannot be obtained by putting together a finite number of triangles, but can be obtained (Fig. 3) by putting together a countable number.

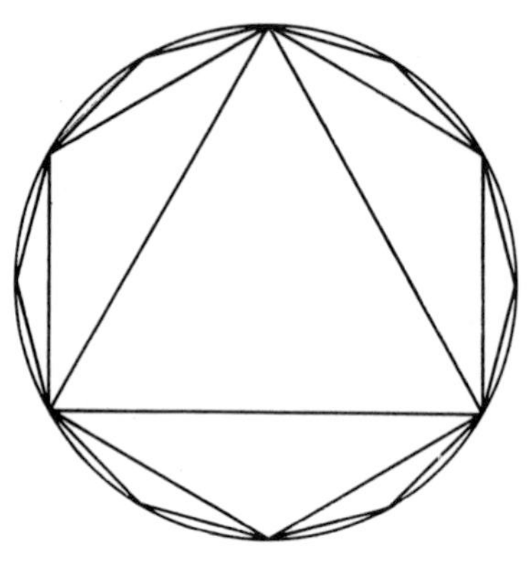

Fig. 3

We denote the sum A of the somas A_j by

$$A = A_1 + A_2 + \cdots \qquad \text{or} \qquad A = \sum_j A_j. \tag{3.2}$$

Now let B be a soma which is disjoint from *each* of the somas A_j occurring in the sum (3.2). We require that this always imply $B \circ A$. On the other hand, no one of the somas A_j (unless it be the empty soma, introduced below) shall be disjoint from A.

The sum A is, by its definition, independent of the order of its summands A_j: in other words, it is *commutative*. We require in addition that it have the property of *associativity* and, in fact, associativity in the strongest sense of the word. By this we mean the following. Consider, say, a system of at most countably many pairwise disjoint somas A_{kj}, and put

$$A = \sum_{k,j} A_{kj}, \quad A_k = \sum_j A_{kj} \quad (k = 1, 2, \ldots). \tag{3.3}$$

By our assumptions, the somas A_k are pairwise disjoint, and consequently have a sum. We now require that this sum be the same as A, so that we may write

$$A = \sum_k A_k. \tag{3.4}$$

It is convenient to adjoin to the set of somas $\mathfrak{M}_0$ a further, improper, soma O, which is called the *empty* (or *null*) *soma* and is characterized by the properties

$$O \circ A, \; O + A = A, \tag{3.5}$$

valid for *every* soma A. As mentioned earlier, it follows from the definition that

$$\text{from} \quad A \circ A \quad \text{it follows that} \quad A = O. \tag{3.6}$$

4. We now deal with the problem of treating in a similar fashion somas that are not pairwise disjoint. To this end, we postulate that somas are decomposable, i.e., that the following holds:

If a finite number of arbitrary somas

$$A_1, A_2, \ldots, A_p \tag{4.1}$$

is given, there exists at least one finite set of pairwise disjoint somas

$$S_1, S_2, \ldots, S_n \tag{4.2}$$

such that each of the somas A_k which is not itself an S_j can be written (Fig. 4) as

$$A_k = S_{j_1} + S_{j_2} + \cdots + S_{j_q}. \tag{4.3}$$

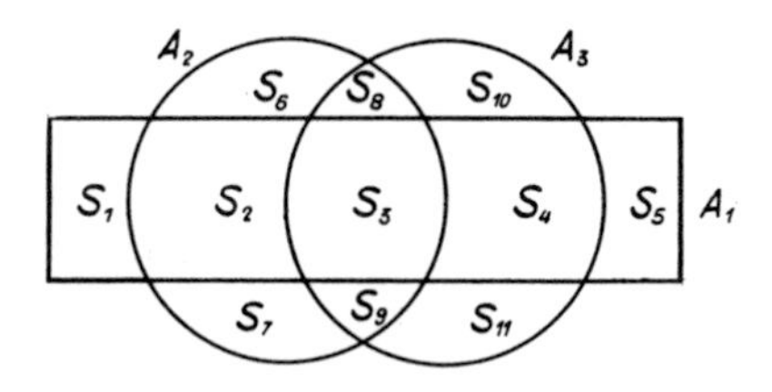

Fig. 4

The last relation can be expressed in much more convenient form if we introduce the following convention: Let S be any soma, and let x denote one of the integers zero or one. By xS we mean the soma S if $x = 1$, and the empty soma O if $x = 0$. Then there is a matrix

$$(a_{kj}) \qquad (k = 1, \ldots, p; \, j = 1, \ldots, n) \tag{4.4}$$

all of whose entries are zeros and ones, by means of which we can rewrite (4.3) as

$$A_k = \sum_{j=1}^{n} a_{kj} S_j \qquad (k = 1, \ldots, p). \quad (4.5)$$

We now define three sequences of integers by putting for $j = 1, 2, \ldots, n$,

$$\left.\begin{aligned} v_j &= \max(a_{1j}, a_{2j}, \ldots, a_{pj}), \\ r_j &= a_{1j} + a_{2j} + \cdots + a_{pj} \pmod 2, \\ d_j &= \min(a_{1j}, a_{2j}, \ldots, a_{pj}) = a_{1j} a_{2j} \ldots a_{pj}. \end{aligned}\right\} \quad (4.6)$$

These integers v_j, r_j, and d_j are all either zero or one, so that we can also form the somas

$$V = \sum_{j=1}^{n} v_j S_j, \quad R = \sum_{j=1}^{n} r_j S_j, \quad D = \sum_{j=1}^{n} d_j S_j. \quad (4.7)$$

If, for example,

$$A_1 = S_1 + S_2, \quad A_2 = S_2 + S_3,$$

then the associated matrix is

$$a_{11} = 1, \quad a_{12} = 1, \quad a_{13} = 0,$$

$$a_{21} = 0, \quad a_{22} = 1, \quad a_{23} = 1,$$

and by the above rule we compute that

$$V = S_1 + S_2 + S_3, \quad R = S_1 + S_3, \quad D = S_2.$$

In this way, we have associated three new somas V, R, and D with each system (4.1) of finitely many somas. It is conceivable that these three somas depend upon the choice of the decomposition (4.2), which by assumption need not be unique.

As the last postulate of our theory of somas, we now require that *for every possible decomposition* (4.2), *the operations* (4.7) *always give the same result.*

Our various requirements are consistent, since the subsets of a given set can be considered as somas. On the other hand, they are certainly redundant. However, since they would lose their elementary character if we were to reduce them to a system of independent axioms, we shall refrain from doing so at this point and we shall make good this omission later (§§ 8-13), in a different way.

5. The three somas (4.7) can be considered to be functions of the somas (4.1). It is advantageous to choose a notation for these functions of such a kind that we obtain a symbolic calculus very similar to ordinary algebra.

We therefore put

$$V = A_1 \dot{+} A_2 \dot{+} \cdots \dot{+} A_p \qquad \text{or} \qquad V = \sum_{k=1}^{p} \dot{+}\, A_k \tag{5.1}$$

and call the soma V the *union* of the somas A_k.

Second, we write

$$R = A_1 \underset{\cdot}{+} A_2 \underset{\cdot}{+} \cdots \underset{\cdot}{+} A_p \qquad \text{or} \qquad R = \sum_{k=1}^{p} \underset{\cdot}{+}\, A_k \tag{5.2}$$

and call R the *conjunction* of the somas A_k.

Finally, we call D the *intersection* of the somas A_k and we write

$$D = A_1 A_2 \ldots A_p \qquad \text{or} \qquad D = \prod_{k=1}^{p} A_k. \tag{5.3}$$

The three somas V, R, and D can thus be thought of as the results of certain *operations*, each of which, by (4.6) and (4.7), satisfies the *commutative* and *associative* laws.

If three numbers a, b, and c are each zero or one, they in every case satisfy the equations

$$\min(a, b) = a\, b,$$

$$\min\big(\max(a, b), c\big) = \max(a, b) \cdot c = \max(a\, c, b\, c), \tag{5.4}$$

$$\min\big((a+b) \bmod 2, c\big) = \big((a+b) \bmod 2\big) \cdot c = (a\, c + b\, c) \pmod 2, \tag{5.5}$$

$$\max(a, b) = (a + b + a\, b) \pmod 2. \tag{5.6}$$

It is easy to prove, using (5.4) and (5.5), that for any three somas A, B, and C, the two distributive laws

$$(A \dot{+} B)\, C = A\, C \dot{+} B\, C, \quad (A \underset{\cdot}{+} B)\, C = A\, C \underset{\cdot}{+} B\, C \tag{5.7}$$

hold.

Similarly, it follows from (5.6) that for any two somas A and B we have

$$A \dot{+} B = A \underset{\cdot}{+} B \underset{\cdot}{+} A\, B. \tag{5.8}$$

Finally, using the empty soma O and the representations $A = 1 \cdot S$, $O = 0 \cdot S$, the equations

$$A \dot{+} O = A, \quad A \underset{\cdot}{+} O = A, \quad A\, O = O, \tag{5.9}$$

$$A \dot{+} A = A, \quad A \underset{\cdot}{+} A = O, \quad A\, A = A \tag{5.10}$$

can be verified. We shall show later that any set of objects that formally satisfy the symbolic calculus the rules for which we have laid down in § 5 is a collection of somas. We next derive some consequences of the last relations.

6. We observe that each of the equations

$$X \underset{\cdot}{+} A = B, \quad X = A \underset{\cdot}{+} B$$

is a consequence of the other. If, for example, the soma X satisfies the first of these equations, then the second equation holds, since

$$A \underset{\cdot}{+} B = B \underset{\cdot}{+} A = (X \underset{\cdot}{+} A) \underset{\cdot}{+} A = X \underset{\cdot}{+} O = X .$$

We have thus proved the following theorem.

THEOREM 1: *The equation*

$$X \underset{\cdot}{+} A = B \tag{6.1}$$

always has one and only one solution, namely

$$X = A \underset{\cdot}{+} B . \tag{6.2}$$

The fact that two somas are disjoint can easily be expressed in our symbolism. For if $A \circ B$, we may put

$$A = S_1, \quad B = S_2 \qquad (S_1 \circ S_2)$$

obtaining, by (4.6), (4.7), and (5.3),

$$A B = O . \tag{6.3}$$

Conversely, if (6.3) is satisfied, then $A \circ B$. For we can always write

$$A = a_{11} S_1 + a_{12} S_2, \quad B = a_{22} S_2 + a_{23} S_3,$$

and by (6.3), we must have $a_{12}\, a_{22} = 0$.

Observe also that, in view of the identity (5.8), (6.3) implies

$$A \dotplus B = A \underset{\cdot}{+} B , \tag{6.4}$$

and, conversely, equations (6.4) and (5.8) yield

$$AB = (A \dotplus B) \underset{\cdot}{+} (A \underset{\cdot}{+} B) = O.$$

We have thus proved the following theorem.

THEOREM 2: *The three relations*

$$A \circ B, \tag{6.5}$$

$$AB = O, \tag{6.6}$$

$$A \dotplus B = A \underset{\cdot}{+} B \tag{6.7}$$

are equivalent, and each implies the relation

$$A \dotplus B = A \underset{\cdot}{+} B = A + B.$$

We can prove yet another result on somas, as follows (cf. § 22): Given countably many somas

$$A_1, A_2, A_3, \ldots, \tag{6.8}$$

we can always determine in one and only one way *pairwise disjoint* somas

$$S_1, S_2, S_3, \ldots \tag{6.9}$$

which satisfy all the equations

$$\left.\begin{aligned} A_1 &= S_1, \\ A_1 \dotplus A_2 \dotplus \cdots \dotplus A_k &= S_1 + S_2 + \cdots + S_k \quad (k = 2, 3, \ldots). \end{aligned}\right\} \tag{6.10}$$

The sum of all the S_j is then a soma A called the *union* of the A_j, and denoted by

$$A = A_1 \dotplus A_2 \dotplus \cdots \qquad \text{or} \qquad A = \sum_j \dotplus A_j. \tag{6.11}$$

7. For the subsets of a fixed set of elements, which, as we have seen, can be considered as a system of somas, the operations $A \dotplus B$ and AB and the relation $A \circ B$ have the same meaning as the operations of the same name defined in set theory. Moreover, the operation $A \underset{\cdot}{+} B$ of conjunction defines the set consisting of all those elements of A not contained in B and all those elements of B not contained in A. Thus $A \underset{\cdot}{+} B$ is obtained by removing the points of AB from $A \dotplus B$.

In Fig. 5 we illustrate the results of the operations $A \dotplus B$ and AB, the significance of the relation $A \circ B$ and, finally, the result of the operation $A \underset{\cdot}{+} B$.

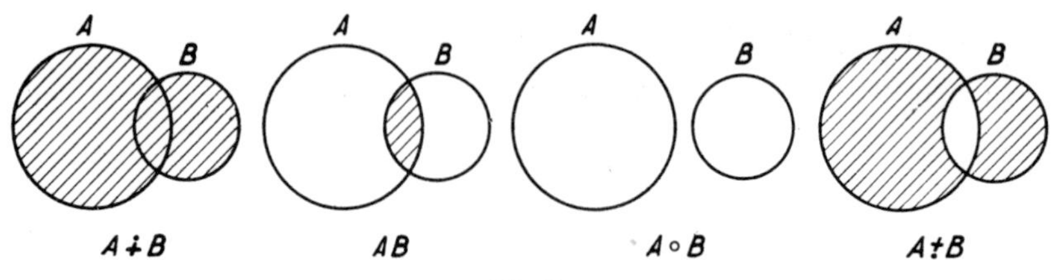

Fig. 5

These operations can be interpreted similarly in the case in which the somas are figures of elementary geometry. In general, however, our somas are abstract systems, susceptible of any number of realizations.

§§ 8-13. Somas as Elements of a Boolean Algebra

8. The fundamental properties by means of which we have described somas thus far are very acceptable from an intuitive point of view but not very convenient for a detailed development of the theory in the simplest possible way. Therefore, we shall now define somas by means of a few independent axioms; as we shall see subsequently, the new definition coincides with the old.

AXIOM 1: *Let a collection of somas $A, B, \ldots,$ be given forming a non-empty set $\mathfrak{M}_0$. To every pair A, B of somas of $\mathfrak{M}_0$ let there be assigned a third soma of $\mathfrak{M}_0$, denoted by $A \underset{\cdot}{+} B$, and called the conjunction of A and B. This operation satisfies*

$$A \underset{\cdot}{+} B = B \underset{\cdot}{+} A, \tag{8.1}$$

$$A \underset{\cdot}{+} (B \underset{\cdot}{+} C) = (A \underset{\cdot}{+} B) \underset{\cdot}{+} C, \tag{8.2}$$

where the equality sign indicates that the two somas are identical, i.e., that the symbols on both sides stand for one and the same soma. Furthermore, for every pair A, B of somas of $\mathfrak{M}_0$, there is at least one soma X of $\mathfrak{M}_0$ for which

$$A \underset{\cdot}{+} X = B. \tag{8.3}$$

In other words, the operation $A \underset{\cdot}{+} B$ applied to the somas of $\mathfrak{M}_0$ makes $\mathfrak{M}_0$ an *abelian group;* this axiom was deliberately stated in such a way as to coincide with the definition of an abelian group.[2]

[2] G. Birkhoff and S. MacLane, *A Survey of Modern Algebra* (New York, 1941), pp. 130 and 131, or any standard text on abstract algebra or group theory. [*Trans.*]

We choose an arbitrary fixed soma A_0 and consider any other soma A. By the last part of Axiom 1, there is a soma O and a soma B such that

$$A_0 \dotplus O = A_0, \quad A_0 \dotplus B = A. \tag{8.4}$$

From this it follows that

$$A \dotplus O = (A_0 \dotplus B) \dotplus O = A_0 \dotplus (B \dotplus O) =$$

$$= A_0 \dotplus (O \dotplus B) = (A_0 \dotplus O) + B = A_0 \dotplus B = A.$$

Thus we have shown that there is at least one soma O satisfying, for *all* X in $\mathfrak{M}_0$,

$$X \dotplus O = X \qquad (X \in \mathfrak{M}_0). \tag{8.5}$$

Let A be a given soma and let X and Y be two further somas for which

$$A \dotplus X = A \dotplus Y. \tag{8.6}$$

By Axiom 1, there is at least one soma B for which

$$A \dotplus B = O.$$

Since by (8.6) we have

$$B \dotplus (A \dotplus X) = B \dotplus (A \dotplus Y),$$

and since, furthermore,

$$(B \dotplus A) \dotplus X = O \dotplus X = X, \quad (B \dotplus A) \dotplus Y = O \dotplus Y = Y,$$

it follows from (8.6) that

$$X = Y. \tag{8.7}$$

We conclude, in consideration of Axiom 1, that (8.3) has a *unique* solution. In particular, there is exactly one soma satisfying (8.5).

THEOREM 1: *There is precisely one soma O, the empty soma, for which the equation*

$$X \dotplus O = X \tag{8.8}$$

holds identically for all X belonging to $\mathfrak{M}_0$. Furthermore, the equation

$$A \dot{+} X = A \tag{8.9}$$

has for any arbitrary A only the one solution $X = O$.

9. We now require that somas can be combined with each other in yet another way:

AXIOM 2: *To each pair A, B of somas of $\mathfrak{M}_0$—in that order—there is assigned uniquely a third soma of $\mathfrak{M}_0$ denoted by AB. For any three somas A, B, and C, the following relations hold:*

$$A(BC) = (AB)C, \tag{9.1}$$

$$(A \dot{+} B)C = AC \dot{+} BC, \tag{9.2}$$

$$C(A \dot{+} B) = CA \dot{+} CB. \tag{9.3}$$

In algebra, a system of elements $A, B, \ldots$ for which Axioms 1 and 2 hold is called a *ring*.[3] It should be observed that we have not assumed that the somas AB and BA must be the same; it is for this reason that we have had to write the distributive law (9.2) and (9.3) as a two-fold equality.

Examples can be given of rings for which $AB \neq BA$ for suitable A and B. For *every* ring, however, we have

$$AB = A(O \dot{+} B) = AO \dot{+} AB,$$

$$BA = (O \dot{+} B)A = OA \dot{+} BA,$$

whence

$$AO = OA = O \qquad (A \in \mathfrak{M}_0). \tag{9.4}$$

10. We now require that the ring constituted by our somas be a *Boolean ring*, i.e., that it satisfy, in addition, the following axiom.

AXIOM 3: *Every soma A satisfies*

$$AA = A. \tag{10.1}$$

Boolean rings are also called *idempotent rings*, since the powers $A^2 = AA$, $A^3 = AAA$, are all equal to A.

---

[3] Birkhoff and Maclane, *loc. cit.*, p. 84, or any standard text on abstract algebra. [*Trans.*]

Boolean rings enjoy remarkable properties. For we have, in particular,

$$A \dotplus B = (A \dotplus B)\,(A \dotplus B),$$

whence, by (9.2) and (9.3),

$$\begin{aligned} A \dotplus B &= A\,(A \dotplus B) \dotplus B\,(A \dotplus B) \\ &= A \dotplus B \dotplus (AB \dotplus BA). \end{aligned}$$

By Theorem 1 of § 8, it follows that

$$AB \dotplus BA = O \tag{10.2}$$

for any two somas A and B. If we put $B = A$, we obtain the general result:

$$A \dotplus A = O. \tag{10.3}$$

The solution X of the equation

$$A \dotplus X = B$$

can now be immediately computed, as in § 6; for we have

$$X = (A \dotplus A) \dotplus X = A \dotplus (A \dotplus X) = A \dotplus B.$$

It follows, in particular, from (10.2) that

$$BA = O \dotplus AB = AB.$$

Combining all these results, we obtain the following theorem.

THEOREM 2: *For any somas A, B the equations*

$$BA \quad = AB, \tag{10.4}$$

$$AO \quad = O, \tag{10.5}$$

$$A \dotplus A = O \tag{10.6}$$

hold and, furthermore,

$$A \dotplus X = B \quad \textit{implies} \quad X = A \dotplus B. \tag{10.7}$$

We call the soma $AB = BA$, as before, the *intersection* of A and B. Comparison of (10.6) with the second equation of (5.10) indicates that it was indeed not misleading, in § 8, to call the operation $A \dotplus B$, conjunction.

11. We now introduce the following definition.

DEFINITION 1: *A soma A is called a subsoma of the soma B if*

$$AB = A. \tag{11.1}$$

To express that A is a subsoma of B, we write

$$A \subseteqq B \quad \textit{or} \quad B \supseteqq A. \tag{11.2}$$

If A and B are two distinct somas for which $A \subseteqq B$, we shall also write

$$A \subset B \quad \textit{or} \quad B \supset A \tag{11.3}$$

and we shall say that A is a proper subsoma of B.

The relation $A \subseteqq B$ has the following properties: First, (10.1) insures that

$$A \subseteqq A; \tag{11.4}$$

second, if we have simultaneously

$$A \subseteqq B \quad \text{and} \quad B \subseteqq C,$$

then, by assumption,

$$AB = A, \ BC = B,$$

so that

$$AC = (AB)\,C = A(BC) = AB = A.$$

Thus $A \subseteqq C$ also holds, and we have proved that

$$A \subseteqq B \text{ and } B \subseteqq C \text{ imply } A \subseteqq C. \tag{11.7}$$

Let us now introduce the following definition.

DEFINITION 2: *A set $\mathfrak{M}_0$ is called partially ordered if a relation $A \subseteqq B$ is defined for certain pairs of elements A, B of $\mathfrak{M}_0$ in such a way that both*

$$A \subseteqq A \ \textit{for all} \ A \in \mathfrak{M}_0 \tag{11.6}$$

and

$$\textit{if } A \subseteqq B \textit{ and } B \subseteqq C, \textit{ then } A \subseteqq C \tag{11.7}$$

hold.

If A and B are somas for which both $A \subseteqq B$ and $B \subseteqq A$ hold, then

$$A = AB, \quad B = AB,$$

so that $A = B$, and we have the following theorem.

THEOREM 3: *Every system $\mathfrak{M}_0$ of somas is a partially ordered set for which*

$$\textit{if } A \subseteqq B \textit{ and } B \subseteqq A, \textit{ then } A = B. \tag{11.8}$$

Note that partially ordered sets exist for which (11.8) does not hold. For example, the points of the (x, y)-plane can be partially ordered by putting $P_1 \subseteqq P_2$ if and only if $x_1 \leqq x_2$ for any two points P_1 and P_2 with coordinates (x_1, y_1) and (x_2, y_2), respectively. Thus, if $x_1 = x_2$, we have both $P_1 \subseteqq P_2$ and $P_2 \subseteqq P_1$ without necessarily having $P_1 = P_2$ (cf. §§ 303-304).

We now state the following theorem.

THEOREM 4: *The empty soma O is a subsoma of every soma X and it is the only such soma.*

Proof: $O \subseteqq X$ is a consequence of (10.5). Furthermore, if O' is a subsoma of every soma, we have simultaneously $O' \subseteqq O$ and $O \subseteqq O'$.

Finally, we have the following theorem.

THEOREM 5: *The intersection $D = AB$ of two somas A and B is the greatest common subsoma of these two somas.*

Proof: First, D is a common subsoma of A and B, since

$$AD = A(AB) = AB = D, \quad BD = B(AB) = AB = D. \tag{11.9}$$

Second, if E is an arbitrary common subsoma of A and B, we have

$$EA = EB = E, \tag{11.10}$$

and we can write

$$ED = (EA)B = EB = E, \tag{11.11}$$

so that $E \subseteqq D$.

12. We are now in a position to formulate the notion of the *union* of two somas, as follows:

THEOREM 6: *Any two somas A and B have a (unique) minimal common containing soma, called their union and denoted by $A \dotplus B$. The union can be defined by*

$$A \dotplus B = A + B + AB. \tag{12.1}$$

Proof: Indeed, letting

$$V = A \underset{\cdot}{+} B \underset{\cdot}{+} AB,$$

we obtain

$$AV = A \underset{\cdot}{+} AB \underset{\cdot}{+} AB = A,$$

and, by virtue of the symmetry in A and B, we also have $BV = B$. V is thus a common containing soma of A and B. But for any common containing soma W of A and B, it follows from

$$AW = A, \quad BW = B,$$

that

$$VW = AW \underset{\cdot}{+} BW \underset{\cdot}{+} ABW = V.$$

Thus $V \subseteqq W$, and the theorem is proved.

Using (12.1), we can prove the following theorem.

THEOREM 7: *A soma A is a subsoma of a soma B if and only if*

$$A \dot{+} B = B. \tag{12.2}$$

Proof: By (12.1), (12.2) is equivalent with the equation

$$A \underset{\cdot}{+} B \underset{\cdot}{+} AB = B,$$

whence it follows that $A \underset{\cdot}{+} B = O$, so that by (10.7),

$$AB = A. \tag{12.3}$$

Conversely, if A is a subsoma of B, (12.3) holds, so that

$$A \dot{+} B = A \underset{\cdot}{+} B \underset{\cdot}{+} A = B.$$

13. The notion of union can be extended to collections of infinitely many somas, as follows:

DEFINITION 3: *We say that $V = \sum_{A \in \mathfrak{A}} \dot{+} A$ is the union of the somas A of some set $\mathfrak{A}$ of somas if V satisfies the two conditions*

$$\textit{if} \quad A \in \mathfrak{A} \quad \textit{then} \quad A \subseteqq V \tag{13.1}$$

and

$$\textit{if} \quad A \subseteqq W \quad \textit{for all} \quad A \in \mathfrak{A} \quad \textit{then} \quad V \subseteqq W. \tag{13.2}$$

Conditions (13.1) and (13.2) ensure that the union of all the somas A of $\mathfrak{A}$, if it exists, is unique. For if two somas V and V' both satisfy these conditions, we have simultaneously $V \subseteqq V'$ and $V' \subseteqq V$, so that $V = V'$.

Using Theorem 6 of § 12, we can verify by mathematical induction that the union of any finite number of somas exists. That the union of countably many somas always exists must, however, be postulated; we formulate this requirement as a new axiom:

AXIOM 4: *Every sequence $A_1, A_2, \ldots$ of countably many somas has a minimal containing soma called the union of the A_j and written*

$$A_1 \dotplus A_2 \dotplus \cdots \quad \text{or} \quad \sum_j \dotplus A_j. \tag{13.3}$$

Axiom 4 does not follow from the previous axioms. For let $\mathfrak{M}_0$ be the set of *bounded* sets in a Euclidean space. As indicated in § 7, the first three axioms are satisfied; nevertheless, the whole space, which is not bounded, can be expressed as a union of countably many bounded sets, so that Axiom 4 is not satisfied.

Likewise, one cannot conclude from Axioms 1 through 4 that unions of arbitrarily many somas exist. For example, we take for our set of somas the sets of measure zero on the real line (i.e., those sets which, given any real number $\varepsilon > 0$, can be covered by intervals the sum of whose lengths is less than ε); these satisfy Axioms 1 through 4. But the individual points x of the interval $0 < x < 1$ constitute a set of somas; yet their union, the entire interval $0 < x < 1$, is not one of our somas, since it is not a set of measure zero.

In our theory we shall allow the possibility that there are sets of somas the union of whose elements does not exist. There are, to be sure, certain particular sets of uncountably many somas whose union, in the sense of Definition 3, does exist. A trivial example of this kind is obtained by taking for somas all the subsets of a given infinite set.

For this reason, we must be careful to prove our theorems in such a way that the proofs remain valid even if the unions involved are of sets of uncountably many somas.

§§ 14-16. The Main Properties of the Union

14. The following theorems follow directly from the definition of the union of somas.

THEOREM 1: *If each soma A of the set of somas $\mathfrak{A}$ is the same soma A_0, then their union V_A exists, and $V_A = A_0$.*

THEOREM 2: *Let $\mathfrak{A}$ denote a set of somas A and $\mathfrak{B}$ a set of somas B whose respective unions, V_A and V_B, exist. If for each soma A of $\mathfrak{A}$ there is at least one soma B of $\mathfrak{B}$ for which $A \subseteqq B$, then $V_A \subseteqq V_B$.*

The union $A_1 \dotplus A_2 \dotplus \ldots \dotplus A_m$ of a finite number of somas is obviously independent of their order. Thus identities such as the following hold:

$$A_1 \dotplus A_2 \dotplus A_3 \dotplus A_4 = (A_1 \dotplus A_2 \dotplus A_3) \dotplus (A_2 \dotplus A_3 \dotplus A_4).$$

Along these same lines, we have the following general theorem.

THEOREM 3: *Let $\mathfrak{A}$ be a set of somas A, and let Λ be a set of elements λ. To each λ of Λ let there be assigned a subset $\mathfrak{A}_\lambda$ of $\mathfrak{A}$, the somas A_λ of which have the union V_λ. Furthermore, let every soma A of $\mathfrak{A}$ be contained in at least one $\mathfrak{A}_\lambda$. Then if one of the two unions*

$$V = \sum_{A \in \mathfrak{A}} \dotplus A, \quad V^* = \sum_{\lambda \in \Lambda} \dotplus V_\lambda,$$

exists, so does the other, and the somas V and V^* coincide.

Proof: Suppose, first, that V exists, and let W be a containing soma of every V_λ. To each soma A of $\mathfrak{A}$, there can be assigned, by hypothesis, a λ in Λ such that $A \subseteqq V_\lambda$. Hence $A \subseteqq W$, and thus $V \subseteqq W$. But V is itself a containing soma of each V_λ, so that V must be the smallest containing soma for all the V_λ, and we must have $V = V^*$. Suppose, second, that V^* exists, and let W be a containing soma of each soma A of $\mathfrak{A}$. Then each A_λ, and hence each V_λ, is a subsoma of W, whence $V^* \subseteqq W$. But as V^* is a containing soma of each A, V must then exist and be equal to V^*.

15. The most important theorem on unions is as follows:

THEOREM 4: *A common containing soma V of all the somas X of a given set $\mathfrak{A}$ of somas, not all of which are the empty soma O, is the union $\sum_{X \in \mathfrak{A}} \dotplus X$ of these somas if and only if, for each non-empty subsoma Y of V, there is at least one soma X of $\mathfrak{A}$ whose intersection XY with Y is non-empty, $XY \neq O$.*

Proof: The condition is necessary: for if it is not satisfied, there is at least one non-empty soma $Y \subseteqq V$ satisfying

$$XY = O \quad \text{for all} \quad X \in \mathfrak{A}. \tag{15.1}$$

Consequently, if $W = V \dotplus Y$,

$$WX = (V \dotplus Y)\, X = VX = X \quad \text{for all} \quad X \in \mathfrak{A},$$

in other words, $V \dotplus Y$ is a common containing soma of all the somas of $\mathfrak{A}$ and V is not their minimal common containing soma.

The condition is also sufficient: for if W is any common containing soma of the somas of $\mathfrak{A}$, we see, putting

$$Y = V \dotplus VW, \tag{15.2}$$

that

$$XY = (V \dotplus VW)\, X = VX \dotplus V(WX) = O \quad \text{for all} \quad X \in \mathfrak{A};$$

by the hypothesis of the theorem, we have $Y = O$, so that by (15.2), we must have

$$V = VW \qquad \text{or} \qquad V \subseteqq W.$$

Consequently,

$$V = \sum_{X \in \mathfrak{A}} \dotplus X. \tag{15.3}$$

The distributive property of union follows without difficulty from the preceding theorem, as follows:

THEOREM 5: *Let $\mathfrak{A}$ denote a set of somas X whose union V exists and let B denote any arbitrary soma. Then the union of the elements of the set $\mathfrak{A}_1$, consisting of all somas of the form*

$$X_1 = XB \qquad (X \in \mathfrak{A}) \tag{15.4}$$

exists and is equal to VB.

Proof: It suffices to prove the theorem under the assumption that $VB \neq O$. In that case, VB is a common containing soma of every element of $\mathfrak{A}_1$; i.e., $X \in \mathfrak{A}$ implies

$$X_1 = XB \subseteqq VB.$$

Suppose now that Y is a non-empty subsoma of VB; then

$$YV = Y, \quad YB = Y, \tag{15.5}$$

and the first of these relations (15.5), by Theorem 4, implies the existence of at least one soma X of $\mathfrak{A}$ for which $XY \neq O$. But by the second of these relations, we have

$$X_1 Y = XBY = XY \neq O,$$

whence, by Theorem 4,

$$VB = \sum_{X \in \mathfrak{A}} \dotplus (XB). \tag{15.6}$$

16. The preceding theorems indicate that the rules of computation for the operation of union differ only slightly from those for the operation of conjunction. Corresponding exactly to (8.1), (8.2), (8.5), and (9.2), in fact, we have

$$A \dotplus B = B \dotplus A, \quad A \dotplus (B \dotplus C) = (A \dotplus B) \dotplus C, \tag{16.1}$$

$$A \dotplus O = A, \quad (A \dotplus B)\, C = AC \dotplus BC, \tag{16.2}$$

and the only difference is that, instead of $A \underset{\cdot}{+} A = O$, we have to write

$$A \dotplus A = A. \tag{16.3}$$

This equation and (16.1) *suffice to prove that the equation*

$$A \dotplus X = B \tag{16.4}$$

has a solution only if $A \dotplus B = B$.

This result, incidentally, also follows from the fact that, according to Theorem 6 of § 12, equation (16.4) has a solution only if $A \subseteqq B$. Conversely, the existence of at least one solution of (16.4) is ensured by the condition $A \subseteqq B$, which by Theorem 7 of § 12, can be expressed by the equation

$$B = A \dotplus B. \tag{16.5}$$

For then we can write, in place of (16.4),

$$A \dotplus X = A \dotplus B, \tag{16.6}$$

and this has at least the solution $X = B$.

To construct all the solutions of (16.6), we expand both sides by (12.1), obtaining

$$X = B \underset{\cdot}{+} AB \underset{\cdot}{+} AX. \tag{16.7}$$

Equations (16.6) and (16.7) are equivalent: each follows from the other. Now

$$A\,(B \underset{\cdot}{+} AB) = AB \underset{\cdot}{+} AB = O,$$

and consequently

$$AX\,(B \underset{\cdot}{+} AB) = O;$$

from (16.7), therefore, it follows that

$$X(B \underset{\cdot}{+} AB) = (B \underset{\cdot}{+} AB)^2 \underset{\cdot}{+} AX(B \underset{\cdot}{+} AB) = B \underset{\cdot}{+} AB. \qquad (16.8)$$

The equations (16.8) and (16.6) together yield the condition

$$B \underset{\cdot}{+} AB \subseteqq X \subseteqq A \dotplus B, \qquad (16.9)$$

which must be satisfied by every solution X of (16.6).

Conversely, if X is any soma for which (16.9) holds, we have the equations

$$(B \underset{\cdot}{+} AB)X = B \underset{\cdot}{+} AB, \quad X(A \dotplus B) = X. \qquad (16.10)$$

Expanding the second of these equations, it follows that

$$X = AX \underset{\cdot}{+} (B \underset{\cdot}{+} AB)X = B \underset{\cdot}{+} AB \underset{\cdot}{+} AX.$$

Thus all the solutions of (16.6) are obtained when we let X run through all of the somas satisfying the condition (16.9). There is always more than one such solution, unless

$$B \underset{\cdot}{+} AB = A \dotplus B = A \underset{\cdot}{+} (B \underset{\cdot}{+} AB),$$

i.e., unless $A = O$.

We obtain a more elegant representation of these solutions by noting that, according to (16.7), every soma X must be of the form

$$X = B \underset{\cdot}{+} AB \underset{\cdot}{+} AY. \qquad (16.11)$$

Letting Y be an *arbitrary* soma, we obtain for the X of (16.11)

$$AX = A(B \underset{\cdot}{+} AB) \underset{\cdot}{+} AY = AY;$$

hence one can always verify, for this X, that equation (16.7), and therefore also (16.6), holds.

§§ 17-22. The Decomposability of Somas

17. We now intend to show that the mathematical objects satisfying Axioms 1 through 4 of §§ 8-13 have all the properties described in §§ 3-4 and therefore are indeed somas in the original sense of that word.

To this end, we introduce the following definition.

DEFINITION: *Two somas A and B are called disjoint, and we write*

$$A \circ B \tag{17.1}$$

if they have no common subsoma other than the empty soma O.

The fact that A and B are disjoint can thus be expressed (in conformity with Theorem 2 of § 6) by the equation

$$AB = O. \tag{17.2}$$

As a corollary to Theorem 5 of § 15, we obtain the following theorem.

THEOREM 1: *If the soma B is disjoint from all the somas X of a set $\mathfrak{A}$ of somas and if the union $V = \sum_{X \in \mathfrak{A}} \dot{+}\, X$ exists, then B is disjoint from V.*

Proof: By assumption, we have

$$XB = O \qquad (X \in \mathfrak{A}), \tag{17.3}$$

and by the above-mentioned theorem and Theorem 1 of § 14, we see that

$$VB = \sum_{X \in \mathfrak{A}} \dot{+}\, (XB) = O. \tag{17.4}$$

18. Just as before (Theorem 2 of § 6), the union $A \dot{+} B$ and the conjunction $A \underset{\cdot}{+} B$ of A and B are the same if and only if $A \circ B$. For from $AB = O$ it follows that

$$A \dot{+} B = A \underset{\cdot}{+} B \underset{\cdot}{+} AB = A \underset{\cdot}{+} B,$$

and from $A \dot{+} B = A \underset{\cdot}{+} B$, it follows that $AB = O$. In this case we shall again speak of a *sum* of somas and use the notation $A + B$.

The symbol $+$ in $A + B$, in contradistinction to $A \dot{+} B$ and $A \underset{\cdot}{+} B$, is meaningful only when $A \circ B$.

In view of Theorem 1, we may define sums of several, and even infinitely many somas A_j, provided only they are pairwise disjoint, by calling their union their sum and denoting it by

$$\sum_j A_j .$$

In addition, if $A \circ B$ then $AC \circ BC$, where C is an arbitrary soma, so that we may write

$$(A + B)\, C = AC + BC. \tag{18.1}$$

It is at times convenient to use a minus sign, writing in place of

$$A + C = B, \tag{18.2}$$

the expression

$$C = B - A. \tag{18.3}$$

Thus the symbol $B - A$ *has meaning only if* $B \subseteqq A$*; and in this case,*

$$B - A = B \dotplus A = B \dotplus AB. \tag{18.4}$$

Since we always have $AB \subseteqq B$, we can write

$$B - AB = B \dotplus AB. \tag{18.5}$$

Many authors call $B - AB$ the difference of B and A; however, one can avoid some possibly unpleasant slip-ups by using the term *difference* only if $(B - A) + A = B$. For similar reasons, I have felt free in this book to replace the expression *symmetric difference,* which until now has been in common use for the operation

$$A \dotplus B = (A - AB) + (B - AB) \tag{18.6}$$

by the word *conjunction.*

19. Two disjoint somas A and A' whose sum is M are said to be *complementary with respect to M.*

We consider any finite number of somas

$$A_1, A_2, \ldots, A_p \tag{19.1}$$

and choose some soma M which satisfies

$$A_1 \dotplus A_2 \dotplus \cdots \dotplus A_p \subseteqq M. \tag{19.2}$$

Then $A_k M = A_k$ for $k = 1, 2, \ldots, p$, and

$$A_k' = M \dotplus A_k = M - A_k. \tag{19.3}$$

We now consider the identity

$$(A_1 + A_1')(A_2 + A_2') \ldots (A_p + A_p') = M \tag{19.4}$$

and expand the left-hand side as a sum of products. We obtain a polynomial whose first and last terms are, respectively,

$$S_1 = A_1 A_2 \dots A_p, \quad S_0 = A'_1 A'_2 \dots A'_p. \tag{19.5}$$

All the other terms are of the form

$$S_j = A_{k_1} A_{k_2} \dots A_{k_\alpha} \cdot A'_{m_1} A'_{m_2} \dots A'_{m_\beta} \quad (\alpha + \beta = p). \tag{19.6}$$

Altogether, there are 2^p somas

$$S_0, S_1, \dots, S_n, \tag{19.7}$$

which, as one can verify immediately, are *pairwise disjoint*. It can happen that some of the somas S_j coincide with the empty soma O.

Now it follows from (19.4) that

$$\left.\begin{aligned} A_k = A_k M = (A_1 + A'_1) \dots \\ \dots (A_{k-1} + A'_{k-1}) (A_k + O) (A_{k+1} + A'_{k+1}) \dots (A_p + A'_p); \end{aligned}\right\} \tag{19.8}$$

if we expand the right-hand side of this identity, the individual terms all turn out to be among the somas listed in (19.7), and we finally obtain

$$A_k = S_{j_1} + S_{j_2} + \dots + S_{j_q}. \tag{19.9}$$

We have thus verified the decomposability required in § 4 for the mathematical objects that satisfy the axioms of §§ 8-13. The last postulate of § 4 is satisfied, since for any decomposition of the somas $A_1, A_2, \dots, A_p$ into pairwise disjoint somas $T_1, T_2, \dots, T_m$, each of the latter is a subsoma of one of the somas $S_1, S_2, \dots, S_n$. Thus the somas introduced in §§ 8ff. have all the properties called for in our first definition.

20. Starting with the somas (19.1) and making use of the operations of conjunction and intersection, i.e., the operations of Boolean algebra (cf. § 10), we form new somas, which are taken to be polynomials in $A_1, \dots, A_p$.

Equations (19.9) show that all these polynomials can be represented as sums of the somas (19.7), where, however, the soma S_0 never occurs. On the other hand, each of the somas $S_1, \dots, S_n$ is such a polynomial and is obtained by expanding the formula

$$S_j = A_{k_1} \dots A_{k_\alpha} (M \dotplus A_{m_1}) \dots (M \dotplus A_{m_\beta}), \tag{20.1}$$

which follows from (19.3) and (19.6).

If none of the decomposition somas S_j is empty, then there are

$$\mathfrak{x}(p) = 2^{2^p-1} - 1 \tag{20.2}$$

distinct polynomials that can be formed by means of the somas $A_1, \ldots, A_p$. These numbers grow very rapidly: we find that

$$\mathfrak{x}(2) = 7, \quad \mathfrak{x}(3) = 127, \quad \mathfrak{x}(4) = 32767, \tag{20.3}$$

and $\mathfrak{x}(5)$ is a ten-digit number. Thus, the formulas for these polynomials cannot be written out *in extenso* even when the number of somas is small. Of great importance, however, is the fact that these formulas are the same as those for the subsets of a set with $2^p - 1$ elements.

21. For two somas A and B, the decomposition somas are

$$S_1 = AB, \quad S_2 = B \dotplus AB, \quad S_3 = A \dotplus AB, \tag{21.1}$$

and the representations in terms of the S_j of the other four polynomials in A and B are

$$\left.\begin{array}{c} A = S_1 + S_3, \quad B = S_1 + S_2, \quad A \dotplus B = S_2 + S_3, \\ A \dot{+} B = S_1 + S_2 + S_3. \end{array}\right\} \tag{21.2}$$

These relations are exhibited in Fig. 6.

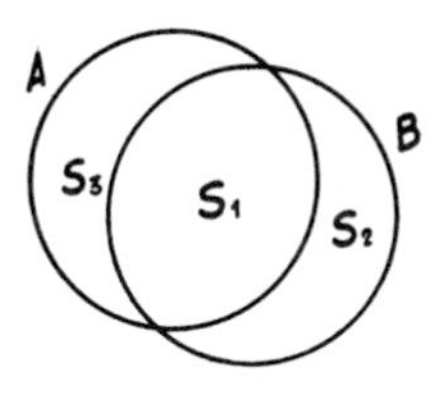

Fig. 6

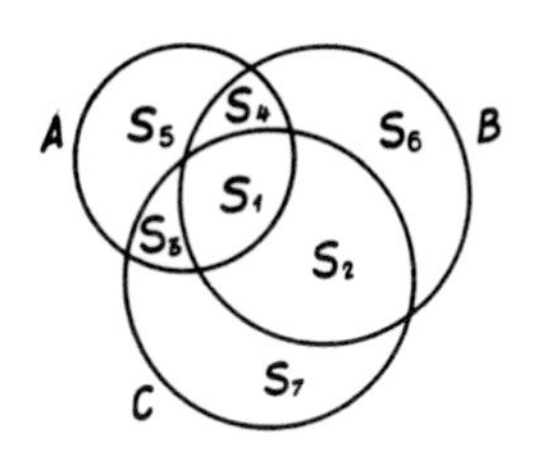

Fig. 7

For three somas A, B, and C, we have (Fig. 7) the decomposition somas

$$\left.\begin{array}{l} S_1 = ABC, \\ S_2 = (M \dotplus A)\, BC = BC \dotplus ABC, \\ S_5 = A(M \dotplus B)\,(M \dotplus C) = A \dotplus AB \dotplus AC \dotplus ABC \end{array}\right\} \tag{21.3}$$

and similar ones obtained from these expressions by cyclic permutations.

Of the 127 formulas which are obtained from these equations by forming sums, we note the following:

$$\left.\begin{aligned} A = S_1 + S_3 + S_4 + S_5, \quad B = S_1 + S_2 + S_4 + S_6, \\ C = S_1 + S_2 + S_3 + S_7, \end{aligned}\right\} \quad (21.4)$$

$$\left.\begin{aligned} C - AC = S_2 + S_7, \quad B - AB = S_2 + S_6, \quad C - BC = S_3 + S_7, \\ C - ABC = S_2 + S_3 + S_7, \\ (C \dot{+} B) - (A \dot{+} B)(C \dot{+} B) = S_7. \end{aligned}\right\} \quad (21.5)$$

From these equations there follow the identities

$$C - ABC = (C - AC) \dot{+} (C - BC), \quad (21.6)$$

$$(C \dot{+} B) - (A \dot{+} B)(C \dot{+} B) = (C - AC)(C - BC), \quad (21.7)$$

as well as the relation

$$C - AC \subseteqq (B - AB) + (C - BC). \quad (21.8)$$

22. Every union

$$V = A_1 \dot{+} A_2 \dot{+} \cdots \quad (22.1)$$

can be represented as the sum of pairwise disjoint somas B_k, and this can be done, moreover, in such a way that each soma B_k can be taken to be a polynomial in $A_1, \ldots, A_k$. For, putting

$$\left.\begin{aligned} A_k^* = A_1 \dot{+} A_2 \dot{+} \cdots \dot{+} A_k, \\ V^* = A_1^* \dot{+} A_2^* \dot{+} \cdots, \end{aligned}\right\} \quad (22.2)$$

we have first, by Theorem 2 of § 14, that from $A_k \subseteqq A_k^*$ it follows that $V \subseteqq V^*$, and second, that from $A_k^* \subseteqq V$ it follows that $V^* \subseteqq V$. Hence

$$V^* = V. \quad (22.3)$$

Now putting

$$B_1 = A_1^* = A_1, \quad B_{k+1} = A_{k+1}^* - A_k^* \quad (k = 1, 2, \ldots), \quad (22.4)$$

the somas B_k are pairwise disjoint, and

$$A_k^* = B_1 + B_2 + \cdots + B_k \quad (k = 1, 2, \ldots). \quad (22.5)$$

In the same way as above, we can conclude that

$$V = B_1 + B_2 + \cdots ; \tag{22.6}$$

but then it follows from (22.4) that

$$B_{k+1} = (A_{k+1} \dotplus A_k^*) \dotplus A_k^* = A_{k+1} - A_{k+1}(A_1 \dotplus A_2 \dotplus \cdots \dotplus A_k), \tag{22.7}$$

which proves our assertion.

§§ 23-24. The Intersection of an Infinite Number of Somas

23. Taking the intersection of a set of somas to be their maximal common subsoma, one can carry over, with appropriate modification, all the results obtained for the union (minimal common containing soma) of somas to the concept of intersection.

DEFINITION: *We say that the somas of a set $\mathfrak{A}$ of somas has an intersection*

$$D = \prod_{A \in \mathfrak{A}} A \tag{23.1}$$

if the two following conditions hold:

$$\text{if } \; A \in \mathfrak{A} \text{ then } A \supseteqq D, \tag{23.2}$$

$$\text{if } \; A \supseteqq E \text{ for all } A \in \mathfrak{A} \text{ then } D \supseteqq E. \tag{23.3}$$

For two somas D and D' satisfying (23.2) and (23.3), we must have the relations $D \supseteqq D'$ and $D' \supseteqq D$. Thus a set $\mathfrak{A}$ of somas can have at most *one* intersection.

The question of whether the intersection D of the somas of a given set $\mathfrak{A}$ exists or does not exist can be reduced to the question of the existence of certain unions of somas by the following procedure: Assuming that D exists, we consider any soma

$$M \supseteqq D, \tag{23.4}$$

and with each soma A of $\mathfrak{A}$ we associate the subsoma

$$A' = M \dotplus MA \tag{23.5}$$

of M. As A ranges over the set $\mathfrak{A}$ of somas, the corresponding A' define a set $\mathfrak{A}'$ of somas.

According to (23.4) and (23.2), we have

$$MD = AD = D;$$

if we put

$$V' = M \dot{+} D, \tag{23.6}$$

we obtain

$$V'A' = (M \dot{+} D)(M \dot{+} MA) = M \dot{+} MA = A'. \tag{23.7}$$

Thus $A' \in \mathfrak{A}'$ implies $A' \subseteqq V'$. Let W' be a common containing soma of all the A'; then

$$W'(M \dot{+} MA) = M \dot{+} MA.$$

Since this equation can also be written

$$(M \dot{+} MW')A = M \dot{+} MW' \qquad (A \in \mathfrak{A}),$$

we see from (23.3) that

$$(M \dot{+} MW')D = M \dot{+} MW'$$

whence also

$$(M \dot{+} D)W' = M \dot{+} D, \tag{23.8}$$

so that $V' \subseteqq W'$. It follows that V' is the union of all the somas A' of $\mathfrak{A}'$.

Conversely, let us consider a set $\mathfrak{A}'$ of somas A' whose union V' exists, and also a containing soma M of V'. Considerations of the same sort as above indicate that the set $\mathfrak{A}$ of somas $A = M \dot{+} A'$ has intersection D given by $D = M \dot{+} V'$. We can therefore state the following theorem.

Theorem 1: *Let the somas A and A' of two sets $\mathfrak{A}$ and $\mathfrak{A}'$ of somas be in one-to-one correspondence with each other, and let corresponding somas be complementary with respect to a fixed soma M. Each of the somas*

$$V' = \sum_{A' \in \mathfrak{A}'} \dot{+} A', \quad D = \prod_{A \in \mathfrak{A}} A \tag{23.9}$$

exists if and only if the other does and, in that case, we have the relations

$$V'D = O, \quad V' + D = M. \tag{23.10}$$

Combining this theorem with Axiom 4 of § 13, we obtain the following theorem.

THEOREM 2: *Every sequence of at most countably many somas $A_1, A_2, \ldots$ has an intersection D, which is represented by either of the two symbols*

$$D = A_1 A_2 A_3 \ldots, \quad D = \prod_j A_j .$$

24. We obtain remarkable formulas by comparison of the theorems of the present sections (§§ 23-24) with those of §§ 14-15. To this end, we consider two sets $\mathfrak{A}$ and $\mathfrak{B}$ of somas A and B respectively; we assume that the union V_A of all somas of $\mathfrak{A}$ as well as the union V_B of all somas of $\mathfrak{B}$ exist. By Theorem 3 of § 14, the soma $V_A \dot{+} V_B$ represents the union of all the somas of $\mathfrak{A}$ and $\mathfrak{B}$. This union can be obtained in another way by forming the union $V_{A \dot{+} B}$ of all somas of the form $A \dot{+} B$, where A ranges over $\mathfrak{A}$ and B ranges over $\mathfrak{B}$, so that we have the identity

$$V_{A \dot{+} B} = V_A \dot{+} V_B \qquad (A \in \mathfrak{A},\ B \in \mathfrak{B}). \quad (24.1)$$

Next, we consider all somas of the form AB, where again A ranges over $\mathfrak{A}$ and B over $\mathfrak{B}$; let us determine the union V_{AB} of all such somas AB. Let $\mathfrak{C}_B$ denote the set of somas $C_B = AB$, where A ranges over $\mathfrak{A}$, and B denotes a fixed soma of $\mathfrak{B}$. By Theorem 5 of § 15, the union V_{C_B} of all the somas C_B exists, and in fact

$$V_{C_B} = B V_A . \quad (24.2)$$

The union V^* of all somas V_{C_B} is, on the one hand, by Theorem 3 of § 14, equal to V_{AB} and on the other hand, by Theorem 5 of § 15, equal to $V_A V_B$, and from this there follows the identity

$$V_{AB} = V_A V_B . \quad (24.3)$$

Equation (24.3) represents the most far-reaching generalization of the distributive law of union and intersection.

Now let M be a containing soma of $V_A \dot{+} V_B$. We consider sets $\mathfrak{A}'$ and $\mathfrak{B}'$ consisting, respectively, of the somas

$$A' = M \dot{-} A \ (A \in \mathfrak{A}) \quad \text{and} \quad B' = M \dot{-} B \ (B \in \mathfrak{B}), \quad (24.4)$$

and we assume that, in addition to the unions V_A and V_B, the unions $V_{A'}$ $V_{B'}$ as well exist. Then, by Theorem 1 of § 23, the intersections D_A, D_B,

$D_{A'}$ and $D_{B'}$ must also all exist, although we shall make use only of the existence of the first two of these intersections.

By (24.1) and (24.3), we have

$$\left.\begin{aligned} V_{A'\dot{+}B} &= V_{A'} \dot{+} V_B, \quad & V_{AB'} &= V_A V_{B'}, \\ V_{A'\dot{+}B'} &= V_{A'} \dot{+} V_{B'}, \quad & V_{A'B'} &= V_{A'} V_{B'}. \end{aligned}\right\} \tag{24.5}$$

But by (24.4),

$$\left.\begin{aligned} A' \dot{+} B &= M \underset{\cdot}{+} (A - AB), \quad & AB' &= A - AB, \\ A' \dot{+} B' &= M \underset{\cdot}{+} AB, \quad & A'B' &= M \underset{\cdot}{+} (A \dot{+} B). \end{aligned}\right\} \tag{24.6}$$

A comparison of the latter relations and equation (24.4) with (24.5), if we apply Theorem 1 of § 23, yields the relations

$$\left.\begin{aligned} M \underset{\cdot}{+} D_{A-AB} &= (M \underset{\cdot}{+} D_A) \dot{+} V_B = M \underset{\cdot}{+} D_A \underset{\cdot}{+} V_B D_A, \\ V_{A-AB} &= V_A (M \underset{\cdot}{+} D_B) = V_A \underset{\cdot}{+} V_A D_B, \\ M \underset{\cdot}{+} D_{AB} &= (M \underset{\cdot}{+} D_A) \dot{+} (M \underset{\cdot}{+} D_B) = M \underset{\cdot}{+} D_A D_B, \\ M \underset{\cdot}{+} D_{(A\dot{+}B)} &= (M \underset{\cdot}{+} D_A)(M \underset{\cdot}{+} D_B) = M \underset{\cdot}{+} (D_A \dot{+} D_B), \end{aligned}\right\} \tag{24.7}$$

and consequently also

$$\left.\begin{aligned} D_{A-AB} &= D_A \underset{\cdot}{+} V_B D_A, \\ D_{AB} &= D_A D_B, \\ D_{A\dot{+}B} &= D_A \dot{+} D_B. \end{aligned}\right\} \tag{24.8}$$

Finally, we compute the union and intersection of somas of the form

$$A \underset{\cdot}{+} B = AB' \dot{+} A'B,$$

obtaining

$$\left.\begin{aligned} V_{A\underset{\cdot}{+}B} &= (V_A \underset{\cdot}{+} V_A D_B) \dot{+} (V_B \underset{\cdot}{+} V_B D_A) \\ &= (V_A \underset{\cdot}{+} V_B) + (V_A V_B - D_A D_B) \\ &= (V_A \dot{+} V_B) - D_A D_B, \end{aligned}\right\} \tag{24.9}$$

$$\left.\begin{aligned} D_{A\underset{\cdot}{+}B} &= (D_A \underset{\cdot}{+} V_B D_A) \dot{+} (D_B \underset{\cdot}{+} V_A D_B) \\ &= D_A \underset{\cdot}{+} D_B \underset{\cdot}{+} V_B D_A \underset{\cdot}{+} V_A D_B \\ &= (V_A \underset{\cdot}{+} V_B)(D_A \underset{\cdot}{+} D_B). \end{aligned}\right\} \tag{24.10}$$

We unite these results in the following theorem.

THEOREM 3: *Let $\mathfrak{A}$ and $\mathfrak{B}$ be sets of somas A and B, respectively, whose respective unions and intersections V_A, D_A, and V_B, D_B all exist. Associated with the Cartesian product $\mathfrak{A} \times \mathfrak{B}$ of the two given sets there are four sets of somas, whose elements are of the form*

$$A \dot{+} B, \quad AB, \quad A - AB, \quad A \underset{\cdot}{+} B.$$

Under the above assumptions, the unions and intersections of each of these four sets of somas exist, and we have the formulas

$$V_{A \dot{+} B} = V_A \dot{+} V_B, \tag{24.11}$$

$$D_{A \dot{+} B} = D_A \dot{+} D_B, \tag{24.12}$$

$$V_{AB} = V_A V_B, \tag{24.13}$$

$$D_{AB} = D_A D_B, \tag{24.14}$$

$$V_{A-AB} = V_A - V_A D_B, \tag{24.15}$$

$$D_{A-AB} = D_A - D_A V_B, \tag{24.16}$$

$$V_{A \underset{\cdot}{+} B} = (V_A \dot{+} V_B) - D_A D_B, \tag{24.17}$$

$$D_{A \underset{\cdot}{+} B} = (V_A \underset{\cdot}{+} V_B)(D_A \underset{\cdot}{+} D_B). \tag{24.18}$$

These formulas also apply in case the set $\mathfrak{B}$ consists of a single soma B; we can then put $V_B = D_B = B$ in (24.11)-(24.18).

§§ 25-32. Limits and Bounds

25. $A \subseteq B$, as a relation between two somas, has the same formal properties as the relation $a \leqq b$ between two real numbers. Thus, Axiom 4 of § 13 is the analogue, in the theory of somas, of the axiom of completeness in the theory of the real numbers. In this sense, the *union*

$$V = \sum_j \dot{+} A_j$$

of a sequence of somas A_j is the precise analogue of the *least upper bound* of a sequence of real numbers. Similarly, the *intersection*

$$D = \prod A_j$$

is the analogue of the *greatest lower bound* of a sequence of real numbers. Consequently, we can imitate the construction of the upper and lower limits of a sequence of real numbers and assign to each sequence

$$A_1, A_2, A_3, \ldots \tag{25.1}$$

of infinitely many somas two new somas, which we shall call the *lower* and *upper limits* of the sequence.

To this end, we construct, using (25.1), two new sequences

$$D_k = \prod_{j=0}^{\infty} A_{k+j}, \qquad V_k = \sum_{j=0}^{\infty} \dot{+}\, A_{k+j} \quad (k = 1, 2, \ldots) \tag{25.2}$$

and we form the somas

$$\underline{A} = \sum_k \dot{+}\, D_k, \quad \bar{A} = \prod_k V_k. \tag{25.3}$$

The soma $\underline{A}$ is called the *lower limit* or *limes inferior* of the sequence (25.1), while the soma $\bar{A}$ is the *upper limit* or *limes superior* of the sequence. Just as in the case of real numbers, we shall use the notation

$$\underline{A} = \underline{\lim}_{k=\infty} A_k, \quad \bar{A} = \overline{\lim}_{k=\infty} A_k. \tag{25.4}$$

For any two positive integers m and k we have, by (25.2), the relations

$$D_k \subseteqq A_{k+m} \subseteqq V_m. \tag{25.5}$$

Hence, for any m,

$$\underline{A} \subseteqq V_m,$$

and consequently

$$\underline{A} \subseteqq \bar{A}. \tag{25.6}$$

Thus, the lower limit of a sequence of somas is always a subsoma of the upper limit of the sequence.

26. Let us denote by

$$A'_j = A_{n_j} \qquad (j = 1, 2, \ldots) \tag{26.1}$$

any infinite subsequence of (25.1). The positive integers $n_1, n_2, \ldots$ are all distinct; we re-index them according to increasing order of magnitude, that is, we write

$$n_{j_1} < n_{j_2} < n_{j_3} < \ldots, \tag{26.2}$$

and we define a monotonically increasing sequence of integers k_p by means of the equations

$$k_p - 1 = \max(j_1, j_2, \ldots, j_p) \quad (p = 1, 2, \ldots). \quad (26.3)$$

The integer n_{k_p+j} for $j \geqq 0$, necessarily appears after $n_{j_1}, \ldots, n_{j_p}$ in the sequence (26.2). It follows as a consequence that $n_{k_p+j} > p$; therefore, putting

$$D'_k = \prod_{j=0}^{\infty} A'_{k+j}, \quad V'_k = \sum_{j=0}^{\infty} \dot{+}\, A'_{k+j}, \quad (26.4)$$

we obtain

$$D'_{k_p} \supseteqq D_p, \quad V'_{k_p} \subseteqq V_p.$$

Denoting the principal limits of the subsequence (26.1) by $\underline{A}'$ and $\bar{A}'$, we see from the last two relations that

$$D_p \subseteqq D'_{k_p} \subseteqq \underline{A}', \quad \bar{A}' \subseteqq V'_{k_p} \subseteqq V_p \quad (p = 1, 2, \ldots);$$

and consequently also

$$\underline{A} \subseteqq \underline{A}' \subseteqq \bar{A}' \subseteqq \bar{A}. \quad (26.5)$$

If the subsequence (26.1) is obtained by a mere rearrangement of the terms of the sequence (25.1), then the two sequences are interchangeable in the above argument, and we obtain the following theorem.

THEOREM 1: *The principal limits of a sequence of somas are independent of the order of the terms.*

We also note that the principal limits remain unchanged if a finite number of terms of the sequence in question are removed. Putting these results together, we have:

THEOREM 2: *The principal limits $\underline{A}$, $\bar{A}$ of a sequence of somas and the principal limits $\underline{A}'$, $\bar{A}'$ of an infinite subsequence are related as follows:*

$$\underline{A} \subseteqq \underline{A}' \subseteqq \bar{A}' \subseteqq \bar{A}. \quad (26.6)$$

If the subsequence is obtained by omission of a finite number of somas from the original sequence, then:

$$\underline{A}' = \underline{A}, \quad \bar{A}' = \bar{A}. \quad (26.7)$$

27. Let us consider two sequences $\{A_k\}$ and $\{A_k'\}$ of somas, whose individual terms are complementary with respect to a fixed soma M, i.e., for each positive integer k,

$$A_k + A'_k = M. \quad (27.1)$$

We define the somas V_k, D_k, V_k', D_k' by the equations (25.2) and (26.4). By Theorem 1 of § 23, we have

$$V_k' + D_k = M, \quad V_k + D_k' = M. \tag{27.2}$$

Applying the same theorem once again, we obtain

$$\underline{A} + \bar{A}' = M, \quad \bar{A} + \underline{A}' = M. \tag{27.3}$$

THEOREM 3: *If the terms of two sequences of somas $\{A_k\}$ and $\{A_k'\}$ are complementary with respect to a fixed soma M, then the upper limit of either of the sequences and the lower limit of the other are complementary with respect to M.*

28. We now consider two infinite sequences

$$A_k', A_k'' \qquad (k = 1, 2, \ldots) \tag{28.1}$$

of somas, from which, by an obvious extension of the notation of § 25, we obtain the somas

$$V_k', D_k', \bar{A}', \underline{A}', V_k'', D_k'', \bar{A}'', \underline{A}''. \tag{28.2}$$

If we do the same also for the sequence of somas

$$A_k = A_k' \dotplus A_k'' \qquad (k = 1, 2, \ldots), \tag{28.3}$$

we find, say by Theorem 3 of § 14, that

$$V_k = V_k' \dotplus V_k'' \qquad (k = 1, 2, \ldots). \tag{28.4}$$

But then

$$\bar{A} \subseteqq V_{k+m} = V_{k+m}' \dotplus V_{k+m}'' \subseteqq V_k' \dotplus V_m'' \quad (k, m = 1, 2, \ldots). \tag{28.5}$$

Taking equation (24.12) into consideration, we conclude from (28.5) that

$$\bar{A} \subseteqq \prod_k (V_k' \dotplus V_m'') = \bar{A}' \dotplus V_m'' \quad (m = 1, 2, \ldots),$$

and by applying (24.12) to this in turn, we obtain the further relation

$$\bar{A} \subseteqq \prod_m (\bar{A}' \dotplus V_m'') = \bar{A}' \dotplus \bar{A}''. \tag{28.6}$$

On the other hand, since

$$V_k = V_k' \dotplus V_k'' \supseteqq V_k' \tag{28.7}$$

holds, we may write

$$\bar{A} = \prod_k V_k \supseteqq \prod_k V_k' = \bar{A}' ; \tag{28.8}$$

and—since we can show in the same way that $\bar{A} \supseteqq \bar{A}''$—we have

$$\bar{A} \supseteqq \bar{A}' \dotplus \bar{A}''. \tag{28.9}$$

Taking (28.6) into account, we conclude that

$$\bar{A} = \bar{A}' \dotplus \bar{A}''. \tag{28.10}$$

29. We shall now examine the lower limit $\underline{A}$ of the sequence (28.3). First of all, it follows from

$$D_k = \prod_{j=0}^{\infty} (A_{k+j}' \dotplus A_{k+j}'') \tag{29.1}$$

and from

$$A_{k+j}' \supseteqq D_k', \quad A_{k+j}'' \supseteqq D_k'' \tag{29.2}$$

that

$$D_k' \dotplus D_k'' \subseteqq D_k.$$

Thus, we also have

$$\left(\sum_k \dotplus D_k'\right) \dotplus \left(\sum_k \dotplus D_k''\right) \subseteqq \sum_k \dotplus D_k ,$$

or

$$\underline{A}' \dotplus \underline{A}'' \subseteqq \underline{A}. \tag{29.3}$$

On the other hand, it follows from (25.2), since $A_{k+j}' \subseteqq V_k'$, that we may write

$$D_k \subseteqq \prod_{j=0}^{\infty} (V_k' \dotplus A_{k+j}'') = V_k' \dotplus D_k'' \subseteqq V_k' \dotplus \underline{A}''.$$

Hence

$$\underline{A} = \sum_{j=0}^{\infty} \dotplus D_{k+j} \subseteqq \sum_{j=0}^{\infty} \dotplus (V_{k+j}' \dotplus \underline{A}'') = V_k' \dotplus \underline{A}'';$$

and consequently

$$\underline{A} \subseteqq \prod_k (V_k' \dotplus \underline{A}'') = \bar{A}' \dotplus \underline{A}'' = (\underline{A}' \dotplus \underline{A}'') \dotplus (\bar{A}' - \underline{A}'). \tag{29.4}$$

In the same way we obtain $\underline{A} \subseteqq \underline{A}' \dotplus \overline{A}''$, from which we conclude that

$$\underline{A} \subseteqq (\overline{A}' \dotplus \underline{A}'')\,(\underline{A}' \dotplus \overline{A}''), \tag{29.5}$$

which can also be written in the form

$$\underline{A} \subseteqq (\underline{A}' \dotplus \underline{A}'') + (\overline{A}' - \underline{A}')\,(\overline{A}'' - \underline{A}''). \tag{29.6}$$

Thus we have proved the following theorem.

THEOREM 4: *The lower and upper limits $\underline{A}'$, $\overline{A}'$, $\underline{A}''$, $\overline{A}''$ of two infinite sequences of somas A_k' and A_k'' and the lower and upper limits $\underline{A}$ and $\overline{A}$ of the sequence*

$$A_k = A_k' \dotplus A_k'' \qquad (k = 1, 2, \ldots) \tag{29.7}$$

are related by

$$\underline{A}' \dotplus \underline{A}'' \subseteqq \underline{A} \subseteqq \frac{\underline{A}' \dotplus \overline{A}''}{\overline{A}' \dotplus \underline{A}''} \subseteqq \overline{A} = \overline{A}' \dotplus \overline{A}'', \tag{29.8}$$

from which the more precise relation (29.6) *follows.*

30. Retaining the notation of § 28, consider a soma M which has all the somas A_k' and A_k'' as subsomas. We now introduce the sequences of somas $\{B_k'\}$ and $\{B_k''\}$, which are defined by the equations

$$A_k' + B_k' = M, \quad A_k'' + B_k'' = M \quad (k = 1, 2, \ldots) \tag{30.1}$$

and also the sequence of somas

$$B_k = B_k' B_k'' \qquad (k = 1, 2, \ldots). \tag{30.2}$$

By Theorem 1 of § 23, we have

$$A_k + B_k = M. \tag{30.3}$$

Furthermore, by Theorem 3 of § 27, the following relations hold among the upper and lower limits of all these sequences:

$$\underline{A}' + \overline{B}' = M, \quad \overline{A}' + \underline{B}' = M, \tag{30.4}$$

$$\underline{A}'' + \overline{B}'' = M, \quad \overline{A}'' + \underline{B}'' = M, \tag{30.5}$$

$$\underline{A} + \overline{B} = M, \quad \overline{A} + \underline{B} = M. \tag{30.6}$$

Then, by Theorem 1 of § 23, we have

$$(\underline{A}' \dotplus \underline{A}'') + \overline{B}'\overline{B}'' = M, \quad (\overline{A}' \dotplus \overline{A}'') + \underline{B}'\underline{B}'' = M; \tag{30.7}$$

in addition, (30.4) implies

$$\underline{A}' \dotplus \overline{B}' \dotplus \overline{A}' \dotplus \underline{B}' = M \dotplus M = O,$$

which can be written also as

$$\overline{A}' - \underline{A}' = \overline{B}' - \underline{B}', \tag{30.8}$$

and we can, similarly, obtain

$$\overline{A}'' - \underline{A}'' = \overline{B}'' - \underline{B}''. \tag{30.9}$$

A comparison of these results with Theorem 4 of § 29, yields:

THEOREM 5: *The lower and upper limits $\underline{B}'$, $\overline{B}'$, $\underline{B}''$, $\overline{B}''$ of two infinite sequences $\{B_k'\}$ and $\{B_k''\}$ of somas and the lower and upper limits $\underline{B}$ and $\overline{B}$ of the sequence of somas*

$$B_k = B_k' B_k'' \qquad (k = 1, 2, \ldots) \tag{30.10}$$

are related by the formulas

$$\underline{B}'\underline{B}'' = \underline{B} \subseqq \begin{matrix} \underline{B}'\overline{B}'' \\ \overline{B}'\underline{B}'' \end{matrix} \subseqq \overline{B} \subseqq \overline{B}'\overline{B}'', \tag{30.11}$$

from which it also follows that

$$\overline{B}'\overline{B}'' - (\overline{B}' - \underline{B}')(\overline{B}'' - \underline{B}'') \subseqq \overline{B}. \tag{30.12}$$

We now apply this theorem to the sequence of somas

$$C_k = A_k' B_k'' = A_k' - A_k' A_k'' \quad (k = 1, 2, \ldots). \tag{30.13}$$

The lower and upper limits $\underline{C}$ and $\overline{C}$ of this sequence then satisfy

$$\underline{C} = \underline{A}'\underline{B}'', \quad \overline{A}'\overline{B}'' - (\overline{A}' - \underline{A}')(\overline{A}'' - \underline{A}'') \subseqq \overline{C} \subseqq \overline{A}'\overline{B}''; \tag{30.14}$$

thus, changing our notation, we can enunciate the following theorem.

THEOREM 6: *The lower and upper limits $\underline{C}'$, $\overline{C}'$, $\underline{C}''$, $\overline{C}''$ of two infinite sequences $\{C_k'\}$ and $\{C_k''\}$ of somas and the lower and upper limits $\underline{C}$ and $\overline{C}$ of the sequence*

$$C_k = C_k' - C_k' C_k'' \qquad (k = 1, 2, \ldots) \quad (30.15)$$

and related by the formulas

$$\underline{C}' - \underline{C}'\,\overline{C}'' = \underline{C} \subseteq \frac{\underline{C}' - \underline{C}'\,\underline{C}''}{\overline{C}' - \overline{C}'\,\overline{C}''} \subseteq \overline{C} \subseteq \overline{C}' - \overline{C}'\,\underline{C}'', \quad (30.16)$$

from which it also follows that

$$(\overline{C}' - \overline{C}'\,\underline{C}'') - (\overline{C}' - \underline{C}')\,(\overline{C}'' - \underline{C}'') \subseteq \overline{C}. \quad (30.17)$$

31. We shall say of a sequence $A_1, A_2, \ldots$ of somas that it *converges* to a soma A if both the lower and upper limits $\underline{A}$ and $\overline{A}$ are equal to A. A is then called the *limit* of the sequence and we write

$$\lim_{k=\infty} A_k = A. \quad (31.1)$$

It follows from the preceding three theorems that if

$$\lim_{k=\infty} A_k = A, \quad \lim_{k=\infty} B_k = B, \quad (31.2)$$

then the three sequences of somas

$$\{A_k \dotplus B_k\}, \{A_k B_k\} \text{ and } \{A_k - A_k B_k\}$$

all converge and we can write

$$\lim_{k=\infty} (A_k \dotplus B_k) \quad = A \dotplus B, \quad (31.3)$$

$$\lim_{k=\infty} A_k B_k \quad = AB, \quad (31.4)$$

$$\lim_{k=\infty} (A_k - A_k B_k) = A - AB. \quad (31.5)$$

Since

$$A_k + B_k = (A_k - A_k B_k) \dotplus (B_k - A_k B_k), \quad (31.6)$$

the sequence of somas $\{A_k + B_k\}$ converges as well, and we have:

THEOREM 7: *From the convergence of the sequences* $\{A_k\}$ *and* $\{B_k\}$ *to the somas* A *and* B *respectively, it follows that the sequences of somas* $\{A_k \mathbin{\underset{\cdot}{+}} B_k\}$ *and* $\{A_k B_k\}$ *also converge, and that*

$$\lim_{k=\infty} (A_k \mathbin{\underset{\cdot}{+}} B_k) = A \mathbin{\underset{\cdot}{+}} B \tag{31.7}$$

and

$$\lim_{k=\infty} A_k B_k = A B. \tag{31.8}$$

From this theorem it is easy to deduce equations (31.3), (31.5), and many others.

Convergent sequences of somas exist, as we see from the following theorem.

THEOREM 8: *A monotone increasing sequence of somas converges to their union, a monotone decreasing sequence, to their intersection.*

As a consequence, every series of the type

$$A_1 \dotplus A_2 \dotplus A_3 \dotplus \cdots \tag{31.9}$$

converges, whereas series of the type

$$A_1 \mathbin{\underset{\cdot}{+}} A_2 \mathbin{\underset{\cdot}{+}} A_3 \mathbin{\underset{\cdot}{+}} \cdots \tag{31.10}$$

only converge in exceptional cases. In particular, the partial sums of the series

$$A \mathbin{\underset{\cdot}{+}} A \mathbin{\underset{\cdot}{+}} A \mathbin{\underset{\cdot}{+}} \cdots$$

are alternately A and O.

32. A comparison of (29.6) with (29.8) shows that the sequence of somas $A_k = A'_k \dotplus A''_k$ converges only if

$$(\underline{A}' \dotplus \underline{A}'') + (\bar{A}' - \underline{A}')(\bar{A}'' - \underline{A}'') = \bar{A}' \dotplus \bar{A}'' \tag{32.1}$$

holds. Expanding this equation, we obtain

$$\underline{A}' \mathbin{\underset{\cdot}{+}} \underline{A}'' \mathbin{\underset{\cdot}{+}} \underline{A}'\underline{A}'' \mathbin{\underset{\cdot}{+}} \bar{A}'\bar{A}'' \mathbin{\underset{\cdot}{+}} \underline{A}'\bar{A}'' \mathbin{\underset{\cdot}{+}} \bar{A}'\underline{A}'' \mathbin{\underset{\cdot}{+}} \underline{A}'\underline{A}'' = \bar{A}' \mathbin{\underset{\cdot}{+}} \bar{A}'' \mathbin{\underset{\cdot}{+}} \bar{A}'\bar{A}'',$$

which can be rewritten as

$$\bar{A}' \mathbin{\underset{\cdot}{+}} \underline{A}' = (\bar{A}'' \mathbin{\underset{\cdot}{+}} \underline{A}'') \mathbin{\underset{\cdot}{+}} (\bar{A}'\underline{A}'' \mathbin{\underset{\cdot}{+}} \underline{A}'\bar{A}''). \tag{32.2}$$

Now the terms on the right-hand side are all subsomas of $\bar{A}''$; therefore $\bar{A}' \mathbin{\underset{\cdot}{+}} \underline{A}' \subseteqq \bar{A}''$, and consequently equation (32.1) implies the relations

$$\bar{A}' \mathbin{\underset{\cdot}{+}} \underline{A}' \subseteqq \bar{A}'', \quad \bar{A}'' \mathbin{\underset{\cdot}{+}} \underline{A}'' \subseteqq \bar{A}'. \tag{32.3}$$

Conversely, (32.3) implies

$$\begin{aligned}(\bar{A}' \mathbin{\underset{\cdot}{+}} \underline{A}') \mathbin{\underset{\cdot}{+}} (\bar{A}'' \mathbin{\underset{\cdot}{+}} \underline{A}'') &= \bar{A}''(\bar{A}' \mathbin{\underset{\cdot}{+}} \underline{A}') \mathbin{\underset{\cdot}{+}} \bar{A}'(\bar{A}'' \mathbin{\underset{\cdot}{+}} \underline{A}'') \\ &= \bar{A}''\underline{A}' \mathbin{\underset{\cdot}{+}} \bar{A}'\underline{A}'',\end{aligned} \tag{32.4}$$

which is equivalent to (32.2), and hence to (32.1). Thus, (32.1) may be replaced by the relations (32.3).

Furthermore, a *sufficient* condition for the convergence of the somas A_k is, by (29.8), that

$$\underline{A}' \dotplus \underline{A}'' = \bar{A}' \dotplus \bar{A}''. \tag{32.5}$$

A necessary and sufficient condition that this equation hold is, in addition to (32.3)—or, what is the same, (32.1)—the equation

$$(\bar{A}' \mathbin{\underset{\cdot}{+}} \underline{A}')(\bar{A}'' \mathbin{\underset{\cdot}{+}} \underline{A}'') = O. \tag{32.6}$$

But this equation can be written as

$$(\bar{A}' \mathbin{\underset{\cdot}{+}} \underline{A}')\bar{A}'' = (\bar{A}' \mathbin{\underset{\cdot}{+}} \underline{A}')\underline{A}'',$$

and we see that the relations (32.3) can be replaced in the present case by the pair of relations

$$\bar{A}' \mathbin{\underset{\cdot}{+}} \underline{A}' \subseteqq \underline{A}'', \quad \bar{A}'' \mathbin{\underset{\cdot}{+}} \underline{A}'' \subseteqq \underline{A}'. \tag{32.7}$$

From the first of the relations (32.7) we obtain

$$\underline{A}' \mathbin{\underset{\cdot}{+}} \underline{A}'\underline{A}'' = \bar{A}' \mathbin{\underset{\cdot}{+}} \bar{A}'\underline{A}'',$$

so that

$$\underline{A}' \dotplus \underline{A}'' = \underline{A}' \mathbin{\underset{\cdot}{+}} \underline{A}'\underline{A}'' \mathbin{\underset{\cdot}{+}} \underline{A}'' = \bar{A}' \mathbin{\underset{\cdot}{+}} \bar{A}'\underline{A}'' \mathbin{\underset{\cdot}{+}} \underline{A}'' = \bar{A}' \dotplus \underline{A}''.$$

The relation

$$\underline{A}' \dotplus \underline{A}'' = \underline{A}' \dotplus \bar{A}''$$

is proved similarly, and we obtain

$$\underline{A}' \dotplus \underline{A}'' = (\bar{A}' \dotplus \underline{A}'') \dotplus (\underline{A}' \dotplus \bar{A}'') = \bar{A}' \dotplus \bar{A}''. \tag{32.8}$$

Thus, (32.5) and (32.7) are equivalent, and we have proved the following theorem.

THEOREM 9: *A necessary condition for the convergence of the sequence* (29.7) *of Theorem* 4 *of* § 29, *is that the two relations*

$$\bar{A}' - \underline{A}' \subseqq \bar{A}'', \quad \bar{A}'' - \underline{A}'' \subseqq \bar{A}' \tag{32.9}$$

hold; and a sufficient condition is that the two relations

$$\bar{A}' - \underline{A}' \subseqq \underline{A}'', \quad \bar{A}'' - \underline{A}'' \subseqq \underline{A}' \tag{32.10}$$

hold.

CHAPTER TWO

SETS OF SOMAS

§§ 33-40. Sets of Somas Closed under a Binary Operation

33. We denote the totality of all somas involved in a given investigation, as before, by $\mathfrak{M}_0$; subsets of $\mathfrak{M}_0$ we denote by capital German letters $\mathfrak{A}$, $\mathfrak{B}$, ...

We shall express the statement that $\mathfrak{B}$ is a (proper or improper) subset of $\mathfrak{A}$, i.e., that

$$\text{if } X \in \mathfrak{B}, \text{ then } X \in \mathfrak{A},$$

by writing

$$\mathfrak{B} \prec \mathfrak{A} \quad \text{or} \quad \mathfrak{A} \succ \mathfrak{B},$$

since, to avoid confusion, the notation $B \subseteqq A$ will be reserved exclusively for somas.

The most important sets of somas are those that are closed under one of the four basic binary operations

$$A \dotplus B, \quad AB, \quad A \mathbin{\underset{\centerdot}{+}} B, \quad A - AB.$$

We introduce the following definitions:

Definition 1: *A set of somas $\mathfrak{A}$ is called additive if whenever $A \in \mathfrak{A}$ and $B \in \mathfrak{A}$, the union $A \dotplus B$ of these two somas is also an element of $\mathfrak{A}$.*

Analogously, a set of somas $\mathfrak{A}$ is called multiplicative, conjunctive, and subtractive, according as $A \in \mathfrak{A}$ and $B \in \mathfrak{A}$ together imply

$$AB \in \mathfrak{A}, \quad A \mathbin{\underset{\centerdot}{+}} B \in \mathfrak{A}, \quad \textit{and} \quad A - AB \in \mathfrak{A}.$$

Definition 2: *A set of somas $\mathfrak{R}$ which is additive, multiplicative, conjunctive, and subtractive is called a ring of somas.*[1]

[1] Another terminology, due to Hausdorff (*Mengenlehre*, 1914), is used in the theory of point sets. In this terminology, a set of point sets that is both additive and multiplicative is called a *ring*. [*Ring*] and a set of this kind that is closed under each of the four basic binary operations is called a *field*. [*Körper*]. Now if the operations on point sets are looked upon as Boolean operations, Hausdorff's *field* and Boole's *ring* become identical notions. This terminological discrepancy becomes unpleasantly noticeable in our present investigation, in which both theories are closely intertwined. In my previous publications, I proceeded under the assumption that in any treatment of the notions of measure and integral, the usages of set theory should be followed; it is for this reason that I used to write of "fields of somas." Of late, however, the study of lattice theory and of Boolean algebra has assumed such dimensions, that my former position in this matter can no longer be supported.

34. From these definitions, we obtain the following theorems.

THEOREM 1: *Every subtractive set of somas is necessarily multiplicative as well.*

Proof: A subtractive set of somas $\mathfrak{A}$ that contains the somas A and B must also contain the soma $A \underset{\cdot}{+} AB$ and therefore must contain the soma

$$A \underset{\cdot}{+} A\,(A \underset{\cdot}{+} AB) = AB$$

as well.

THEOREM 2: *Every set of somas that is conjunctive or subtractive (and, in particular, every ring of somas) contains the empty soma O.*

Proof: This follows directly from the identities

$$A \underset{\cdot}{+} A = O, \quad A \underset{\cdot}{+} AA = O.$$

THEOREM 3: *A set of somas $\mathfrak{R}$ is a ring if it is either*

a) *additive and conjunctive,*
b) *additive and subtractive,*
c) *multiplicative and conjunctive, or*
d) *conjunctive and subtractive.*

Proof: Under assumption a), if the set of somas $\mathfrak{R}$ contains A and B, it also contains the somas $A \dotplus B$ and $A \underset{\cdot}{+} B$, and thus it contains the soma

$$(A \dotplus B) \underset{\cdot}{+} (A \underset{\cdot}{+} B) = AB$$

and, finally, the soma $A \underset{\cdot}{+} AB$. Hence, it is a ring.

Under assumption b), if $\mathfrak{R}$ contains A and B, it also contains the somas $A \dotplus B$ and $A \underset{\cdot}{+} AB$. Then, by Theorem 1, it contains the soma AB and consequently also the soma

$$(A \dotplus B) \underset{\cdot}{+} AB\,(A \dotplus B) = A \underset{\cdot}{+} B.$$

Under assumption c), if $\mathfrak{R}$ contains A and B it also contains AB and $A \underset{\cdot}{+} B$ and thus contains $A \underset{\cdot}{+} AB$ and $(A \underset{\cdot}{+} B) \underset{\cdot}{+} AB = A \dotplus B$.

Finally, under assumption d), the set of somas $\mathfrak{R}$ is, by Theorem 1, multiplicative and conjunctive. Thus, by virtue of what we have just proved, $\mathfrak{R}$ is a ring.

THEOREM 4: *Let $\mathfrak{A}$ be a subtractive set of somas and let M be a soma of $\mathfrak{A}$. The set $\mathfrak{B}(M)$ consisting of all those somas of $\mathfrak{A}$ which are subsomas of M (including, of course, M itself) is a ring of somas.*

Proof: The set of somas $\mathfrak{B}(M)$ obviously has the same property as $\mathfrak{A}$ of being subtractive, and hence multiplicative. If now A and B are two somas of $\mathfrak{A}$ satisfying $A \subseteqq M$ and $B \subseteqq M$, then the three somas

$$M \dotplus A, \quad M \dotplus B, \quad (M \dotplus A)(M \dotplus B) = M \dotplus (A \dotplus B)$$

belong to $\mathfrak{B}(M)$, and the same is also true of

$$M \dotplus (M \dotplus (A \dotplus B)) = A \dotplus B.$$

Thus $\mathfrak{B}(M)$ is also an additive set of somas and, by Theorem 3, b), is therefore a ring.

35. Let $\mathfrak{N}$ be an arbitrary set of somas, and let $A_1, A_2, \ldots, A_p$ be any finite number of somas of $\mathfrak{N}$. Every additive set of somas that contains all the somas of $\mathfrak{N}$ must then also contain the soma

$$A = A_1 \dotplus A_2 \dotplus \cdots \dotplus A_p. \tag{35.1}$$

We now adjoin to $\mathfrak{N}$ all those somas that can be written in the form (35.1) and, in so doing, we obtain an *additive* set of somas; for if the soma (35.1) and the soma

$$B = B_1 \dotplus B_2 \dotplus \cdots \dotplus B_q \tag{35.2}$$

belong to our enlarged set of somas, so does $A \dotplus B$. This enlarged set of somas is denoted by $\mathfrak{N}^{\dotplus}$ and is called the *additive closure* of the set of somas $\mathfrak{N}$.

The additive closure $\mathfrak{N}^{\dotplus}$ of $\mathfrak{N}$ is thus the smallest additive set of somas containing all the somas of $\mathfrak{N}$.

In the same way, we can generate the smallest multiplicative and conjunctive sets of somas containing all the somas of $\mathfrak{N}$. These are called the *multiplicative* and *conjunctive closures* of $\mathfrak{N}$. We denote these sets of somas by $\mathfrak{N}^{\times}$ and $\mathfrak{N}^{+}$, respectively.

36. The *subtractive closure* $\mathfrak{N}^{-}$ of a set of somas $\mathfrak{N}$, i.e., the smallest subtractive set of somas containing every soma of $\mathfrak{N}$, must be constructed by a somewhat different method.

To this end, we denote by

$$\mathfrak{S}(A_1, \ldots, A_p) \tag{36.1}$$

the subtractive closure of the finite number of somas $A_1, A_2, \ldots, A_p$. The set of somas (36.1) also consists of a finite number of somas, which can be computed one after the other, in sequence.

Indeed, the somas of the set (36.1), with the possible exception of the empty soma, are all to be found among the polynomials in $A_1, \ldots, A_p$, which, as we saw in § 20, are finite in number.

Now, if

$$A \in \mathfrak{S}(A_1, \ldots, A_p), \quad B \in \mathfrak{S}(B_1, B_2, \ldots, B_q), \tag{36.2}$$

each of the somas A, B is an element of $\mathfrak{S}(A_1, \ldots, A_p, B_1, \ldots, B_q)$, and thus it follows that

$$A \dot{+} AB \in \mathfrak{S}(A_1, \ldots, A_p, B_1, \ldots, B_q). \tag{36.3}$$

The subtractive closure $\mathfrak{N}^-$ of an arbitrary set of somas is thus obtained by forming the sets analogous to (36.1) from all possible combinations of a finite number of somas $A_1, \ldots, A_p$ of $\mathfrak{N}$ and adjoining them to the set $\mathfrak{N}$.

37. It is important for what follows to prove that the set of somas (36.1) contains all $2^p - 1$ of the decomposition somas

$$S_1, S_2, \ldots, S_n \tag{37.1}$$

that, by § 19, can be formed from $A_1, \ldots, A_p$.

Indeed, if we denote the $2^{p-1} - 1$ decomposition somas of $A_1, \ldots, A_{p-1}$ by

$$T_1, T_2, \ldots, T_m, \tag{37.2}$$

then the somas (37.1) can be written as

$$S_{2j-1} = T_j A_p, \quad S_{2j} = T_j \dot{+} T_j A_p \quad (j = 1, \ldots, m), \tag{37.3}$$

$$S_n = A_p \dot{+} (T_1 + T_2 + \cdots + T_m) A_p. \tag{37.4}$$

All the somas (37.3) are in the set of somas

$$\mathfrak{S}(T_1, T_2, \ldots, T_m, A_p); \tag{37.5}$$

and, in fact, the same is true of the soma (37.4). Indeed, putting

$$U_k = A_p \dot{+} (T_1 + T_2 + \cdots + T_k) A_p \quad (k = 1, 2, \ldots, m), \tag{37.6}$$

we have

$$U_{k+1} = U_k \dot{+} T_{k+1} A_p = U_k \dot{+} T_{k+1} U_k. \tag{37.7}$$

If U_k is an element of (37.5), then U_{k+1} is also an element of (37.5), provided $k < m$. Now, since U_1 is a soma of (37.5), $S_n = U_m$ must also be an element of (37.5). Therefore, if we assume that the set of somas

$$\mathfrak{S}(A_1, \ldots, A_{p-1})$$

contains all the somas (37.2), we see that all the somas (37.1) are elements of (36.1). Our result is therefore valid for all p by induction, since it obviously holds for $p = 1$.

38. We now state the following theorems concerning the additive closure of a set of somas.

THEOREM 5: *The additive closure $\mathfrak{A}^{\dot{+}}$ of a multiplicative set of somas $\mathfrak{A}$ is itself multiplicative.*

Proof: Let

$$\left.\begin{aligned} A &= A_1 \dot{+} A_2 \dot{+} \cdots \dot{+} A_p, \\ B &= B_1 \dot{+} B_2 \dot{+} \cdots \dot{+} B_q \end{aligned}\right\} \tag{38.1}$$

be any two somas of $\mathfrak{A}^{\dot{+}}$, where all the somas on the right-hand side—and in similar cases in future we shall tacitly make an analogous assumption—are understood to be somas of the set $\mathfrak{A}$. We may write

$$AB = \sum_{j,k} \dot{+}\, A_j B_k \cdot \tag{38.2}$$

By assumption, each of the somas $A_j B_k$ is in $\mathfrak{A}$; consequently, AB is in $\mathfrak{A}^{\dot{+}}$.

Likewise, the multiplicative closure of an additive set of somas is additive. A proof is obtained by interchanging union and intersection in the proof of Theorem 5.

THEOREM 6: *The additive closure of a subtractive set of somas is a ring.*

Proof: Let $\mathfrak{B}$ be a subtractive set of somas; consider two somas

$$\left.\begin{aligned} A &= A_1 \dot{+} A_2 \dot{+} \cdots \dot{+} A_p, \\ B &= B_1 \dot{+} B_2 \dot{+} \cdots \dot{+} B_q \end{aligned}\right\} \tag{38.3}$$

in the additive closure $\mathfrak{B}^{\dot{+}}$ of $\mathfrak{B}$. All the somas of the subtractive set of somas

$$\mathfrak{S}(A_1, \ldots, A_p, B_1, \ldots, B_q) \tag{38.4}$$

are in $\mathfrak{B}$, by hypothesis. In particular, all the decomposition somas of the family $A_1, \ldots, A_p, B_1, \ldots, B_p$ are, by § 37, in $\mathfrak{B}$, and thus all those somas that can be represented as sums of these decomposition somas are in $\mathfrak{B}^{\dot{+}}$. Now, since the soma $A \dot{+} B$ can be represented as such a sum, the set $\mathfrak{B}^{\dot{+}}$ of somas is not only additive, but also conjunctive. Hence, by Theorem 3 of § 34, $\mathfrak{B}^{\dot{+}}$ is a ring, which is what we wished to show.

39. We state the following theorem concerning conjunctive closures.

THEOREM 7: *The conjunctive closure of an additive or of a multiplicative set of somas is a ring.*

Proof: Let $\mathfrak{A}^{\underset{\cdot}{+}}$ denote the conjunctive closure of the set $\mathfrak{A}$ of somas. If

$$\left.\begin{aligned} A &= A_1 \underset{\cdot}{+} A_2 \underset{\cdot}{+} \cdots \underset{\cdot}{+} A_p, \\ B &= B_1 \underset{\cdot}{+} B_2 \underset{\cdot}{+} \cdots \underset{\cdot}{+} B_q \end{aligned}\right\} \tag{39.1}$$

are two somas of $\mathfrak{A}^{\underset{\cdot}{+}}$, they satisfy

$$AB = \sum_{j,k} \underset{\cdot}{+} A_j B_k. \tag{39.2}$$

Now, if, in our first case, $\mathfrak{A}$ is an additive set of somas, $A_j \dot{+} B_k$ is in $\mathfrak{A}$ whenever A_j and B_k are in $\mathfrak{A}$, and so $\mathfrak{A}^{\underset{\cdot}{+}}$ contains the soma

$$A_j B_k = (A_j \dot{+} B_k) \underset{\cdot}{+} A_j \underset{\cdot}{+} B_k \tag{39.3}$$

Consequently, the soma (39.2) also must be in $\mathfrak{A}^{\underset{\cdot}{+}}$.

If, in our second case, $\mathfrak{A}$ is a multiplicative set of somas, then the somas $A_j B_k$ are in $\mathfrak{A}$, and so, again, the soma (39.2) must be in $\mathfrak{A}^{\underset{\cdot}{+}}$.

Thus, under the assumptions of our theorem, the set $\mathfrak{A}^{\underset{\cdot}{+}}$ is always multiplicative. Since it is also conjunctive, it is a ring, by Theorem 3 of § 34.

40. The preceding theorems give several methods for the construction of the smallest ring of somas $\mathfrak{R}(\mathfrak{N})$ containing all the somas of $\mathfrak{N}$ (or, as we shall also say: the ring *generated* by $\mathfrak{N}$).

First, one can form the subtractive closure $\mathfrak{N}^-$ of $\mathfrak{N}$ and then the additive closure of $\mathfrak{N}^-$. By Theorem 6 of § 38, we obtain in this way a ring $\mathfrak{R}(\mathfrak{N})$ of somas; furthermore, every ring of somas containing all the somas of $\mathfrak{N}$ must contain all of the somas of $\mathfrak{R}(\mathfrak{N})$, as well.

Second, one can form the additive closure $\mathfrak{N}^{\dot{+}}$ of $\mathfrak{N}$; by the last theorem, $\mathfrak{R}(\mathfrak{N})$ is the same as the conjunctive closure of $\mathfrak{N}^{\dot{+}}$.

Third, $\mathfrak{R}(\mathfrak{N})$ is the same as the conjunctive closure of the multiplicative closure of $\mathfrak{N}$, which we denoted in § 35 by $\mathfrak{N}^{\times}$.

Last, one can form the conjunctive closure of $\mathfrak{N}^-$, since, by Theorem 1 of § 34, $\mathfrak{N}^-$ is a multiplicative set of somas.

Thus we may write

$$\mathfrak{R}(\mathfrak{N}) = (\mathfrak{N}^-)^{\dot{+}} = (\mathfrak{N}^{\dot{+}})^{\underset{\cdot}{+}} = (\mathfrak{N}^{\times})^{\underset{\cdot}{+}} = (\mathfrak{N}^-)^{\underset{\cdot}{+}}. \tag{40.1}$$

The set $\mathfrak{N}$ of somas is called a *base* for the ring $\mathfrak{R}(\mathfrak{N})$.

§§ 41-46. Complete Rings

41. The operations of union and of intersection can each be applied to countably many somas (Axiom 4 of § 13; Theorem 2 of § 23). Hence, we are led to distinguish the particular classes of additive and multiplicative sets of somas given by the following definition.

DEFINITION: *A set* $\mathfrak{A}$ *of somas is called* (i) *countably additive and* (ii) *countably multiplicative if, whenever the elements* $A_1, A_2, \ldots$ *of an at most countable set of somas are in* $\mathfrak{A}$, (i) *the union* $\sum_j \dot{+} A_j$ *and* (ii) *the intersection* $\prod_j A_j$, *respectively, is in* $\mathfrak{A}$.

The following examples suggest the wisdom of distinguishing not only additive and multiplicative sets of somas, but also countably additive and countably multiplicative sets of somas: If we adjoin the empty set to the totality of all open cubes in a euclidean space, we obtain a multiplicative set of somas which is neither additive nor countably multiplicative; the complements of these cubes, if we adjoin the whole space, yield an additive set of somas which is neither multiplicative nor countably additive; the totality of all open sets in a euclidean space is both countably additive and multiplicative, but not countably multiplicative.

42. Again, let $\mathfrak{R}$ be a set of somas. We denote by $\mathfrak{R}_\sigma$ the set of all somas which can be represented as a union of at most countably many somas of $\mathfrak{R}$. Every countably additive set of somas that contains all the somas of $\mathfrak{R}$ also contains every soma of $\mathfrak{R}_\sigma$. On the other hand, the set of somas $\mathfrak{R}_\sigma$ is, by Theorem 3 of § 14, *countably additive;* thus, it is the smallest countably additive set of somas that contains $\mathfrak{R}$ as a subset; $\mathfrak{R}_\sigma$ will therefore be called the *countably additive closure* of $\mathfrak{R}$.

The *countably multiplicative closure* $\mathfrak{R}_\delta$ of $\mathfrak{R}$ is constructed quite similarly. The set $\mathfrak{R}_\delta$ of somas consists of all somas that can be written as an intersection of at most countably many somas of $\mathfrak{R}$.

Of course, we have the relations

$$(\mathfrak{R}_\sigma)_\sigma = \mathfrak{R}_\sigma, \quad (\mathfrak{R}_\delta)_\delta = \mathfrak{R}_\delta. \tag{42.1}$$

One may, however, obtain new sets of somas by an alternate iteration of the operations leading from $\mathfrak{R}$ to $\mathfrak{R}_\sigma$ and $\mathfrak{R}_\delta$. This procedure gives rise to two monotonically increasing sequences of sets of somas:

$$\mathfrak{R}_\sigma \prec \mathfrak{R}_{\sigma\delta} \prec \mathfrak{R}_{\sigma\delta\sigma} \prec \cdots, \tag{42.2}$$

$$\mathfrak{R}_\delta \prec \mathfrak{R}_{\delta\sigma} \prec \mathfrak{R}_{\delta\sigma\delta} \prec \cdots. \tag{42.3}$$

If, in either sequence, two consecutive terms are the same, then all the later terms of the sequence are the same, and the sequence terminates. Since $\mathfrak{N} \prec \mathfrak{N}_\sigma$ and $\mathfrak{N} \prec \mathfrak{N}_\delta$, it follows that

$$\mathfrak{N}_\delta \prec \mathfrak{N}_{\sigma\delta}, \quad \mathfrak{N}_\sigma \prec \mathfrak{N}_{\delta\sigma} \quad \text{etc.,} \tag{42.4}$$

from which it is easy to see that each of the sequences (42.2) and (42.3) of sets of somas terminates if the other does. It can happen, however, that neither of the sequences terminates, so that transfinite induction (Theorem 4 of § 52) has to be used to find the smallest set of somas that contains $\mathfrak{N}$ and is both countably additive and countably multiplicative.

The sets of somas $\mathfrak{N}_{\sigma\delta}$ and $\mathfrak{N}_{\delta\sigma}$ need not be the same. For example, if $\mathfrak{N}$ consists of all the open subsets of euclidean space, then $\mathfrak{N}_\sigma = \mathfrak{N}$ and $\mathfrak{N}_{\sigma\delta} = \mathfrak{N}_\delta$, whereas $\mathfrak{N}_{\delta\sigma}$ contains sets which are not in $\mathfrak{N}_\delta$.[2]

If the set $\mathfrak{N}$ of somas is countable, it does not follow that $\mathfrak{N}_\sigma$ or $\mathfrak{N}_\delta$ need be countable. For example, if $\mathfrak{N}$ consists of all the intervals with rational endpoints on the real line, then $\mathfrak{N}$ is countable. The sets $\mathfrak{N}_\sigma$ and $\mathfrak{N}_\delta$, however, contain respectively all the open intervals and all the closed intervals whatsoever (as well as other sets of points), and so are not countable.

43. We now introduce the following important concept:

DEFINITION: *A ring of somas which is at the same time a countably additive set of somas is called a complete ring.*

In the terminology of Hausdorff, which we have already mentioned in the footnote on p. 52, complete rings are referred to as "σ-fields." The somas of a complete ring satisfy the four axioms of §§ 8-13. From the two theorems of § 23, we immediately obtain the following theorem.

THEOREM 1: *Every complete ring is a countably multiplicative set of somas.*

The totality of bounded subsets of a euclidean space can be considered as a ring of somas which, not being countably additive is not a complete ring and yet is a countably multiplicative set of somas. There is no need, however, to consider the class of countably multiplicative rings apart from the class of complete rings.

For, the totality of somas of a countably multiplicative ring that are subsomas of a fixed soma M of the ring, is automatically a complete ring. Indeed, more generally, we have the following result.

[2] By a well-known theorem of W. H. Young, *Ber. Ges. Wiss. Leipzig* 55, pp. 287-293 (1903), $\mathfrak{N}_\delta$ can contain only those at most countable sets which have no subsets that are dense in themselves. On the other hand, every countable set is in $\mathfrak{N}_{\delta\sigma}$.

THEOREM 2: *Let $\mathfrak{A}$ be a subtractive and countably multiplicative set of somas, and let M be any fixed soma of $\mathfrak{A}$. Then $\mathfrak{B}(M)$, the totality of all those somas of $\mathfrak{A}$ that are subsomas of M, is a complete ring.*

Proof: The set of somas $\mathfrak{B}(M)$ is a subset of $\mathfrak{A}$ and is obviously countably multiplicative. Let $A_1, A_2, \ldots$ be countably many (not necessarily distinct) somas of $\mathfrak{B}(M)$; we introduce the notation

$$B_j = M \dot{+} A_j, \quad A = \sum_j \dot{+} A_j, \quad B = \prod_j B_j \tag{43.1}$$

and observe that, by Theorem 1 of § 23,

$$A = M \dot{+} B. \tag{43.2}$$

Now by Theorem 4 of § 34, the set of somas $\mathfrak{B}(M)$ is a ring. Thus, since the A_j are elements of $\mathfrak{B}(M)$, so are the B_j; consequently B, and hence A as well, is in $\mathfrak{B}(M)$. The ring $\mathfrak{B}(M)$ is countably additive and thus is a complete ring.

44. To verify that a given ring is indeed a complete ring, we can use Theorem 3 of § 34, from which we immediately obtain the following theorem.

THEOREM 3: *A set of somas that is either* (i) *conjunctive and countably additive or* (ii) *subtractive and countably additive is a complete ring.*

Since every complete ring is a countably multiplicative set of somas, we also have the following results.

THEOREM 4: *A countably additive set of somas that is not countably multiplicative is neither conjunctive nor multiplicative.*

An example of a set of somas that is countably additive but not countably multiplicative is furnished by the totality of open subsets of a euclidean space.

45. Let $\mathfrak{A}$ be a multiplicative set of somas. We consider two somas

$$A = \sum_j \dot{+} A_j, \quad B = \sum_k \dot{+} B_k \tag{45.1}$$

of the countably additive closure $\mathfrak{A}_\sigma$ of $\mathfrak{A}$. By assumption, $\mathfrak{A}$ contains the somas $A_j B_k$. Furthermore, in virtue of Theorem 5 of § 15, we have the identity

$$AB = \sum_k \dot{+} AB_k = \sum_{j,k} \dot{+} A_j B_k, \tag{45.2}$$

and consequently the following theorem.

THEOREM 5: *The countably additive closure of a multiplicative set of somas is itself multiplicative.*

This theorem is an analogue of Theorem 5 of § 38; however, no strict analogue exists for Theorem 6 of that section. We have only a narrower result, which we formulate as follows:

THEOREM 6: *The countably additive closure $\mathfrak{A}_\sigma$ of a subtractive set of somas $\mathfrak{A}$ is itself subtractive (or conjunctive) if and only if it is itself countably multiplicative; in that case, $\mathfrak{A}_\sigma$ is a complete ring.*

Proof: If $\mathfrak{A}_\sigma$ is a subtractive (or conjunctive) set of somas, then, by Theorem 3 of § 44, $\mathfrak{A}_\sigma$ is a complete ring, and so is countably multiplicative, i.e., $\mathfrak{A}_\sigma = \mathfrak{A}_{\sigma\delta}$.

Conversely, if $\mathfrak{A}_\sigma = \mathfrak{A}_{\sigma\delta}$, then, whenever $C_1, C_2, \ldots$ is an infinite sequence of somas of $\mathfrak{A}_\sigma$, their upper limit

$$\bar{C} = \overline{\lim_{j=\infty}}\, C_j \tag{45.3}$$

is also a soma of $\mathfrak{A}_\sigma$. For, by § 25, the upper limit can be written as an intersection of countably many somas of $\mathfrak{A}_\sigma$.

Every soma in $\mathfrak{A}_\sigma$ can be written as a union of countably many, not necessarily distinct somas of $\mathfrak{A}$. Suppose, then, that

$$A = \sum_j \dot{+} A'_j, \quad B = \sum_j \dot{+} B'_j \tag{45.4}$$

are two such somas. Writing

$$A_n = \sum_{j=1}^{n} \dot{+} A'_j, \quad B_n = \sum_{j=1}^{n} \dot{+} B'_j \quad (n = 1, 2, \ldots), \tag{45.5}$$

A_n and B_n are elements of the additive closure $\mathfrak{A}^+$ of $\mathfrak{A}$, and by Theorem 6 of § 38, $A_n \dot{+} B_n$ is therefore also an element of $\mathfrak{A}^+$, and so, a fortiori, an element of $\mathfrak{A}_\sigma$.

At the same time, Theorem 8 of § 31, asserts that

$$A = \lim_{n=\infty} A_n, \quad B = \lim_{n=\infty} B_n. \tag{45.6}$$

Theorem 7 of § 31 implies that the somas $A_n \dot{+} B_n$ converge to $A \dot{+} B$, so that we can write

$$A \dot{+} B = \overline{\lim_{n=\infty}}\, (A_n \dot{+} B_n). \tag{45.7}$$

$A \dot{+} B$ is then a soma of $\mathfrak{A}_\sigma$, by what we have already shown, and so $\mathfrak{A}_\sigma$ is a conjunctive set of somas and hence is a complete ring (Theorem 3 of § 44).

46. We supplement this result with the following theorem.

THEOREM 7: *The countably additive closure of a ring need not be either subtractive or conjunctive.*

Proof: We consider those subsets of the real line which are unions of at most a finite number of points and open intervals. It can be verified immediately that the totality $\mathfrak{R}$ of all these point sets is both additive and subtractive and, consequently (Theorem 3 of § 34), is a ring. The countably additive closure $\mathfrak{R}_\sigma$ of $\mathfrak{R}$ consists of those subsets of the real line that are the union of a (possibly empty) open subset and an at most countable subset. A proper interval A and a countable everywhere dense subset B of A are both always in $\mathfrak{R}_\sigma$. The set $A \dotplus B = A - AB$ is then not in $\mathfrak{R}_\sigma$, however, and so $\mathfrak{R}_\sigma$ is neither subtractive nor conjunctive.

Similarly one can prove the following result.

THEOREM 8: *The smallest ring containing a countably additive set of somas need not be a complete ring.*

Proof: By Theorem 7 of § 39, the conjunctive closure $\mathfrak{A}^+$ of the totality $\mathfrak{A}$ of all open subsets of the real line is the ring generated by (see § 40) the countably additive set of somas $\mathfrak{A}$. If M is a soma of $\mathfrak{A}^+$, that is, if it is the conjunction of a finite number k of open subsets of the line, and if M' is the complement of M in the real line, then at least one of the two sets M and M' contains a proper interval (proof by mathematical induction on k). Each one-point set, being the conjunction of its complement, which is open, with the entire real line, belongs to $\mathfrak{A}^+$. Therefore, if it were countably additive, this ring would contain all countable subsets of the real line—for example, the set N of all rational points; neither N nor its complement N', however, contains a proper interval. It follows that the ring $\mathfrak{A}^+$ cannot contain the soma N and so cannot be countably additive, i.e., cannot be a complete ring.

We gather from all these results that the problem of determining the smallest complete ring containing a given set $\mathfrak{B}$ of somas is of a completely different nature from the analogous problem, solved in § 40, for ordinary rings of somas. The next few sections (§§ 47-53) will be devoted to a discussion of this problem.

§§ 47-53. Ordinal Numbers of the Second Class

47. Let $\mathfrak{a}$ be a *partially ordered* set (cf. Definition 2 of § 11), whose elements we denote by $a, b, \dots$. We express the relation "a precedes b," for $a \neq b$, by

$$a < b.$$

If *for every pair a, b* of elements of $\mathfrak{a}$ *one and only one* of the relations

$$a < b, \quad a = b, \quad b < a \tag{47.1}$$

holds, then $\mathfrak{a}$ is called an *ordered* (or *totally ordered*) set; in ordered sets, we also express $a < b$ by saying "a comes before b" or "b comes after a." If there is an element a_1 of $\mathfrak{a}$ for which

$$\text{if} \quad x \in \mathfrak{a} \quad \text{then} \quad a_1 \leqq x, \tag{47.2}$$

then a_1 is called the *first* element of $\mathfrak{a}$; the *last* element of $\mathfrak{a}$, if it exists, is defined similarly.

The subsets of an ordered set, of course, are also ordered sets. With each subset $\mathfrak{b}$ of an ordered set $\mathfrak{a}$ we associate a new subset $\mathfrak{m}(\mathfrak{b})$ of $\mathfrak{a}$, which is uniquely defined by the following conditions:

$$\left.\begin{array}{l} \text{if } y > x \text{ for all } x \in \mathfrak{b}, \text{ then } y \in \mathfrak{m}(\mathfrak{b}); \\ \text{if } y \in \mathfrak{m}(\mathfrak{b}) \text{ and } x \in \mathfrak{b}, \text{ then } y > x; \\ \mathfrak{m}(\mathfrak{b}) \text{ is empty if with each } y \in \mathfrak{a} \text{ there} \\ \text{is associated an } x \in \mathfrak{b} \text{ such that } y \leqq x. \end{array}\right\} \tag{47.3}$$

In addition, we introduce the set

$$\mathfrak{n}(\mathfrak{b}) = \mathfrak{a} - \mathfrak{m}(\mathfrak{b}), \tag{47.4}$$

which we call the *cut* of the ordered set $\mathfrak{a}$ generated by $\mathfrak{b}$.

If $\mathfrak{b}$ consists of a single element b, we shall write $\mathfrak{m}(b)$ and $\mathfrak{n}(b)$, respectively, instead of $\mathfrak{m}(\mathfrak{b})$ and $\mathfrak{n}(\mathfrak{b})$. An element c of $\mathfrak{a}$ for which $\mathfrak{m}(c) = O$ must then be the *last* element of $\mathfrak{a}$; such an element need not exist, however.

If x is any element of $\mathfrak{m}(\mathfrak{b})$, every element y of $\mathfrak{a}$ for which $y > x$ is itself an element of $\mathfrak{m}(\mathfrak{b})$. Thus, every subset $\mathfrak{b}_1$ of $\mathfrak{a}$ whose intersection $\mathfrak{b}_1\mathfrak{m}(\mathfrak{b})$ with $\mathfrak{m}(\mathfrak{b})$ is non-empty satisfies

$$\mathfrak{m}(\mathfrak{b}) \succ \mathfrak{m}(\mathfrak{b}_1).$$

If, however, this intersection is empty, that is, if $\mathfrak{b}_1$ is a subset of $\mathfrak{n}(\mathfrak{b})$, then $\mathfrak{m}(\mathfrak{b})$ satisfies

$$\mathfrak{m}(\mathfrak{b}) \prec \mathfrak{m}(\mathfrak{b}_1).$$

Observe that, if $\mathfrak{b}_1, \mathfrak{b}_2, \ldots$ is a finite or infinite collection of subsets of $\mathfrak{a}$, and $\mathfrak{v}$ denotes their union, we have the equations

$$\left.\begin{array}{l} \mathfrak{m}(\mathfrak{v}) = \mathfrak{m}(\mathfrak{b}_1)\,\mathfrak{m}(\mathfrak{b}_2)\ldots, \\ \mathfrak{n}(\mathfrak{v}) = \mathfrak{n}(\mathfrak{b}_1) \dotplus \mathfrak{n}(\mathfrak{b}_2) \dotplus \cdots. \end{array}\right\} \tag{47.5}$$

48. An ordered set $\mathfrak{a}$ is called *well-ordered* if *each* non-empty subset $\mathfrak{b}$ of $\mathfrak{a}$ has a *first* element. The sequence of positive integers in their natural order is well-ordered.

Let $\mathfrak{a}$ be a well-ordered set, and let a be an element of $\mathfrak{a}$ different from the last element (if a last element exists). Then the set $\mathfrak{m}(a)$ defined in § 47 is non-empty, and so has a first element a_1; and no element x of $\mathfrak{a}$ satisfies both relations

$$a < x \quad \text{and} \quad x < a_1.$$

We express this result as follows.

THEOREM 1: *With the exception of the last element, if it exists, of a well-ordered set $\mathfrak{a}$, every element a of $\mathfrak{a}$ has an immediate successor a_1, i.e., an element a_1 that immediately follows a.*

The real numbers in their natural order form an example of an ordered, but not well-ordered set.

49. Considering the sequence of positive integers as a well-ordered set, we can associate with each positive integer p the subsets $\mathfrak{m}(p)$ and $\mathfrak{n}(p)$ described in § 47. It can be shown by mathematical induction that $\mathfrak{m}(p)$ is never empty, so that the sequence of positive integers has no last element, and moreover that $\mathfrak{n}(p)$ always consists of only a finite number of elements.

Now let $\mathfrak{a}$ be a well-ordered set that has both of the above-mentioned properties: for each a in $\mathfrak{a}$, $\mathfrak{m}(a)$ is non-empty and $\mathfrak{n}(a)$ consists of only a finite number of elements.

We denote the first element of $\mathfrak{a}$ by a_1, and associate it with the integer 1. We denote the first element of $\mathfrak{m}(a_1)$ by a_2, and associate it with the integer 2. An element a_n of $\mathfrak{a}$ having been associated with the integer n, we associate with the integer $n + 1$ the first element of $\mathfrak{m}(a_n)$ and we denote this element by a_{n+1}.

In this way, we have inductively defined a one-to-one mapping from the subset

$$a_1, a_2, a_3, \ldots \tag{49.1}$$

of $\mathfrak{a}$ onto the sequence of positive integers; the mapping is *order-preserving*, by which we mean that if n and m are two positive integers with $n < m$, then the corresponding elements a_n and a_m of $\mathfrak{a}$ are related by $a_n < a_m$; two sets related by an order-preserving mapping will be called *similar*.

Moreover, we see, also by induction, that for each a_k in (49.1), the set $\mathfrak{n}(a_k)$ consists of the elements $a_1, a_2, \ldots, a_k$.

We shall now show that the sequence (49.1) is identical with $\mathfrak{a}$. Indeed, if there were an element a of $\mathfrak{a}$ that did not appear in (49.1), then the relation

$a_n < a$ would hold for every positive integer n and thus the set $\mathfrak{n}(a)$ would contain the infinitely many elements (49.1), contrary to hypothesis.

50. If $\mathfrak{a}$ is an *infinite* well-ordered set, then $\mathfrak{m}(a)$ is non-empty whenever $\mathfrak{n}(a)$ consists of only a finite number of elements. The method used in § 49 enables us to prove the following theorem.

Theorem 2: *Every infinite well-ordered set* $\mathfrak{a}$ *contains a countable subset* $\mathfrak{a}_1$ *which is uniquely defined by the conditions*

$\mathfrak{a}_1$ *is similar to the sequence of positive integers, and*
$\mathfrak{n}(\mathfrak{a}_1) = \mathfrak{a}_1$.

The elements of $\mathfrak{a}_1$ may be represented by the positive integers

$$1, 2, 3, \ldots \tag{50.1}$$

in their natural order. If $\mathfrak{m}(\mathfrak{a}_1)$ is empty, then $\mathfrak{a} = \mathfrak{a}_1$; if, on the other hand, $\mathfrak{m}(\mathfrak{a}_1)$ is not empty, we denote by ω the first element of this well-ordered set and say that ω is a *transfinite* number. If $\mathfrak{m}(\omega)$ is non-empty, we denote its first element by $\omega + 1$. Similarly, we denote by $\omega + (n+1)$ the first element of $\mathfrak{m}(\omega + n)$, provided that this set is non-empty. We assume now once and for all that we will never have occasion to speak of a number x for which the well-ordered set $\mathfrak{m}(x)$ is empty. Then we obtain first a well-ordered set

$$\omega, \quad \omega + 1, \quad \omega + 2, \quad \ldots, \tag{50.2}$$

which we denote by $\mathfrak{a}_2$, and we write 2ω for the first element of $\mathfrak{m}(\mathfrak{a}_2)$. Next, we successively define the elements

$$2\,\omega + 1, \quad 2\,\omega + 2, \quad 2\,\omega + 3, \quad \ldots, \tag{50.3}$$

whose totality we denote by $\mathfrak{a}_3$; and we determine the first element 3ω of $\mathfrak{m}(\mathfrak{a}_3)$. Continuing in this way, we obtain elements denoted by $k\omega + n$, where k is a positive integer and n a non-negative integer. Denoting by $\mathfrak{a}_\omega$ the subset of $\mathfrak{a}$ consisting of

$$\omega, \quad 2\,\omega, \quad 3\,\omega, \quad \ldots, \tag{50.4}$$

$\mathfrak{m}(\mathfrak{a}_\omega)$ contains none of the elements $k\omega + n$, and the first element of $\mathfrak{m}(\mathfrak{a}_\omega)$ must be denoted by a new symbol; we call it ω^2. It is possible to continue in this way and to give each of the symbols

$$\omega^n, \quad \omega^\omega, \quad \omega^{\omega^\omega}, \quad \omega^{\omega^{\omega^{\omega \cdots}}}, \tag{50.5}$$

as well as mony others, a precise meaning in terms of the ordering of the elements of $\mathfrak{a}$.

51. It is conceivable, however, that it is impossible to exhaust the well-ordered set $\mathfrak{a}$ by successive enumeration of its elements, and any ordinary mathematician would have found this to be an insuperable difficulty.

Considerations of this sort, however, inspired Georg Cantor to discover the higher classes of ordinal numbers. We shall discuss the ordinal numbers of the *second* class, these being the only ones we shall have need of in the sequel. To this end, we remark that, for each element a of $\mathfrak{a}$ that is named or mentioned in the formulas (5.1) through (50.5), the subset of $\mathfrak{a}$ that we have denoted by $\mathfrak{n}(a)$ is always *at most countable.* Now Cantor discovered a sufficient condition for the procedure described in § 50 to continue indefinitely, namely: $\mathfrak{m}(\mathfrak{b})$ *is never empty for any at most countable subset* $\mathfrak{b}$ *of* $\mathfrak{a}$.

If we now postulate not only that the properties of $\mathfrak{n}(a)$ and $\mathfrak{m}(\mathfrak{b})$ mentioned above shall hold but also that well-ordered sets for which this is the case are all *similar* one to another, then, in the terminology of Cantor, the "order-type" common to all these well-ordered sets represents a set of "numbers," which Cantor called the *ordinal numbers of the second class.* We note that in this definition of ordinal numbers of the second class, the positive integers (ordinal numbers of the *first* class) are included as a subset.

We shall not expatiate any further on these very convincing ideational constructs of Cantor,[3] and we shall merely content ourselves with stating the following axiom.

AXIOM OF ORDINAL NUMBERS OF THE SECOND CLASS: *There are well-ordered sets* $\mathfrak{a}$ *characterized by the following properties:*

1. $\mathfrak{n}(a)$ *is at most countable for each element* a *of* $\mathfrak{a}$;
2. $\mathfrak{m}(\mathfrak{b})$ *is non-empty for every at most countable subset* $\mathfrak{b}$ *of* $\mathfrak{a}$.

All such sets are similar to each other, and any one of them can be used to determine the ordinal numbers of the second class.

[3] To learn more about questions of this sort, the reader is referred, first and foremost, to Cantor himself, whose collected works are available in an edition edited by E. Zermelo: *Gesammelte Abhandlungen* (Berlin, 1932). The most pertinent of the papers are the "Beiträge zur Begründung der transfiniten Mengenlehre" (pp. 282ff.). An outstanding and detailed exposition of Cantor's theory of order types is to be found in Chapters IV and V of Hausdorff's *Grundzüge der Mengenlehre* (Leipzig, 1914; repr., New York, 1949) or in Chapters III and IV of the third edition of the same book *Mengenlehre* (Berlin and Leipzig, 1935), which is also available in English translation: *Set Theory* (2nd ed., New York, 1962). Finally, the critical remarks of H. Lebesgue in *Note sur les nombres transfinis,* which is reprinted on p. 314 of his book *Leçons sur l'Intégration* (2nd ed., Paris, 1928) is well worth reading. It may be added that the *axiom of ordinal numbers of the second class,* formulated below, is provable in the theory of well-ordered sets and ordinal numbers.

52. If $\mathfrak{b}$ is a countable set of ordinal numbers of the second class, then the first element of the non-empty set $\mathfrak{m}(\mathfrak{b})$ is not contained in $\mathfrak{b}$. Thus, we have the following theorem.

THEOREM 3: *The set* $\mathfrak{Z}$ *of ordinal numbers of the second class is not countable.*

Finally, we prove the following result.

THEOREM 4: *A subset* $\mathfrak{Z}_1$ *of the set* $\mathfrak{Z}$ *of ordinal numbers of the second class is identical with* $\mathfrak{Z}$ *if both*

(i) *the first element* 1 *of* $\mathfrak{Z}$ *is in* $\mathfrak{Z}_0$; *and*

(ii) *the first element of* $\mathfrak{m}(\mathfrak{b})$ *is in* $\mathfrak{Z}_0$ *whenever* $\mathfrak{b}$ *is an at most countable subset of* $\mathfrak{Z}_1$.

Proof: Let $\mathfrak{Z}_0$ be a proper subset of $\mathfrak{Z}$ that contains the element 1, and let a be the first element of the complement $\mathfrak{Z} - \mathfrak{Z}_0$ of $\mathfrak{Z}_0$ in $\mathfrak{Z}$. By removing the element a from the set $\mathfrak{n}(a)$, we obtain an at most countable subset $\mathfrak{b}$ of $\mathfrak{Z}_0$. Now the first element of $\mathfrak{m}(\mathfrak{b})$ is a, which is not an element of $\mathfrak{Z}_0$. This contradiction proves the theorem.

53. We shall now construct the smallest complete ring $\overline{\mathfrak{N}}$ of somas containing a given set $\mathfrak{N}$ of somas; we shall call $\mathfrak{N}$ the *complete ring generated by* $\mathfrak{N}$. To his end, we associate with each ordinal number a of the second class a well-defined ring $\mathfrak{R}_a$ that contains all the somas of $\mathfrak{N}$ and is contained in $\overline{\mathfrak{N}}$.

With the integer 1, we associate the ring $\mathfrak{R}_1$ generated by the countably additive closure $\mathfrak{N}_\sigma$ of $\mathfrak{N}$ (cf. §§ 40 and 42).

Let $\mathfrak{b}$ be a set of at most countably many ordinal numbers $a_1, a_2, \ldots$ of the second class with which we have already associated rings $\mathfrak{R}_{a_1}, \mathfrak{R}_{a_2}, \ldots$; and let a be the first element of $\mathfrak{m}(\mathfrak{b})$. We then put

$$\mathfrak{W} = \mathfrak{R}_{a_1} \dotplus \mathfrak{R}_{a_2} \dotplus \cdots,$$

and we let $\mathfrak{R}_a$ be the ring generated by the countably additive closure $\mathfrak{W}_\sigma$ of $\mathfrak{W}$.

In this way, with every ordinal number a of the second class, we have associated a ring $\mathfrak{R}_a$ that contains every soma of $\mathfrak{N}$ and is contained in $\overline{\mathfrak{N}}$. We show that this ring is independent of the choice of the $\mathfrak{b}$ for which a is the first element of $\mathfrak{m}(\mathfrak{b})$. For suppose $\mathfrak{R}_a'$ is a second association of the same sort; let $\mathfrak{c}$ be the set of ordinal numbers a of the second class for which $\mathfrak{R}_a'$ and $\mathfrak{R}_a$ are different. We assume that $\mathfrak{c}$ is not empty and we denote its first element by a_1; let $\mathfrak{b}$ be the at most countable subset of $\mathfrak{Z}$ consisting of all the elements of $\mathfrak{n}(a_1)$ with the exception of a_1 itself. Since a_1 must be > 1, the set $\mathfrak{b}$ is not empty, and a_1 is the first element of $\mathfrak{m}(\mathfrak{b})$. For each element a of $\mathfrak{b}$, $\mathfrak{R}_a = \mathfrak{R}_a'$; hence $\mathfrak{R}_{a_1} = \mathfrak{R}'_{a_1}$, which contradicts our assumption. From this it follows that $\mathfrak{c}$ is empty.

The totality $\mathfrak{S}$ of all somas contained in the various $\mathfrak{R}_a$ is a complete ring. Let us consider a set of at most countably many somas $A_1, A_2, \ldots$ of $\mathfrak{S}$ and their union V. Each of these somas A_j is contained in some first ring $\mathfrak{R}_{a_j}$; let $\mathfrak{b}$ denote the countable set of all these ordinal numbers a_j and let a_0 be the first element of $\mathfrak{m}(\mathfrak{b})$. By construction, the ring $\mathfrak{R}_{a_0}$ contains the soma V, from which it follows that $\mathfrak{S}$ is countably additive. Similarly, it is easy to see that if A and B are somas of $\mathfrak{S}$, the soma $A \dotplus B$ lies in at least one of the rings $\mathfrak{R}_a$; thus, $\mathfrak{S}$ is conjunctive, and hence is a complete ring. On the other hand, every soma in $\mathfrak{S}$ is an element of the smallest complete ring $\overline{\mathfrak{R}}$, to which all the somas of $\mathfrak{R}$ belong, and so we have shown that $\mathfrak{S} = \overline{\mathfrak{R}}$, where $\overline{\mathfrak{R}}$ is the complete ring generated by $\mathfrak{R}$.

§§ 54-55. Hereditary Sets of Somas

54. DEFINITION 1: *A set of somas $\mathfrak{B}$ is called hereditary if every subsoma of a soma of $\mathfrak{B}$ is a soma of $\mathfrak{B}$, i.e., if*

$$\text{if} \quad X \subseteqq B \quad \text{and} \quad B \in \mathfrak{B} \quad \text{then} \quad X \in \mathfrak{B}. \tag{54.1}$$

Given two sets of somas $\mathfrak{A}$ and $\mathfrak{B}$, $\mathfrak{B}$ is said to be hereditary with respect to $\mathfrak{A}$, or $\mathfrak{A}$-hereditary, if every soma of $\mathfrak{A}$ that is a subsoma of a soma of $\mathfrak{B}$ is itself a soma of $\mathfrak{B}$, i.e., if

$$\text{if} \quad X \subseteqq B \quad \text{and} \quad X \in \mathfrak{A}, \quad B \in \mathfrak{B} \quad \text{then} \quad X \in \mathfrak{B}. \tag{54.2}$$

If $\mathfrak{B}$ is hereditary with respect to a subtractive set $\mathfrak{A}$ of somas, and $\mathfrak{B}$ is a subset of $\mathfrak{A}$, then the set $\mathfrak{B}$ of somas is itself subtractive. For if $A \in \mathfrak{B}$ and $B \in \mathfrak{B}$, then A and B belong to $\mathfrak{A}$ and consequently so does $A \dotplus AB$. Since, furthermore, $A \dotplus AB \subseteqq A$, we see by (54.2) that $A \dotplus AB \in \mathfrak{B}$. The corresponding result for multiplicative $\mathfrak{A}$ also holds.

The notion of a *hereditary ring* is similar to the notion of an *ideal* in algebra. For an ideal is defined[4] as a ring containing all the products AB, where A is any element of the ideal and B need not belong to the ideal. But in our case $AB \subseteqq A$, and in fact every soma $C \subseteqq A$ can be written in the form $C = AC$.

[4] See Birkhoff and MacLane, *A Survey of Modern Algebra*, p. 350, or any standard text on abstract algebra. [*Trans.*]

As examples of complete hereditary rings, we mention the ring consisting of the empty soma O alone, and the ring of all the subsomas of a given fixed soma M. To this latter ring there corresponds the algebraic notion of a principal ideal.

Incidentally, there are complete rings that are not hereditary, as well as hereditary rings that are not complete rings. If A is a soma containing a non-empty subsoma distinct from A, then the ring consisting of the two somas O and A is a complete ring, but is not hereditary. On the other hand, the family of all bounded subsets of a euclidean space forms a hereditary ring that is not a complete ring.

55. DEFINITION 2: *Let $\mathfrak{B}$ be a set of somas, and let $\mathfrak{B}_\sigma$ be its countably additive closure. The $\mathfrak{B}$-coverable part of an arbitrary set $\mathfrak{A}$ of somas consists of all those somas of $\mathfrak{A}$ that are subsomas of at least one soma of $\mathfrak{B}_\sigma$.*

The $\mathfrak{B}$-coverable part of $\mathfrak{A}$, which we denote by $\mathfrak{A}_\mathfrak{B}$, is $\mathfrak{A}$-hereditary. For let $X \subseteqq A$, where $X \in \mathfrak{A}$ and $A \in \mathfrak{A}_\mathfrak{B}$. Then there is a soma B of $\mathfrak{B}_\sigma$ for which $A \subseteqq B$ and consequently $X \subseteqq B$. Thus $X \in \mathfrak{A}_\mathfrak{B}$, as was to be shown.

If $\mathfrak{A}$ is countably additive, the $\mathfrak{B}$-coverable part $\mathfrak{A}_\mathfrak{B}$ of $\mathfrak{A}$ is countably additive. If $\mathfrak{A}$ is a complete ring, $\mathfrak{A}_\mathfrak{B}$ is not only countably additive, but also, by § 54, subtractive, and hence, by Theorem 3 of § 44, it is a complete ring. For the case in which $\mathfrak{B}$ is a subset of $\mathfrak{A}$, we have the following theorem.

THEOREM 1: *Where $\mathfrak{B}$ is any subset of a complete ring $\mathfrak{A}$, the $\mathfrak{B}$-coverable part $\mathfrak{A}_\mathfrak{B}$ of $\mathfrak{A}$ is identical with the smallest complete $\mathfrak{A}$-hereditary ring $\mathfrak{B}^*$ that contains every soma of $\mathfrak{B}$.*

Proof: It is clear that $\mathfrak{A}_\mathfrak{B}$ is a complete $\mathfrak{A}$-hereditary ring that contains every soma of $\mathfrak{B}$. If $\mathfrak{B}_1$ is a second ring having these properties, $\mathfrak{B}_1$ must include not only the set of somas $\mathfrak{B}$ but also its countably additive closure $\mathfrak{B}_\sigma$. Then, if X is any soma of $\mathfrak{A}_\mathfrak{B}$, X is a soma of $\mathfrak{A}$ for which there exists a soma $C \supseteqq X$ in $\mathfrak{B}_\sigma$, so that, since $C \in \mathfrak{B}_1$ and $\mathfrak{B}_1$ is $\mathfrak{A}$-hereditary, X belongs to $\mathfrak{B}_1$. Hence $\mathfrak{A}_\mathfrak{B}$ is a subset of $\mathfrak{B}_1$ that must coincide with $\mathfrak{B}^*$.

From this argument we immediately have the following theorem.

THEOREM 2: *The complete ring $\mathfrak{B}$ generated by a set of somas $\mathfrak{B}$ is always $\mathfrak{B}$-coverable.*

Now let $\mathfrak{B}_1^*$ and $\mathfrak{B}_2^*$ denote two complete $\mathfrak{A}$-hereditary rings that are contained in $\mathfrak{A}$, where $\mathfrak{A}$ denotes a complete ring; furthermore, let $\mathfrak{B}_1^* \dotplus \mathfrak{B}_2^*$ denote the totality of somas in $\mathfrak{B}_1^*$ or $\mathfrak{B}_2^*$. Finally, let $\mathfrak{B}^*$ be the $(\mathfrak{B}_1^* \dotplus \mathfrak{B}_2^*)$-coverable part of $\mathfrak{A}$, and let $\mathfrak{B}^{\dotplus}$ and $\mathfrak{B}^+$ be the additive and conjunctive closures, respectively, of $\mathfrak{B}_1^* \dotplus \mathfrak{B}_2^*$.

Since the sets $\mathfrak{B}_1^*$ and $\mathfrak{B}_2^*$ of somas are countably additive, there can be associated with each soma X of $\mathfrak{B}^*$ a soma B_1 of $\mathfrak{B}_1^*$ and a soma B_2 of $\mathfrak{B}_2^*$ in such a way that

$$X \subseteqq B_1 \dotplus B_2 \,. \tag{55.1}$$

If we put

$$X_1 = X\,(B_1 \underset{\cdot}{+} B_1 B_2)\,, \quad X_2 = X B_2\,, \tag{55.2}$$

X_1 is a soma of $\mathfrak{B}_1^*$ and X_2 is a soma of $\mathfrak{B}_2^*$, since each of these sets of somas is $\mathfrak{A}$-hereditary.

Consequently,

$$X = X_1 \dotplus X_2 \tag{55.3}$$

is an element of the additive closure $\mathfrak{B}^{\dotplus}$ of $\mathfrak{B}_1^* \dotplus \mathfrak{B}_2^*$, and so the set $\mathfrak{B}^*$ of somas is included in $\mathfrak{B}^{\dotplus}$. Conversely, each soma of $\mathfrak{B}^{\dotplus}$ belongs to $\mathfrak{B}^*$, since $\mathfrak{B}^*$ is additive, and so we have

$$\mathfrak{B}^* = \mathfrak{B}^{\dotplus}. \tag{55.4}$$

The equation

$$\mathfrak{B}^* = \mathfrak{B}^{\underset{\cdot}{+}} \tag{55.5}$$

is proved in a similar way, for the somas X_1 and X_2 of (55.2) are disjoint, so that equation (55.3) can also be written in the form

$$X = X_1 \underset{\cdot}{+} X_2 \,.$$

Taking § 40 and Theorem 1 above into consideration, we see that we have proved the following theorem.

Theorem 3: *Let a complete ring $\mathfrak{A}$ include the complete $\mathfrak{A}$-hereditary rings $\mathfrak{B}_1^*$ and $\mathfrak{B}_2^*$. Then the additive and conjunctive closures of the set of somas $\mathfrak{B}_1^* \dotplus \mathfrak{B}_2^*$ coincide with each other and with the ring generated by all the somas of $\mathfrak{B}_1^*$ and $\mathfrak{B}_2^*$. This ring, furthermore, is a complete $\mathfrak{A}$-hereditary ring and forms the $(\mathfrak{B}_1^* \dotplus \mathfrak{B}_2^*)$-coverable part $\mathfrak{B}^*$ of $\mathfrak{A}$.*

§§ 56-64. Homomorphisms of Rings of Somas

56. We consider a complete ring $\mathfrak{A}$ of somas $A, B, \ldots$ and a set $\mathfrak{A}_0'$ of somas $A', B', \ldots$ in another system. Let there be assigned to each soma A of $\mathfrak{A}$ a uniquely determined soma A' of $\mathfrak{A}_0'$; we express this by writing

$$A' = \sigma A \qquad (A \in \mathfrak{A}). \tag{56.1}$$

However, it remains possible for *different* somas from $\mathfrak{A}$ to have the *same* image in $\mathfrak{A}_0'$.

A mapping of this kind, for example, is an orthogonal projection of the points (x, y, z) of three-dimensional euclidean space onto the (x, y)-plane.

The totality of somas A' for which (56.1) holds forms a subset of $\mathfrak{A}_0'$, which we denote by $\mathfrak{A}'$. We may also write

$$\mathfrak{A}' = \sigma\,\mathfrak{A} \tag{56.2}$$

without danger of confusion.

DEFINITION: *The mapping* $\mathfrak{A}' = \sigma\mathfrak{A}$ *is called a homomorphism if, first,*

$$A_j \in \mathfrak{A} \quad (j = 1, 2, \ldots) \quad \textit{and} \quad A = \sum_j \dot{+}\, A_j \tag{56.3}$$

whenever

$$\sigma A = \sum_j \dot{+}\, \sigma A_j, \tag{56.4}$$

and, second, $\sigma A \circ \sigma B$ *whenever* $A \circ B$.

These conditions are independent: The orthogonal projection discussed above satisfies the first condition, but not the second, since two distinct points may have the same projection. On the other hand, if we denote the subsets of a euclidean space by $A, B, \ldots$, and if we let

$$A' = \sigma A$$

denote the interior of A (i.e., the totality of interior points of A), then the second condition is satisfied, but not the first.

An example in which both conditions are satisfied is obtained by choosing a fixed non-empty subset A_0 of a euclidean space and, for each subset A, putting

$$A' = \sigma A = A \dot{+} A A_0. \tag{56.5}$$

57. If σ is a homomorphism, the relation $\sigma B \subseteqq \sigma A$ is a consequence of $B \subseteqq A$. For, the last relation can also be written as

$$A \dot{+} B = A;$$

by assumption, then, we have

$$\sigma A = \sigma(A \dot{+} B) = \sigma A \dot{+} \sigma B,$$

whence it follows that $\sigma B \subseteqq \sigma A$.

Now if A and B are any two somas of $\mathfrak{A}$, let us consider the two somas

$$X = B \underset{\cdot}{+} AB, \quad Y = AB, \tag{57.1}$$

which can be characterized[5] by the relations

$$X \circ A, \quad Y \subseteqq A, \quad X \dotplus Y = B. \tag{57.2}$$

Now from (57.2), it follows that

$$\sigma X \circ \sigma A, \quad \sigma Y \subseteqq \sigma A, \quad \sigma X \dotplus \sigma Y = \sigma B, \tag{57.3}$$

and this means that we can write

$$\sigma X = \sigma B \underset{\cdot}{+} \sigma A \, \sigma B, \quad \sigma Y = \sigma A \, \sigma B, \tag{57.4}$$

or, taking (57.1) into account,

$$\sigma(B \underset{\cdot}{+} AB) = \sigma B \underset{\cdot}{+} \sigma A \, \sigma B, \quad \sigma(AB) = \sigma A \, \sigma B. \tag{57.5}$$

Now observe that we have the relations

$$(A \underset{\cdot}{+} AB) \circ (B \underset{\cdot}{+} AB), \quad (A \underset{\cdot}{+} B) = (A \underset{\cdot}{+} AB) \dotplus (B \underset{\cdot}{+} AB).$$

From these relations it follows that

$$\begin{aligned} \sigma(A \underset{\cdot}{+} B) &= \sigma(A \underset{\cdot}{+} AB) \dotplus \sigma(B \underset{\cdot}{+} AB) \\ &= \sigma(A \underset{\cdot}{+} AB) \underset{\cdot}{+} \sigma(B \underset{\cdot}{+} AB); \end{aligned}$$

consequently, using (57.5), we see that

$$\sigma(A \underset{\cdot}{+} B) = \sigma A \underset{\cdot}{+} \sigma B. \tag{57.6}$$

The empty soma O, which must be an element of the complete ring $\mathfrak{A}$, satisfies

$$\sigma O = \sigma(A \underset{\cdot}{+} A) = \sigma A \underset{\cdot}{+} \sigma A = O', \tag{57.7}$$

where O' denotes the empty soma of the second system.

---

[5] Indeed, it follows from these relations that

$$AX = O, \quad AY = Y, \quad AB = AX \dotplus AY = Y, \quad XY = XAB = O,$$
$$X = B \underset{\cdot}{+} Y \underset{\cdot}{+} XY = B \underset{\cdot}{+} AB.$$

We conclude from all these equations and from (56.4) that the set of somas

$$\mathfrak{A}' = \sigma\,\mathfrak{A} \tag{57.8}$$

contained in the set $\mathfrak{A}_0'$ is a complete ring.

If the somas A and B are complementary with respect to a soma M, then σA and σB must be complementary with respect to σM. We consider two sequences of somas $\{A_j\}$ and $\{B_j\}$ satisfying

$$A_j + B_j = M \qquad (j = 1, 2, \ldots) \tag{57.9}$$

and define the somas V and D by

$$V = \sum_j \dot{+}\, B_j, \quad D = M \dot{+} V. \tag{57.10}$$

By what we have already shown, we have

$$\sigma\,A_j + \sigma\,B_j = \sigma\,M\,, \quad \sigma\,V = \sum_j \dot{+}\,\sigma\,B_j\,, \quad \sigma\,D = \sigma\,M \dot{+} \sigma\,V. \tag{57.11}$$

From (57.10) and (57.11), we obtain (Theorem 1 of § 23) that

$$D = \prod_j A_j\,, \quad \sigma\,D = \prod_j \sigma\,A_j\,. \tag{57.12}$$

We summarize all these results in the following theorem.

THEOREM 1: *A homomorphism σ always satisfies the following two relations:*

$$\sigma(A \dot{+} B) = \sigma\,A \dot{+} \sigma\,B\,, \tag{57.13}$$

$$\sigma(\prod_j A_j) = \prod_j \sigma\,A_j\,. \tag{57.14}$$

Furthermore, by § 25, we have the following theorem.

THEOREM 2: *A homomorphism maps the upper and the lower limits of a sequence of somas into the corresponding limits of the sequence of images.*

58. Let $\mathfrak{N}$ denote the totality of somas U that are mapped onto the empty soma O'; by (57.7), the set $\mathfrak{N}$ contains at least the empty soma O. It is immediately obvious that the union $U_1 \dot{+} U_2 \dot{+} \ldots$ of at most countably many somas of $\mathfrak{N}$ is itself a soma of $\mathfrak{N}$, and that the same is true of a subsoma of any soma of $\mathfrak{N}$ that is a soma of $\mathfrak{A}$.

We have thus proved the following theorem.

THEOREM 3: *The set of somas $\mathfrak{N}$ whose elements $U, V, \ldots$ are mapped onto the empty soma O' by a homomorphism is a complete $\mathfrak{A}$-hereditary ring.*

If

$$\sigma A = \sigma B, \tag{58.1}$$

then, by (57.13),

$$\sigma(A \underset{\cdot}{+} B) = \sigma A \underset{\cdot}{+} \sigma B = O',$$

that is,

$$A \underset{\cdot}{+} B = U \qquad (U \in \mathfrak{N}), \tag{58.2}$$

or

$$A = B \underset{\cdot}{+} U \qquad (U \in \mathfrak{N}). \tag{58.3}$$

Conversely, (58.1) is a direct consequence of (58.3).

We deduce from the condition (58.3) that

$$A \dotplus BU = (B \underset{\cdot}{+} U) + BU = B \dotplus U,$$

which can also be written as

$$A \dotplus U_1 = B \dotplus V_1 \qquad (U_1, V_1 \in \mathfrak{N}), \tag{58.4}$$

since the ring $\mathfrak{N}$ is $\mathfrak{A}$-hereditary. But now, since equation (58.1) follows from (58.4) also, we may combine all these results in the following theorem.

THEOREM 4: *Two somas A and B in $\mathfrak{A}$ satisfy*

$$\sigma A = \sigma B,$$

if and only if one of the two equivalent equations

$$A \underset{\cdot}{+} B = U \qquad (U \in \mathfrak{N}), \tag{58.5}$$

$$A \dotplus U_1 = B \dotplus V_1 \qquad (U_1, V_1 \in \mathfrak{N}) \tag{58.6}$$

holds.

Similarly, from

$$\sigma A \subseteqq \sigma B \tag{58.7}$$

there follows the relation

$$\sigma(A \underset{\cdot}{+} AB) = \sigma A \underset{\cdot}{+} \sigma A \, \sigma B = O',$$

which is equivalent to

$$A \underset{\cdot}{+} AB = U \qquad (U \in \mathfrak{N}). \qquad (58.8)$$

But this equation implies

$$A = AB \underset{\cdot}{+} U \subseteqq AB \dotplus U \subseteqq B \dotplus U; \qquad (58.9)$$

conversely, if $A \subseteqq B \dotplus U$, we have

$$\sigma A \subseteqq \sigma(B \dotplus U) = \sigma B \dotplus \sigma U = \sigma B,$$

and we have thus proved the following theorem.

Theorem 5: *Two somas A and B satisfy*

$$\sigma A \subseteqq \sigma B \qquad (58.10)$$

if and only if one of the two equivalent relations

$$A = AB \underset{\cdot}{+} U \qquad (U \in \mathfrak{N}), \qquad (58.11)$$

$$A \subseteqq B \dotplus V \qquad (V \in \mathfrak{N}) \qquad (58.12)$$

holds.

59. Theorem 3 allows of the following converse:

Theorem 6: *Let $\mathfrak{N}$ be a complete $\mathfrak{A}$-hereditary ring contained in $\mathfrak{A}$. Then a homomorphism $A' = \sigma A$ can be found which maps the somas of $\mathfrak{N}$, and these alone, onto the empty soma O'.*

Proof: Define the *congruence*

$$A \equiv B \pmod{\mathfrak{N}} \qquad (59.1)$$

by either of the equations

$$A = B \underset{\cdot}{+} U \qquad (U \in \mathfrak{N}), \qquad (59.2)$$

$$A \dotplus U_1 = B \dotplus V_1 \qquad (U_1, V_1 \in \mathfrak{N}), \qquad (59.3)$$

which are of course equivalent, as can be verified by a procedure similar to that in the proof of Theorem 4 above.

Congruences of the type (59.1), to be sure, are meaningful only if (i) $A \equiv A$ and (ii) $B \equiv C$ whenever $A \equiv B$ and $A \equiv C$. But these properties follow immediately from (59.3) and the observation that $\mathfrak{N}$ is an additive set of somas.

We can calculate with these congruences. For the relations

$$A_1 \equiv B_1 \pmod{\mathfrak{N}}, \quad A_2 \equiv B_2 \pmod{\mathfrak{N}} \tag{59.4}$$

are equivalent with

$$A_1 = B_1 \dotplus U_1, \quad A_2 = B_2 \dotplus U_2 \qquad (U_1, U_2 \in \mathfrak{N}). \tag{59.5}$$

Now,

$$U_1 \dotplus U_2 \in \mathfrak{N}, \quad (B_2 U_1 \dotplus B_1 U_2 \dotplus U_1 U_2) \in \mathfrak{N}; \tag{59.6}$$

the first, since $\mathfrak{N}$ is a ring, and the second, since it is $\mathfrak{A}$-hereditary. Thus, we can state the following:

$$\left.\begin{aligned} &\text{If } A_1 \equiv B_2 \text{ and } A_1 \equiv B_2 \pmod{\mathfrak{N}} \text{ then} \\ &A_1 \dotplus A_2 \equiv B_1 \dotplus B_2 \text{ and } A_1 A_2 \equiv B_1 B_2 \pmod{\mathfrak{N}}. \end{aligned}\right\} \tag{59.7}$$

We consider the at most countable sequences of somas A_j and B_j satisfying

$$A_j \equiv B_j \pmod{\mathfrak{N}} \qquad (j = 1, 2, \ldots). \tag{59.8}$$

By (59.3), these congruences may be written as

$$A_j \dotplus U_j = B_j \dotplus V_j \qquad (U_j, V_j \in \mathfrak{N}). \tag{59.9}$$

Consequently,

$$\Big(\sum_j \dotplus A_j\Big) \dotplus \Big(\sum_j \dotplus U_j\Big) = \Big(\sum_j \dotplus B_j\Big) \dotplus \Big(\sum_j \dotplus V_j\Big), \tag{59.10}$$

and since $\mathfrak{N}$ is a complete ring, we have

$$\sum_j \dotplus U_j \in \mathfrak{N}, \quad \sum_j \dotplus V_j \in \mathfrak{N}, \tag{59.11}$$

so that

$$\sum_j \dotplus A_j \equiv \sum_j \dotplus B_j \pmod{\mathfrak{N}} \tag{59.12}$$

follows from (59.10), and hence from (59.8).

60. We call the set of those somas which are congruent, in the sense of (59.1), to a given soma A, a *congruence-class* with *representative* A. Each such congruence class, which we shall denote by $Cl(A)$, is to be considered a single mathematical entity. With these conventions agreed upon, the two relations

$$B \in Cl(A), \tag{60.1}$$

$$A \equiv B \pmod{\mathfrak{N}} \tag{60.2}$$

are obviously equivalent.

Thus, the statement:

$$\text{if } A \equiv B \text{ and } A \equiv C, \text{ then } B \equiv C$$

is equivalent with the statement:

$$\text{if } B \in Cl(A), \text{ then } Cl(A) = Cl(B).$$

Thus, any soma which is an element of a congruence class can be chosen as a representative of that class.

61. We introduce the operations of conjunction and multiplication into the system of congruence classes, as follows. Let Cl_1 and Cl_2 be two congruence classes and let A_1 and A_2 be representatives of these classes. Define

$$Cl_1 \dot{+} Cl_2 = Cl(A_1 \dot{+} A_2), \tag{61.1}$$

$$Cl_1 \cdot Cl_2 = Cl(A_1 A_2). \tag{61.2}$$

By (59.7), these definitions are independent of the choice of representatives and they convert the system of congruence classes into a Boolean ring. In fact, the operations (61.1) and (61.2) satisfy all the conditions of Axioms 1, 2, and 3 of §§ 8-10.

To show, finally, that the congruence classes can be interpreted as somas, we must verify Axiom 4 of § 13, i.e., we must show that for each countable sequence of classes

$$Cl_j \qquad (j = 1, 2, \ldots) \tag{61.3}$$

there is a minimal class containing all the classes of the sequence. Let

$$A_j \qquad (j = 1, 2, \ldots) \tag{61.4}$$

be representatives of the classes (61.3). Put

$$Cl^v = Cl\Big(\sum_j \dot{+} A_j\Big). \tag{61.5}$$

First, the result at the end of § 59 assures us that the class Cl^v is independent of the choice of representatives A_j of the classes Cl_j. Next,

$$Cl_k \cdot Cl^v = Cl(A_k)\, Cl\Big(\sum_j \dot{+} A_j\Big) = Cl\Big(A_k \sum_j \dot{+} A_j\Big) = Cl(A_k) = Cl_k. \tag{61.6}$$

Thus, Cl^v is a containing class common to all the Cl_k.

Finally, if Cl^w is a containing class common to all the Cl_j, and W is a representative of Cl^w, then from

$$Cl_j \cdot Cl^w = Cl_j \qquad (j = 1, 2, \ldots), \qquad (61.7)$$

we deduce, one after the other, the relations

$$Cl(A_j)\ Cl(W) = Cl(A_j),$$
$$Cl(A_j W) = Cl(A_j),$$
$$A_j \equiv A_j W \ (\mathrm{mod}\ \mathfrak{N}),$$

and by (59.12) and Theorem 5 of § 15,

$$\sum_j \dot{+} A_j \equiv W \sum_j \dot{+} A_j \ (\mathrm{mod}\ \mathfrak{N}),$$
$$Cl\Big(\sum_j \dot{+} A_j\Big) = Cl\Big(W \sum_j \dot{+} A_j\Big) = Cl(W)\ Cl\Big(\sum_j \dot{+} A_j\Big),$$

so that, by (61.5),

$$Cl^v = Cl^w\ Cl^v. \qquad (61.8)$$

It follows from (61.6) and (61.8) that Cl^v is indeed the minimal common containing class of the sequence Cl_j $(j = 1, 2, \ldots)$. Thus, we may write

$$Cl^v = \sum_j \dot{+}\ Cl_j. \qquad (61.9)$$

The congruence classes thus form a system of somas A', B', ..., in which the empty soma O' is given by the equation

$$O' = Cl(A) \dot{+} Cl(A) = Cl(A \dot{+} A) = Cl(O). \qquad (61.10)$$

The relation between a soma A of the original ring $\mathfrak{A}$ and the congruence class $Cl(A)$, of which A is a representative, can be expressed by a mapping

$$A' = \sigma A = Cl(A). \qquad (61.11)$$

This mapping is a homomorphism; for not only do we have the equation (61.5) which, in conjunction with (61.9), is equivalent to the relation (56.4), but also whenever $A \circ B$ we have

$$\sigma A \cdot \sigma B = \sigma(AB) = \sigma(O) = O'.$$

Finally, the somas of $\mathfrak{N}$ are the only ones belonging to the congruence class $Cl(O)$; this completes the proof of Theorem 6 of § 59.

62. Let

$$A' = \sigma A, \quad B'' = \tau B \qquad (A, B \in \mathfrak{A})$$

be two homomorphisms that map the *same* complete $\mathfrak{A}$-hereditary ring $\mathfrak{N}$ onto the empty somas O' and O'', respectively. We can associate with each soma A' in $\mathfrak{A}' = \sigma\mathfrak{A}$ a unique soma A'' in $\mathfrak{A}'' = \tau\mathfrak{A}$ by finding any soma A for which $A' = \sigma A$ and letting $A'' = \tau A$. This mapping $A'' = \varrho A'$ is clearly a homomorphism for which each soma A'' is the image of *exactly one* soma A'.

Let us make the following definition.

DEFINITION: *A homomorphism in which the mapping $A' = \sigma A$ is one to one, is called an isomorphism.*

There are many investigations in which isomorphic rings of somas can be considered as equivalent mathematical objects. In that case, we have the following theorem.

THEOREM 7: *Every homomorphism is determined uniquely to within isomorphism by the subring $\mathfrak{N}$ consisting of those somas of $\mathfrak{A}$ that are mapped onto the empty soma O'.*

63. Suppose that a given homomorphism

$$A' = \sigma A \tag{63.1}$$

maps a subset $\mathfrak{B} \prec \mathfrak{A}$ onto the set

$$\mathfrak{B}' = \sigma \mathfrak{B}. \tag{63.2}$$

From the formulas of §§ 56-57, it is clear that if $\mathfrak{B}$ is additive, countably additive, multiplicative, countably multiplicative, conjunctive, or subtractive, then so is $\mathfrak{B}'$, and conversely.

The property of being hereditary is also carried over from $\mathfrak{B}$ to $\mathfrak{B}'$. On the assumption that $\mathfrak{B}$ is $\mathfrak{A}$-hereditary, it must be shown that

$$\text{if } A' \in \mathfrak{B}',\ B' \in \mathfrak{A}' \text{ and } B' \subseteqq A' \text{ then } B' \in \mathfrak{B}'. \tag{63.3}$$

By Theorem 5 of § 58, the relation $B' \subseteqq A'$ implies that there are three somas A, B, and U such that $B = AB \dotplus U$, where

$$\left.\begin{array}{l} A \in \mathfrak{B}, \quad B \in \mathfrak{A}, \quad U \in \mathfrak{N}, \\ \sigma A = A', \quad \sigma B = B', \quad \sigma U = O' \end{array}\right\} \tag{63.4}$$

Since $\mathfrak{B}$ is $\mathfrak{A}$-hereditary by assumption, the soma

$$B \dot{+} U = AB, \tag{63.5}$$

being a subsoma of A, is in $\mathfrak{B}$. Hence

$$\sigma(B \dot{+} U) = \sigma B \dot{+} \sigma U = \sigma B = B' \tag{63.6}$$

is in $\sigma\mathfrak{B} = \mathfrak{B}'$ and, as was to be shown, $B' \in \mathfrak{B}'$.

64. Again, let $\mathfrak{A}$ be a complete ring of somas; in addition, let $\mathfrak{R}_1$ and $\mathfrak{R}_2$ be two complete $\mathfrak{A}$-hereditary rings included in $\mathfrak{A}$. Then, by Theorem 6 of § 59, there are two homomorphisms

$$A' = \sigma_1 A, \quad A'' = \sigma_2 A, \tag{64.1}$$

determined uniquely to within isomorphism, that map the somas of the rings $\mathfrak{R}_1$ and $\mathfrak{R}_2$ onto the empty somas O' and O'', respectively.

By § 63, the set of somas

$$\mathfrak{R}_2' = \sigma_1 \mathfrak{R}_2 \tag{64.2}$$

is a complete $\mathfrak{A}'$-hereditary ring contained in

$$\mathfrak{A}' = \sigma_1 \mathfrak{A}. \tag{64.3}$$

Consequently, there is a homomorphism

$$A^* = \tau_2 A' \tag{64.4}$$

mapping $\mathfrak{A}'$ onto the ring of somas

$$\mathfrak{A}^* = \tau_2 \mathfrak{A}', \tag{64.5}$$

for which the set of somas mapped onto the empty soma O^* is precisely $\mathfrak{R}_2'$.

The relation (64.4) can be interpreted as a mapping

$$A^* = \tau_2(\sigma_1 A) = \varrho A \tag{64.6}$$

from the set $\mathfrak{A}$ of somas onto the set $\mathfrak{A}^*$; this mapping can easily be shown to be a homomorphism. We denote by $\mathfrak{R}^*$ the totality of somas of $\mathfrak{A}$ that are mapped onto the empty soma O^* by this homomorphism.

The set $\mathfrak{R}^*$, then, consists of all the somas X of $\mathfrak{A}$ for which $\sigma_1 X$ is in the ring $\mathfrak{R}_2'$. It follows that a soma U_2 in $\mathfrak{R}_2$ can be associated with each soma X of $\mathfrak{R}^*$ in such a way that

$$\sigma_1 X = \sigma_1 U_2. \tag{64.7}$$

By Theorem 4 of § 58, there must then be a soma $U_1 \in \mathfrak{N}_1$ for which

$$X = U_1 \dotplus U_2 ; \tag{64.8}$$

moreover, this relation is equivalent to (64.7).

Accordingly, the ring $\mathfrak{N}^*$ can be represented as the conjunctive closure of the set of somas $\mathfrak{N}_1 \dotplus \mathfrak{N}_2$. By Theorem 3 of § 55, therefore, it is the ring generated by all the somas of $\mathfrak{N}_1$ and $\mathfrak{N}_2$.

In virtue of this result, the roles of $\mathfrak{N}_1$ and $\mathfrak{N}_2$ can be interchanged in the computation of $\mathfrak{N}^*$, and we obtain the following theorem.

Theorem 8: *Let $\mathfrak{N}_1$ and $\mathfrak{N}_2$ be two complete $\mathfrak{A}$-hereditary rings included in the complete ring $\mathfrak{A}$, and let $\mathfrak{N}^*$ be the ring generated by all the somas of $\mathfrak{N}_1$ and $\mathfrak{N}_2$. Let*

$$A' = \sigma_1 A , \quad A'' = \sigma_2 A \tag{64.9}$$

denote homomorphisms carrying the rings $\mathfrak{N}_1$ and $\mathfrak{N}_2$ into the empty somas O' and O'', respectively. In addition, put

$$\mathfrak{N}_2' = \sigma_1 \mathfrak{N}_2 , \quad \mathfrak{N}_1'' = \sigma_2 \mathfrak{N}_1 , \tag{64.10}$$

and let

$$\tau_2 A' , \quad \tau_1 A'' \tag{64.11}$$

denote homomorphisms carrying the rings $\mathfrak{N}_2'$ and $\mathfrak{N}_1''$ into the empty soma. Then the homomorphism

$$A^* = \varrho A , \tag{64.12}$$

which carries the ring $\mathfrak{N}^*$ into the empty soma O^* can be represented, to within isomorphism, by the equations

$$A^* = \tau_2(\sigma_1 A) = \tau_1(\sigma_2 A) = \varrho A . \tag{64.13}$$

In the case in which, in the notation of the theorem, $\mathfrak{N}_1 \prec \mathfrak{N}_2$, we of course have that $\mathfrak{N}_2 = \mathfrak{N}^*$, and hence also that

$$\tau_1 A'' = A'' , \quad \varrho A = \sigma_2 A . \tag{64.14}$$

This latter case occurs quite often in applications.

CHAPTER THREE

PLACE FUNCTIONS

§§ 65-68. Finitely-valued Place Functions

65. Our next goal is to develop a notion that plays the same role in the theory of somas as does that of point function in euclidean spaces (and in abstract spaces). Inasmuch as somas need not be composed of individual elements (compare § 311), the usual definition of point function must of course be replaced by another definition that is suited to our theory as well.

With this purpose in mind, we consider a finite number of distinct real numbers

$$-\infty,\ y_1,\ y_2,\ \ldots,\ y_m \tag{65.1}$$

and assign to each point P in the domain of definition of the point function $f(P)$ the largest of the numbers (65.1) which is $\leqq f(P)$. In this way, we obtain a new function $\varphi_m(P)$, which takes on only a finite number of values and is therefore called *finitely-valued.*

If, then, $\{y_\nu\}$ is an infinite sequence of distinct real numbers that is everywhere dense on the real line and if the y_j of (65.1) are taken to be the first m elements of this sequence, we see first that

$$\varphi_1(P) \leqq \varphi_2(P) \leqq \varphi_3(P) \leqq \ldots$$

and second that

$$f(P) = \lim_{m=\infty} \varphi_m(P).$$

Thus, every point function can be obtained as the least upper bound of a sequence of finitely-valued functions.

This process can be carried over, word for word, to the theory of somas.

66. We begin, then, by constructing finitely-valued functions. To this end, we consider decompositions of a *given fixed* soma M into a finite number of *non-empty,* pairwise disjoint somas M_j,

$$M = M_1 + M_2 + \cdots + M_p, \tag{66.1}$$

and to each of these somas we assign a finite real number y_j or one of the numbers $\pm\infty$. Just as a country is made up of towns, each with its own name, so our configuration is made up of a mosaic of somas M_j, each named by one of the numbers y_j. Such configurations will therefore be called *finitely-valued place functions, with domain of definition M*; we shall also use, alternatively, the less suggestive but more compact term *functionoid*. In what follows, place functions will be denoted by lower-case italic letters, e.g., by

$$f, g, \ldots .$$

Sometimes we will express finitely-valued place functions, more explicitly, as

$$f = \sum_j y_j M_j . \tag{66.2}$$

The results to be obtained in this chapter all stem from the fundamental fact that the finitely-valued place functions, as well as the more general place functions that we shall introduce later, can be partially ordered.

Indeed, if

$$M = M_1' + M_2' + \cdots + M_p', \quad M = M_1'' + M_2'' + \cdots + M_q'' \tag{66.3}$$

are two decompositions of M, then M is also the sum of all the *non-empty* intersections $M_i'M_j''$. Now if

$$f = \sum_i y_i M_i', \quad g = \sum_j z_j M_j'' \tag{66.4}$$

are two place functions, we shall say that

$$f \leqq g \tag{66.5}$$

if

$$M_i' M_j'' \neq 0$$

for every pair of indices i, j such that

$$y_i \leqq z_j .$$

We can easily verify that the conditions

$$\left.\begin{array}{c} f \leqq f, \\ \text{if } f \leqq g \text{ and } g \leqq h \text{ then } f \leqq h \end{array}\right\} \tag{66.6}$$

of Definition 2 of § 11 are satisfied.

It is quite important to require in addition that two finitely-valued place functions f and g which satisfy both $f \leqq g$ and $g \leqq f$, be viewed as the same mathematical entity. It follows from this requirement that every soma M_j on which a finitely-valued place function is constant can be replaced by any of its decompositions, and two somas M_j and M_k on which f assumes the same value, can be replaced by their sum. Thus, the representation of f in the form (66.2) can be replaced by another having the property that $y_j \neq y_k$ whenever $j \neq k$.

Likewise, there is no loss of generality, whenever a finite number of finitely-valued place functions $f', f'', \ldots, f^{(p)}$ are given, if we use, for each of them, a decomposition of their common domain of definition M that is made up of the same somas. Thus, we may always write

$$f' = \sum_j y_j' M_j, \quad f'' = \sum_j y_j'' M_j, \quad \ldots, \quad f^{(p)} = \sum_j y_j^{(p)} M_j. \tag{66.7}$$

A place function that has the constant value a everywhere on its domain of definition M will from now on be denoted by the letter a itself. This convention has the advantage, among others, that it allows us to set up equations such as

$$f = 0,$$

in which the right-hand side denotes the constant place function, zero.

67. Let two finitely-valued place functions

$$f = \sum_j y_j M_j, \quad g = \sum_j z_j M_j \tag{67.1}$$

be given; if we put

$$h = \sum_j \max(y_j, z_j) M_j, \tag{67.2}$$

then h is a finitely-valued place function that satisfies the relations

$$f \leqq h, \quad g \leqq h. \tag{67.3}$$

For any other place function

$$h^* = \sum_j w_j M_j \tag{67.4}$$

that satisfies the conditions

$$f \leqq h^*, \quad g \leqq h^*, \tag{67.5}$$

the inequalities

$$y_j \leqq w_j, \quad z_j \leqq w_j, \quad \max(y_j, z_j) \leqq w_j$$

hold, from which it follows that

$$h \leqq h^*. \tag{67.6}$$

Since, by the penultimate paragraph of § 66, there is no loss of generality in writing three arbitrary finitely-valued place functions f, g, h^* in the forms (67.1) and (67.4), we have thus demonstrated the existence of a smallest function

$$h = \max(f, g)$$

that is greater than or equal to each of the original place functions f and g.

In the same way, we can show that there exists a largest function

$$\min(f, g) = \sum_j \min(y_j, z_j)\, M_j$$

that is less than or equal to each of the functions f and g.

A partially ordered set of elements $f, g, \ldots$, that has the above-mentioned properties, is called a *lattice*.[1]

68. We now consider arbitrary infinite sequences

$$\{f_\nu\}\colon f_1, f_2, f_3, \cdots \tag{68.1}$$

of finitely-valued place functions. The equations

$$g_1 = f_1, \quad g_2 = \max(g_1, f_2), \quad \ldots, \quad g_{\nu+1} = \max(g_\nu, f_{\nu+1}), \quad \ldots \tag{68.2}$$

define a new sequence of such functions that satisfies the condition

$$g_1 \leqq g_2 \leqq g_3 \leqq \cdots, \tag{68.3}$$

i.e., that is monotonically increasing.

Now, it is conceivable that from a certain positive integer n on $(N \geqq n)$, all the g_N are equal to g_n. Then g_n is the "least upper bound" of the sequence (68.1), that is, there is a smallest *finitely-valued* place function that is $\geqq$ all the f_ν. But even a consideration of finitely-valued point functions, which are but a special case of place functions, shows that this is only rarely the case.

We find ourselves in the same situation as we did at one point in the theory of real numbers, where we found that the least upper bounds of monotonically increasing sequences of rational numbers need not be rational

[1] For the theory of lattices, see the new edition of the first volume of the *Enzyklopadie der Mathematischen Wissenschaften* (Algebra und Zahlentheorie) I, 1, 13: H. Hermes and G. Köthe, "Die Theorie der Verbände" (as of 1939); or see G. Birkhoff, *Lattice Theory* (Amer. Math. Soc. Colloquium Publications, Vol. 25; 2nd ed., 1948).

numbers and that such sequences can be used for defining irrational numbers.[2]

In complete analogy with this procedure, the at most countable sets $\{f_\nu\}$ of finitely-valued place functions can not only be partially ordered but can also be considered to be the elements of a "closed" lattice which is a generalization of the lattice of finitely-valued place functions; that is, these sets can be embedded in the "closure" of the lattice of finitely-valued place functions. The elements $\{f_\nu\}$ of this extended lattice can thus be viewed as "general" place functions. It is more convenient to achieve this result in a somewhat different way. We shall produce the lattice of general place functions by a direct construction; we shall then show that this lattice contains the least upper bound and the greatest lower bound of each of the at most countable subsets of its elements; and we shall finally prove that, conversely, each of its elements can be represented as the least upper bound of a sequence of finitely-valued place functions.

§§ 69-75. Nests of Somas

69. In order to carry out this program, we represent the finitely-valued place functions

$$f = \sum_j y_j M_j \tag{69.1}$$

by means of a new association of real numbers and somas, obtainable in a determinate way from the original. In this new association, there corresponds to each real number y that is not one of the y_j a soma $S(y)$ which is determined as follows: If none of the y_j is $-\infty$, and if y is less than all the y_j, let $S(y)$ be the empty soma O. In every other case, let $y_{j_1}, y_{j_2}, \ldots, y_{j_k}$ be those numbers y_j that are less than y, and put

$$S(y) = M_{j_1} + M_{j_2} + \cdots + M_{j_k} \quad (y \neq y_1, y_2, \ldots). \tag{69.2}$$

If y and z are two numbers that are different from all the y_j and for which $y < z$, then we obviously have

$$S(y) \subseteqq S(z). \tag{69.3}$$

We now make the following definition.

DEFINITION: *A family of somas $S(y)$, defined for every value $(-\infty < y < +\infty)$ of the real parameter y, and satisfying the condition*

$$\textit{if} \quad y < z \quad \textit{then} \quad S(y) \subseteqq S(z), \tag{69.4}$$

will be called a nest of somas, or a ray.

---

[2] See the article by K. Knopp in the *Enzyklopadie* mentioned above, I, 1, 4, p. 8.

In the sequel, $S(y)$ will continue to designate an individual soma of a nest of somas; the nest of somas itself, taken as a whole, will be denoted by the symbol $[S(y)]$.

The one-parameter family of somas defined by (69.2) can be extended in various ways to form a nest of somas. To this end, we assume, in accordance with § 66, that whenever, in our representation of f, $j \neq k$, we also have $y_j \neq y_k$; and we choose a positive real number ε that is less than any of the various non-zero differences $|y_j - y_k|$ that can be formed from pairs of the numbers y_j that appear in (69.1); we then put

$$S(y_j) = S(y_j - \varepsilon) + N_j, \tag{69.5}$$

where

$$O \subseteqq N_j \subseteqq S(y_j + \varepsilon) - S(y_j - \varepsilon).$$

All these nests of somas are uniquely determined by a knowledge of the y_j, M_j, and N_j; since they depend on a finite set of data, they are called *finitely presented.*

Every finitely presented nest of somas uniquely determines a finitely-valued place function. A representation of this function in the form (69.1) is easily obtained from the data that define the nest of somas.

70. Let us denote by $[T(y)]$ one of the nests of somas belonging to a second place function

$$g = \sum_j y'_j M_j. \tag{70.1}$$

In conformity with (66.7), we represent each of the finitely-valued functions f and g by means of the same subsomas M_j of M.

Let us first consider the case

$$g \leqq f; \tag{70.2}$$

then for all $j = 1, 2, \ldots, p$

$$y'_j \leqq y_j.$$

For each value y_0 of y that is not one of the values y_j or y_j', we then have that each of $y_{j_1}, y_{j_2}, \ldots, y_{jk}$ is less than y_0 if the same is true of each of $y'_{j_1}, y'_{j_2}, \ldots, y'_{jk}$, from which we conclude that

$$S(y_0) \subseteqq T(y_0). \tag{70.3}$$

Given two real numbers y and z, of which y, say, is the smaller, there always exists at least one intermediate number y_0 that is different from all the y_j and y_j'. But since

$$y < y_0 < z,$$

it follows that

$$S(y) \subseteqq S(y_0), \quad T(y_0) \subseteqq T(z), \tag{70.4}$$

and, by comparing (70.3) with (70.4), we obtain the relation

$$S(y) \subseteqq T(z), \tag{70.5}$$

which thus holds without exception whenever $y < z$, provided $g \leqq f$.

In our second case, we assume that the relation $g \leqq f$ is not satisfied. Then among the indexes $1, 2, \ldots, p$ there is an index j_0 for which

$$y_{j_0} < y'_{j_0},$$

and we can choose y and z in such a way that

$$y_{j_0} < y < z < y'_{j_0}.$$

For each such choice of y and z, the soma M_{j_0}, although contained in $S(y)$, is not contained in $T(z)$, showing that (70.5) does not hold in this case. Thus, we have proved the following theorem.

THEOREM 1: *If $[S(y)]$ and $[T(y)]$ are finitely presented nests of somas corresponding to the finitely-valued place functions f and g, respectively, we have $g \leqq f$ if and only if,*[3] *for all y and z,*

$$\text{if} \quad y < z \quad \text{then} \quad S(y) \subseteqq T(z). \tag{70.6}$$

71. The preceding theorem gives us the means with which to partially order the most general nests of somas.

We make the following definition.

DEFINITION: *The relation*

$$[T(y)] \leqq [S(y)] \tag{71.1}$$

is said to hold between two nests $[S(y)]$ and $[T(y)]$ of somas if

$$S(y) \subseteqq T(z) \tag{71.2}$$

for every pair of real numbers y and z for which $y < z$.

Clearly, the relation (71.1) fulfills the two conditions of Definition 2 of § 11.

Now let

$$[S_\nu(y)] \qquad (\nu = 1, 2, \ldots) \tag{71.3}$$

[3] In particular, two nests of somas $[S(y)]$ and $[T(y)]$ represent the same place function f if, whenever $y < z$, both $S(y) \subseteqq T(z)$ and $T(y) \subseteqq S(z)$ (cf. § 72 below).

be any sequence of nests of somas. We put

$$S(y) = \prod_{\nu} S_\nu(y), \quad S'(y) = \sum_{\nu} \dot{+}\, S_\nu(y) \tag{71.4}$$

and observe that both $[S(y)]$ and $[S'(y)]$ are themselves nests of somas. For every pair of real numbers y and z for which $y < z$, we have

$$S(y) \subseteqq S_\nu(y) \subseteqq S_\nu(z), \quad S_\nu(y) \subseteqq S'(y) \subseteqq S'(z) \quad (\nu = 1, 2, \ldots),$$

and from these relations it follows that

$$[S_\nu(y)] \leqq [S(y)], \quad [S_\nu(y)] \geqq [S'(y)] \quad (\nu = 1, 2, \ldots). \tag{71.5}$$

Let $[T(y)]$ and $[T'(y)]$ be two further nests of somas for which the similar relations

$$[S_\nu(y)] \leqq [T(y)], \quad [S_\nu(y)] \geqq [T'(y)] \quad (\nu = 1, 2, \ldots) \tag{71.6}$$

hold. Then, if $y < z$,

$$T(y) \subseteqq S_\nu(z), \quad S_\nu(y) \subseteqq T'(z) \qquad (\nu = 1, 2, \ldots),$$

and therefore, applying (71.4),

$$T(y) \subseteqq S(z), \quad S'(y) \subseteqq T'(z),$$

or, in another notation,

$$[S(y)] \leqq [T(y)], \quad [S'(y)] \geqq [T'(y)].$$

Thus, the nest $[S(y)]$ of somas is the least upper bound of the sequence (71.3) and the nest $[S'(y)]$ is the greatest lower bound.

Thus, the general nests of somas form a lattice in which each at most countable set of elements has a least upper bound and a greatest lower bound.

72. We are finally in a position to introduce the notion of a *general place function*. To this end, given a nest $[S(y)]$ of somas, we consider the totality of all nests $[T(y)]$ of somas that satisfy the two relations

$$[T(y)] \leqq [S(y)], \quad [S(y)] \leqq [T(y)]; \tag{72.1}$$

we call such a class of nests of somas a *place function* (or *functionoid*) f.

The individual somas of two nests of somas $[S(y)]$ and $[T(y)]$ that belong to the same place function f are related as follows:

$$\text{if} \quad y < z \quad \text{then} \quad S(y) \subseteqq T(z) \quad \text{and} \quad T(y) \subseteqq S(z), \tag{72.2}$$

which is equivalent to (72.1). These conditions can be put into a more convenient form.

We take two monotone sequences of real numbers, $\{y_j'\}$ and $\{y_k''\}$, satisfying

$$\left.\begin{aligned} &y_1' < y_2' < \ldots, \quad \lim_{n=\infty} y_n' = y, \\ &y_1'' > y_2'' > \ldots, \quad \lim_{n=\infty} y_n'' = y, \end{aligned}\right\} \tag{72.3}$$

and we define

$$S_0(y) = \lim_{n=\infty} S(y_n'), \quad S^0(y) = \lim_{n=\infty} S(y_n''). \tag{72.4}$$

These last definitions are meaningful, since the sequences of somas $\{S(y_n')\}$ and $\{S(y_n'')\}$ are monotone and therefore converge (Theorem 8 of § 31).

The monotonicity of these two sequences of somas also implies the two conditions

$$S_0(y) \subseteqq S(y) \subseteqq S^0(y), \tag{72.5}$$

$$\text{if} \quad y < z \quad \text{then} \quad S^0(y) \subseteqq S_0(z). \tag{72.6}$$

By (72.2), every nest of somas $[T(y)]$ of the function f satisfies, in the notation of (72.3),

$$S(y_n') \subseteqq T(y) \subseteqq S(y_n'') \qquad (n = 1, 2, \ldots),$$

and by (72.4), it follows that

$$S_0(y) \subseteqq T(y) \subseteqq S^0(y) \quad (-\infty < y < +\infty). \tag{72.7}$$

Conversely, if a one-parameter family of somas $T(y)$ satisfies (72.7), it follows, by virtue of (72.5) and (72.6), that if $y < z$, then

$$\left.\begin{aligned} T(y) \subseteqq S^0(y) \subseteqq S_0(z) \subseteqq S(z), \\ S(y) \subseteqq S^0(y) \subseteqq S_0(z) \subseteqq T(z). \end{aligned}\right\} \tag{72.8}$$

Thus, if v is any real number such that $y < v < z$, then we have

$$T(y) \subseteqq S(v) \subseteqq T(z),$$

so that $[T(y)]$ is a nest of somas that satisfies (72.2), that is, $[T(y)]$ is a nest of somas of f. (72.7) holds for $T(y) = S_0(y)$ and for $T(y) = S^0(y)$.

Hence $[S_0(y)]$ and $[S^0(y)]$ are themselves nests of somas of f; and in fact, we have

$$S_0(y) = \prod S(y), \quad S^0(y) = \sum \dot{+} S(y), \tag{72.9}$$

where the product and the sum is taken over all nests of somas $[S(y)]$ of f, for fixed y.

From this we conclude that these extremal nests of somas are independent of the particular choice of nest of somas representing f that is used in constructing them, and also independent of the choice of the sequences (72.3)—facts that are not difficult to prove directly. In some cases, it can happen that for every value of y,

$$S_0(y) = S^0(y),$$

so that the place function f has only the one nest of somas.

Thus, we have the following theorem.

THEOREM 2: *There are two distinguished, though not necessarily distinct, nests of somas among the nests of somas associated with a place function f: the lower nest of somas $[S_0(y)]$ and the upper nest of somas $[S^0(y)]$.*

A set of somas $T(y)$ dependent on the parameter y is a nest of somas of f if and only if it satisfies

$$S_0(y) \subseteqq T(y) \subseteqq S^0(y) \quad (-\infty < y < +\infty). \tag{72.10}$$

73. If f and g are two place functions, we say that $f \leqq g$ if, whenever two nests of somas $[S(y)]$ and $[T(y)]$ represent f and g respectively, then $[S(y)] \leqq [T(y)]$. From this there follows Theorem 3.

THEOREM 3: *If $[S(y)]$ and $[T(y)]$ are two nests of somas belonging to the place functions f and g, respectively, then $f \leqq g$ if and only if, for all real numbers y and z,*

$$\textit{if} \quad y < z \quad \textit{then} \ T(y) \subseteqq S(z). \tag{73.1}$$

A sufficient condition that (73.1) hold for every pair y and z of real numbers is that it hold for every pair of real numbers y and z belonging to an everywhere-dense subset of the real line.

Proof: The last assertion of our theorem is almost obvious: if (73.1) holds under the given assumptions, then whenever $y < z$, we must always have $T^0(y) \subseteqq S_0(z)$.

By Theorem 1 of § 70, the partial ordering of the general place functions agrees with that of the finitely-valued place functions which we set up in § 66. The result at the end of § 71 can now be expressed as follows:

THEOREM 4: *Every at most countable sequence $\{f_\nu\}$ of arbitrary place functions has a least upper bound g and a greatest lower bound h. Thus, we can write*

$$g = \sup(f_1, f_2, \ldots), \tag{73.2}$$

$$h = \inf(f_1, f_2, \ldots). \tag{73.3}$$

74. To complete the program sketched at the end of § 68, it remains to show that every general place function f can also be considered, in particular, as the least upper bound of a sequence of *finitely-valued* place functions.

Let $[S(y)]$ be a nest of somas of f, and let $\{y_\nu\}$ be a countable sequence of real numbers that forms a dense subset of the real line $-\infty < y < +\infty$. Moreover, let

$$N = \lim_{y=+\infty} S(y). \tag{74.1}$$

We consider a sequence of finitely presented nests of somas $[S_\nu'(y)]$ that are defined by

$$S_\nu'(y) = \begin{cases} S(y_\nu) & \text{for} \quad y < y_\nu, \\ N & \text{for} \quad y \geqq y_\nu \end{cases} \tag{74.2}$$

and denote by f_ν' the two-valued place functions determined by these nests of somas.

By § 69, each of the functions f_ν' has the value $-\infty$ on the soma $S(y_\nu)$ and the value y_ν on the soma $N \dotplus S(y_\nu)$.

Consequently, if y is a fixed real number and p_ν denotes all those positive integers for which $y_{p_\nu} > y$, while q_ν denotes all the others, we have, by (74.2),

$$S_{p_\nu}'(y) = S(y_{p_\nu}), \quad S_{q_\nu}'(y) = N, \tag{74.3}$$

and therefore we can write

$$\prod_\nu S_\nu'(y) = N \prod_\nu S(y_{p_\nu}) = S^0(y). \tag{74.4}$$

This equation is equivalent with

$$f = \sup(f_1', f_2', \ldots), \tag{74.5}$$

which is what we wished to prove.

Similarly, by making use of the nests of somas $[S_\nu''(y)]$ defined by the equations

$$S_\nu''(y) = \begin{cases} O & \text{for } y \leqq y_\nu, \\ S(y_\nu) & \text{for } y > y_\nu, \end{cases} \tag{74.6}$$

we obtain the relation

$$\sum_\nu \dot{+} S_\nu''(y) = S_0(y). \tag{74.7}$$

The two-valued place functions f_ν'' associated with the nests of somas (74.6) therefore satisfy the equation

$$f = \inf(f_1'', f_2'', \ldots), \tag{74.8}$$

and we thus have the following theorem.

THEOREM 5: *Every general place function can be represented not only as a least upper bound of a sequence of finitely-valued place functions, but also as a greatest lower bound of a sequence of finitely-valued place functions.*

We can now also prove the following theorem.

THEOREM 6: *A necessary and sufficient condition that two general place functions f and g satisfy*

$$f \leqq g \tag{74.9}$$

is that all finitely-valued place functions $f' \leqq f$ and $g'' \geqq g$ satisfy

$$f' \leqq g''. \tag{74.10}$$

Proof: By Theorem 5, it is possible to find sequences $\{f_\nu'\}$ and $\{g_\nu''\}$ of finitely-valued place functions which satisfy

$$f = \sup(f_1', f_2', \ldots), \quad g = \inf(g_1'', g_2'', \ldots).$$

But in order that (74.10) hold, we must have, for each pair ν, μ of positive integers,

$$f_\nu' \leqq g_\mu'' \qquad (\nu, \mu = 1, 2, \ldots),$$

and from this we obtain, in succession, the relations

$$f_\nu' \leqq \inf(g_1'', g_2'', \ldots) = g,$$

$$f = \sup(f_1', f_2', \ldots) \leqq g.$$

75. In conclusion, we should like to exhibit a procedure for generating the most general place function, a procedure that bears a certain resemblance to the formulas of § 74 and is important for certain applications.

We consider, on the one hand, a sequence of real numbers

$$y_1, y_2, y_3, \dots, \tag{75.1}$$

forming an everywhere-dense set of points on the real line

$$-\infty < y < +\infty$$

and, on the other hand, a sequence of somas

$$C_1, C_2, C_3, \dots \tag{75.2}$$

that are contained in M but are otherwise entirely arbitrary. Let y be a (finite) real number; let

$$y_{q_1}, y_{q_2}, y_{q_3}, \dots \tag{75.3}$$

be the subsequence of (75.1) consisting of all the terms $y_\nu < y$; and, similarly, let

$$y_{r_1}, y_{r_2}, y_{r_3}, \dots \tag{75.4}$$

be the subsequence of all $y_\nu > y$. If we now put

$$S_0(y) = \sum_j \dot{+}\, C_{q_j}, \quad S^0(y) = \prod_j S_0(y_{r_j}), \tag{75.5}$$

we obtain the lower and upper nests of somas of a place function f.

It is clear that every place function f can be computed in this way: we need only choose any nest of somas $[S(y)]$ of f and put

$$C_\nu = S(y_\nu) \qquad (\nu = 1, 2, \dots). \tag{75.6}$$

In particular, if all the somas C_ν are one and the same subsoma $C \subseteqq M$, we obtain a place function i_C, which is determined by the nest of somas $[S(y)]$ for which

$$S(y) = S_0(y) = S^0(y) = C \quad (-\infty < y < +\infty). \tag{75.7}$$

The place function i_C has the value $-\infty$ on the soma C, the value $+\infty$ on the soma $M \dot{+} C$, and can assume no other value. If

$$C = O,$$

i_C represents the constant function $+\infty$; if

$$C = M,$$

i_C represents the constant function $-\infty$.

The fact that, given the values y_ν, every sequence of somas $\{C_\nu\}$ uniquely determines a place function, allows us, among other things, to single out certain classes of place functions; for example, we may consider those place functions for which the somas C_ν are specialized in some way or other (cf. § 154).

§§ 76-79. Altering the Domain of Definition

76. Let us consider, in addition to a place function f with the nest of somas $[S(y)]$, one of the place functions i_C that we have just defined.

The function

$$\max(i_C, f), \tag{76.1}$$

which has the nest of somas

$$[C\, S(y)], \tag{76.2}$$

agrees with f on the soma C and assumes the value $+\infty$ on the soma $M \dot{+} C$, while the function

$$\min(i_C, f), \tag{76.3}$$

which has the nest of somas

$$[C \dot{+} S(y)], \tag{76.4}$$

assumes the value $-\infty$ on the soma C and agrees with f on the soma $M \dot{+} C$.

We now consider a decomposition

$$M = M_1 + M_2 + \cdots \tag{76.5}$$

of M into at most countably many somas M_j, and a like number of place functions f_j defined on M and corresponding to the nests $[S_j(y)]$. Putting

$$f_j^* = \max(i_{M_j}, f_j) \qquad (j = 1, 2, \ldots), \tag{76.6}$$

$$f = \inf(f_1^*, f_2^*, \ldots), \tag{76.7}$$

we obtain a nest of somas $[S(y)]$ of f by writing

$$S(y) = \sum_j \dot{+} M_j\, S_j(y)\,; \tag{76.8}$$

and thus, we have:

THEOREM 1: *If a place function f_j with nest of somas $[S_j(y)]$ is assigned to each subsoma M_j of an at most countable decomposition*

$$M = M_1 + M_2 + \cdots \tag{76.9}$$

of M, then the nest of somas $[S(y)]$ given by

$$S(y) = \sum_j \dot{+} M_j\, S_j(y) \tag{76.10}$$

determines the place function f that agrees with f_j on the corresponding soma M_j.

77. If $[S(y)]$ is a nest of somas of a place function f whose domain of definition is M, and if X denotes an arbitrary *non-empty* subsoma of M, then

$$[T(y)] = [X\, S(y)] \tag{77.1}$$

is a nest of somas of the function that agrees with f on X and has the value $+\infty$ on $M \dot{+} X$. But $[T(y)]$ can also be interpreted as a nest of somas belonging to a place function with domain of definition X; in this way, we can define the given place function f on all the somas of a set of somas—in what follows we shall always denote this set by $\mathfrak{A}$—that consists of all the *non-empty* subsomas X of M. Incidentally, since this set of somas $\mathfrak{A}$ does not contain the empty soma O, it is not a subtractive set of somas and is therefore not a ring.

The lower and upper nests of somas of a constant place function c with domain of definition X are obtained from the formulas

$$S_0(y) = \begin{cases} O \text{ for } y \leqq c, \\ X \text{ for } y > c, \end{cases} \qquad S^0(y) = \begin{cases} O \text{ for } y < c, \\ X \text{ for } y \geqq c, \end{cases} \tag{77.2}$$

with appropriate modification in the case of infinite c.

If there is a finite real number c for which $c \leqq f$ on X, then $T(y) \subseteqq S_0(z)$ whenever $y < z$, and so, for every $y < c$,

$$T(y) = X\, S(y) = O. \tag{77.3}$$

Conversely, if the condition (77.3) holds for all $y < c$, then whenever $y < z$ we have $T(y) \subseteqq S_0(z)$, and hence also $c \leqq f$.

Under the same hypotheses, then, there exists a number $\alpha(X)$, which we call the *infimum of f on the soma X* and which is defined as the least upper bound of the set of all values c of the functions for which $c \leqq f$. By the above, $\alpha(X)$ is computed from the equation

$$\alpha(X) = \sup(y; X\,S(y) = O). \tag{77.4}$$

Clearly, under this definition it is possible to have $\alpha(X) = +\infty$. If, however, $\alpha(X) < +\infty$, equation (77.4) is equivalent, as we can readily satisfy ourselves, with

$$\alpha(X) = \inf(y; X\,S(y) \neq O).$$

Of course, this equation also holds in case $\alpha(X) = -\infty$, when (77.4) fails us. Finally, we obtain the definitive equations

$$\alpha(X) = \begin{cases} \sup(y; X\,S(y) = O) & \text{for } \alpha(X) > -\infty, \\ \inf(y; X\,S(y) \neq O) & \text{for } \alpha(X) < +\infty. \end{cases} \tag{77.5}$$

In the same way, we define the *supremum* $\beta(X)$ *of f on the soma X* by means of the formula

$$\beta(X) = \begin{cases} \inf(y; X\,S(y) = X) & \text{for } \beta(X) < +\infty, \\ \sup(y; X\,S(y) \neq X) & \text{for } \beta(X) > -\infty, \end{cases} \tag{77.6}$$

which also holds without restriction. Moreover, $\beta(X)$, if it is not equal to $+\infty$, can be interpreted as the greatest lower bound of the set of all place functions $c \geqq f$ that are constant on X.

We have at all times

$$\alpha(X) \leqq \beta(X); \tag{77.7}$$

indeed, if $\alpha(X) > -\infty$ and $y < \alpha(X)$, then $XS(y) = O$, whence $XS(y) \neq X$, i.e., $y \leqq \beta(X)$, so that the assumption that $\beta(X) < \alpha(X)$ would lead to a contradiction.

78. If the two numbers $\alpha(X)$ and $\beta(X)$ are finite, the place function f is said to be *bounded on the soma X*. If this is the case, there are finite numbers a and b that satisfy

$$a \leqq \alpha(X) \leqq \beta(X) \leqq b. \tag{78.1}$$

If this relation holds for a soma X, then, for every positive integer n, the conditions

$$X \circ S\left(a - \frac{1}{n}\right), \quad X \subseteqq S\left(b + \frac{1}{n}\right) \tag{78.2}$$

hold, by (77.5) and (77.6); therefore, we have

$$X \subseteqq S^0(b) \dotplus S_0(a). \tag{78.3}$$

Conversely, the relations (78.1) follow from (78.3) and $a \leqq b$.

If $\alpha(M)$ and $\beta(M)$ are finite, the place function f is called, simply, *bounded.* Thus, a place function is bounded if there are two finite numbers $a \leqq b$ for which we have

$$M = S^0(b) \dotplus S_0(a). \tag{78.4}$$

If the soma

$$E(y) = S^0(y) \dotplus S_0(y) \tag{78.5}$$

is non-empty for a particular value of y, we see by the above that

$$\alpha(E(y)) = \beta(E(y)) = y; \tag{78.6}$$

if this is the case, we shall say that f *takes,* or *assumes,* the value y—more precisely, that f *assumes* the value y *on* $E(y)$. If, on the other hand, $E(y) = O$, we say that f *does not assume* the value y. We shall also say that f assumes the value y *in* a soma X of the domain of definition, if $XE(y) \neq O$.

If the soma $E(-\infty)$, which is defined by the equation

$$E(-\infty) = \lim_{y=-\infty} S(y) = S^0(-\infty) \tag{78.7}$$

is non-empty, we shall say that f assumes the value $-\infty$ on this soma. In the same way, we say that f takes the value $+\infty$ on the soma $E(+\infty)$, if $E(+\infty)$ is non-empty, where $E(+\infty)$ is defined by the equation

$$M \dotplus E(+\infty) = \lim_{y=+\infty} S(y) = S_0(+\infty). \tag{78.8}$$

A point function takes on one definite value at each point in its domain of definition. Likewise, a finitely-valued place function $f = \Sigma y_j M_j$ takes the value y_j on the corresponding soma M_j. In contrast to this, it is possible, as we shall see in § 122, to construct place functions that *do not assume any values at all.* The question whether a given place function assumes a certain value or not will, however, play only a very minor rôle in our theory.

If neither of the values $\pm\infty$ are taken, i.e., if both $E(+\infty)$ and $E(-\infty)$ are empty, we say of the place function f that it is *finite.*

The domain of definition M of the function f can be decomposed into the somas $E(+\infty)$, $E(-\infty)$, and an at most countable number of pairwise disjoint somas M_j on which f is bounded.

79. By the *oscillation* of a place function f on a soma X is meant the difference

$$\sigma(X) = \beta(X) - \alpha(X) \tag{79.1}$$

between the supremum and the infimum of f on X.

If f is now bounded, there are two finite numbers a and b that satisfy

$$S(a) = O, \quad S(b) = M. \tag{79.2}$$

Choose a positive number ε and a finite set of numbers y_j for which

$$a < y_1 < y_2 < \ldots < y_p < b \tag{79.3}$$

holds and for which the differences

$$y_1 - a, \quad y_2 - y_1, \quad \ldots, \quad b - y_p$$

are all $< \varepsilon$. Let those somas among

$$S(y_1) \dot{+} S(a), \quad S(y_2) \dot{+} S(y_1), \quad \ldots, \quad S(b) \dot{+} S(y_p)$$

that are non-empty be denoted by $M_1, M_2, \ldots, M_q$. In this way we obtain a decomposition

$$M = M_1 + M_2 + \cdots + M_q \tag{79.4}$$

of M, one that satisfies

$$\sigma(M_j) = \beta(M_j) - \alpha(M_j) < \varepsilon \quad (j = 1, 2, \ldots, q). \tag{79.5}$$

Now if X is a non-empty subsoma of M, and $X_1, X_2, \ldots, X_r$ denote all the non-empty somas of the form XM_j, we also have $\sigma(X_j) < \varepsilon$, and we may state the following theorem.

THEOREM 1: *Let ε be an arbitrary positive number and let f be a place function bounded on M. Then every non-empty subsoma X of M can be represented as the sum of a finite number of pairwise disjoint somas X_j,*

$$X = X_1 + X_2 + \cdots + X_r \tag{79.6}$$

in such a way that the oscillation on each of these somas satisfies

$$\sigma(X_j) < \varepsilon . \tag{79.7}$$

§§ 80-88. Principal Properties of the Soma Functions $\alpha(X)$ and $\beta(X)$

80. The equations

$$\alpha(X) = \begin{cases} \sup(y; X S(y) = O) & \text{for } \alpha(X) > -\infty, \\ \inf(y; X S(y) \neq O) & \text{for } \alpha(X) < +\infty, \end{cases} \tag{80.1}$$

$$\beta(X) = \begin{cases} \inf(y; X S(y) = X) & \text{for } \beta(X) < +\infty, \\ \sup(y; X S(y) \neq X) & \text{for } \beta(X) > -\infty, \end{cases} \tag{80.2}$$

which we derived at the end of § 77, assign real numbers to the somas of the set of somas $\mathfrak{A}$ (cf. § 77), consisting of M and all the non-empty subsomas X of M. In this way we obtain "soma functions" in the argument X and with the set $\mathfrak{A}$ as domain of definition.

If $Y \subseteqq X$, then every value of y satisfying $XS(y) = O$ also satisfies $YS(y) = O$; thus, (80.1) yields the implication

$$\text{if} \quad O \subset Y \subseteqq X \quad \text{then} \quad \alpha(Y) \geqq \alpha(X). \tag{80.3}$$

In the same way, we find:

$$\text{if} \quad O \subset Y \subseteqq X \quad \text{then} \quad \beta(Y) \leqq \beta(X). \tag{80.4}$$

We introduce the following definition.

DEFINITION: *A real soma function $\omega(X)$ is called monotonically decreasing if $\omega(Y) \geqq \omega(X)$ whenever the somas X and Y in the domain of definition satisfy $Y \subseteqq X$. A real soma function $\Omega(X)$ is called monotonically increasing if $\Omega(Y) \leqq \Omega(X)$ whenever $Y \subseteqq X$. A soma function is called monotone if it is either monotonically increasing or monotonically decreasing.*

According to this definition, the infimum $\alpha(X)$ of a place function f is a monotonically decreasing soma function and the supremum $\beta(X)$, a monotonically increasing soma function, for which, in addition, $\alpha(X) \leqq \beta(X)$ holds.

81. Using the soma functions $\alpha(X)$ and $\beta(X)$, we can develop a very intuitive interpretation of the somas $S^0(y)$ and $S_0(y)$ that occur in the two extremal nests of somas. Indeed, if $y' > y$, then by (72.8) $S^0(y) \subseteqq S(y')$, so that by (80.2),

$$\beta(S^0(y)) \leqq y',$$

and, in the limit,

$$\beta(S^0(y)) \leqq y. \tag{81.1}$$

Now let X be a soma for which $\beta(X) < +\infty$, and let n be a positive integer. By (80.2), there is at least one number y' that satisfies the pair of relations

$$\left.\begin{array}{c} \beta(X) \leqq y' \leqq \beta(X) + \dfrac{1}{n}, \\ X \subseteqq S(y'). \end{array}\right\} \tag{81.2}$$

From this it follows that, for every positive integer n,

$$X \subseteqq S\left(\beta(X) + \frac{1}{n}\right),$$

and consequently

$$X \subseteqq S^0(\beta(X)) \qquad (\beta(X) < +\infty). \tag{81.3}$$

If $\beta(X) \leqq y$, we then have

$$X \subseteqq S^0(y). \tag{81.4}$$

A comparison of the last result with (81.1) yields the first half of the following theorem; the second half is proved in a similar way.

THEOREM 1: *For every value of y for which it is not empty, the soma $S^0(y)$ is equal to the union of all the somas X that satisfy*

$$\beta(X) \leqq y \tag{81.5}$$

and moreover is itself such a soma.

The soma $M \dotplus S_0(y)$, if it is non-empty, is equal to the union of all the somas X that satisfy

$$\alpha(X) \geqq y \tag{81.6}$$

and is itself such a soma.

82. We are now in a position to give an "intrinsic" characterization of the supremum $\beta(X)$ of an arbitrary place function f. We have the following theorem.

THEOREM 2: *Let $\beta(X)$ be a monotonically increasing soma function defined on the set $\mathfrak{A}$ of all non-empty subsomas X of a soma M. Such a function is the supremum of a place function f if and only if, for each y, the set $\mathfrak{B}(y)$ of all somas X for which*

$$\beta(X) \leqq y \tag{82.1}$$

contains (provided it is not empty) a maximal soma $S^0(y)$.

Proof: The condition is: If $\mathfrak{B}(y)$ is empty, then

$$\beta(X) > y$$

for every X in $\mathfrak{A}$; if, however, $\mathfrak{B}(y)$ is non-empty, then there is a soma $S^0(y)$ that satisfies the two conditions

$$\left.\begin{array}{c} \beta(S^0(y)) \leqq y\,, \\ \text{if} \quad \beta(X) \leqq y \quad \text{then} \quad X \subseteqq S^0(y). \end{array}\right\} \tag{82.2}$$

It also follows, conversely, that if $X \subseteqq S^0(y)$, then $\beta(X) \leqq y$; for in that case, we have $\beta(X) \leqq \beta(S^0(y)) \leqq y$.

Now, Theorem 1 of § 81 shows that the condition is necessary. But the condition is also sufficient.

For, assuming the condition holds, let us set $S^0(y) = O$ whenever $\mathfrak{B}(y)$ is empty and let us define $S^0(y)$ by condition (82.2) otherwise. Then $S^0(y) \subseteqq S^0(z)$ whenever $y < z$, so that $[S^0(y)]$ is the nest of somas of a place function f.

Now let X be any soma of $\mathfrak{A}$. If we suppose, to begin with, that $\beta(X) = +\infty$, then

$$X\, S^0(y) \neq X$$

for each y; thus $\beta(X)$, in this case, satisfies the second equation of (80.2). If, instead,

$$\beta(X) = y' < +\infty, \tag{82.3}$$

then, by (82.2), $X \subseteqq S^0(y')$, so that $XS^0(y) = X$ for every $y > y'$. Thus, putting

$$\lambda(X) = \inf(y;\, X\, S^0(y) = X), \tag{82.4}$$

we have

$$\lambda(X) \leqq \beta(X). \tag{82.5}$$

Conversely, for every $y > \lambda(X)$, we have $X \subseteqq S^0(y)$, and, since $\beta(X)$ is assumed to be monotonically increasing, it follows from (82.2) that

$$\beta(X) \leqq \beta(S^0(y)) \leqq y$$

and therefore that

$$\beta(X) \leqq \lambda(X). \tag{82.6}$$

Thus, for every soma X of $\mathfrak{A}$ for which $\beta(X) < +\infty$, we have

$$\beta(X) = \inf(y;\ X\, S^0(y) = X). \tag{82.7}$$

This last equation is identical with the first equation of (80.2) and states that $\beta(X)$ is the supremum of that place function whose nest of somas $[S^0(y)]$ is defined by (82.2). This completes the proof of Theorem 2. Moreover, the soma $S^0(y)$, by the wording of the theorem, is equal to the union of all the somas X of $\mathfrak{B}(y)$ and, consequently, gives rise to the upper nest of somas of f.

83. The soma functions $\alpha(X)$ and $\beta(X)$ are not independent of each other: each of them can be computed from the other.

If to begin with, either $\alpha(X) = +\infty$ or $\beta(X) = -\infty$, then $\alpha(X) = \beta(X)$. We need thus consider only such somas X of $\mathfrak{A}$ as satisfy both $\alpha(X) < +\infty$ and $\beta(X) > -\infty$. Under these assumptions, then, let y_1 and y_2 be two numbers which are subject to no restrictions other than that they satisfy the conditions

$$y_1 > \alpha(X), \quad y_2 < \beta(X). \tag{83.1}$$

By (80.1), there is at least one number y' between $\alpha(X)$ and y_1 for which $XS(y')$ is non-empty; and since $[S(y)]$ is a nest of somas, we see that

$$Z_1 = X\, S(y_1) \neq O.$$

In a completely similar way, we can also prove that

$$Z_2 = X \dotplus X\, S(y_2) \neq O.$$

Now, the somas Z_1 and Z_2 satisfy the relations

$$Z_1 S(y_1) = Z_1, \quad Z_2 S(y_2) = O \quad (Z_1, Z_2 \subseteqq X),$$

from which, again by (80.1) and (80.2), the inequalities

$$\beta(Z_1) \leqq y_1, \quad \alpha(Z_2) \geqq y_2 \qquad (Z_1, Z_2 \subseteqq X) \tag{83.2}$$

follow.

We now introduce the soma functions

$$\left.\begin{aligned} \bar{\beta}(X) &= \sup(\alpha(Y);\ Y \subseteqq X), \\ \underline{\alpha}(X) &= \inf(\beta(Y);\ Y \subseteqq X); \end{aligned}\right\} \tag{83.3}$$

in conformity with (83.2), we then have

$$\bar{\beta}(X) \geqq y_2, \quad \underline{\alpha}(X) \leqq y_1,$$

and since these relations hold for all y_1 and y_2 that satisfy the inequalities (83.1), it follows that

$$\bar{\beta}(X) \geqq \beta(X), \quad \underline{\alpha}(X) \leqq \alpha(X). \tag{83.4}$$

On the other hand, if $Y \subseteqq X$, we must have

$$\beta(X) \geqq \beta(Y) \geqq \alpha(Y), \quad \alpha(X) \leqq \alpha(Y) \leqq \beta(Y),$$

and therefore, by (83.3),

$$\beta(X) \geqq \bar{\beta}(X), \quad \alpha(X) \leqq \underline{\alpha}(X). \tag{83.5}$$

A comparison of (83.4) and (83.5) with (83.3) yields the following theorem.

THEOREM 3: *Each of the soma functions $\alpha(X)$ and $\beta(X)$ can be computed from the other. The following formulas hold:*

$$\beta(X) = \sup(\alpha(Y); Y \subseteqq X), \tag{83.6}$$

$$\alpha(X) = \inf(\beta(Y); Y \subseteqq X). \tag{83.7}$$

It should be observed that these formulas remain valid if $\alpha(X) = +\infty$ or if $\beta(X) = -\infty$.

84. The last theorem leads us to the consideration of soma functions $\beta(X)$ that are defined by equations of the form

$$\beta(X) = \sup(\omega(Y); Y \subseteqq X), \tag{84.1}$$

where $\omega(X)$ denotes a monotonically decreasing soma function with domain of definition $\mathfrak{A}$. Since, with increasing X, the set of Y that appears in the right-hand side of (84.1) also increases, we see that $\beta(X_1) \geqq \beta(X)$ whenever $X_1 \supseteqq X$. Hence, the soma function $\beta(X)$ is monotonically increasing. Moreover, it follows from the defining equation (84.1) that

$$\omega(X) \leqq \beta(X) \tag{84.2}$$

for every X in $\mathfrak{A}$. Now let $\mathfrak{A}_1$ be a subset of $\mathfrak{A}$, the union

$$V = \sum_{X \in \mathfrak{A}_1} \dot{+} X \tag{84.3}$$

of whose elements exists. We compute the number

$$\Lambda = \sup(\beta(X); X \in \mathfrak{A}_1). \tag{84.4}$$

Since $\beta(V) \geqq \beta(X)$ for every soma X of $\mathfrak{A}_1$, it follows that

$$\beta(V) \geqq \Lambda. \tag{84.5}$$

By Theorem 4 of § 15, it is possible to assign to each non-empty subsoma Y of V a corresponding soma X in $\mathfrak{A}_1$ for which $XY \neq O$. Using (84.2) and the fact that $\omega(X)$ is monotonically decreasing and $\beta(X)$ monotonically increasing, we obtain

$$\omega(Y) \leqq \omega(XY) \leqq \beta(XY) \leqq \beta(X) \leqq \Lambda.$$

It follows further that

$$\beta(V) = \sup(\omega(Y);\ Y \subseteqq V) \leqq \Lambda,$$

and, taking (84.5) and (84.4) into consideration, we obtain as our final result:

$$\beta(V) = \sup(\beta(X);\ X \in \mathfrak{A}_1). \tag{84.6}$$

Similarly, if we put

$$\alpha(X) = \inf(\Omega(Y);\ Y \subseteqq X), \tag{84.7}$$

where $\Omega(Y)$ denotes an arbitrary monotonically increasing soma function defined on $\mathfrak{A}$, we can prove, in exactly the same way, that

$$\alpha(V) = \inf(\alpha(X);\ X \in \mathfrak{A}_1). \tag{84.8}$$

Consequently, the following theorem holds.

THEOREM 4: *Let $\omega(X)$ be a monotonically decreasing and $\Omega(X)$. a monotonically increasing soma function both defined on $\mathfrak{A}$; put*

$$\beta(X) = \sup(\omega(Y);\ Y \subseteqq X), \tag{84.9}$$

$$\alpha(X) = \inf(\Omega(Y);\ Y \subseteqq X). \tag{84.10}$$

Furthermore, let $\mathfrak{A}_1$ denote any subset of $\mathfrak{A}$ and assume that the union

$$V = \sum_{X \in \mathfrak{A}_1} \dot{+}\, X \tag{84.11}$$

of all the somas of $\mathfrak{A}_1$ exists. Then the following equations hold:

$$\beta(V) = \sup(\beta(X);\ X \in \mathfrak{A}_1), \tag{84.12}$$

$$\alpha(V) = \inf(\alpha(X);\ X \in \mathfrak{A}_1). \tag{84.13}$$

Theorem 3 of § 83 asserts that the assumptions (84.9) and (84.10) are satisfied by the supremum as well as the infimum of any place function. Hence, (84.12) and (84.13) hold for these functions.

85. We are now in a position to supplement Theorem 2 of § 82 in the best possible way by adjoining a similar theorem, which is due to A. Bischof.[4]

THEOREM 5: *The following two conditions are a necessary and sufficient set of conditions for a soma function $\beta(X)$ defined on $\mathfrak{A}$ to be the supremum of a place function f:*

1. *If, for each real number y, we form the set $\mathfrak{B}(y)$ of all non-empty somas X of $\mathfrak{A}$ for which $\beta(X) \leqq y$, then, provided $\mathfrak{B}(y)$ is non-empty, the union $S(y)$ of all these somas exists.*

2. *There is at least one monotonically decreasing soma function $\omega(X)$ defined on $\mathfrak{A}$ for which we have*

$$\beta(X) = \sup\big(\omega(Y);\ Y \subseteqq X\big). \tag{85.1}$$

Proof: By Theorem 2 of § 82 and Theorem 3 of § 83, these conditions are satisfied as soon as $\beta(X)$ represents the supremum of a place function f; thus they are necessary.

But they are also sufficient: for, by Theorem 4 of § 84,

$$\beta\big(S(y)\big) = \sup\big(\beta(X);\ X \in \mathfrak{B}(y)\big) \leqq y, \tag{85.2}$$

so that all the hypotheses of Theorem 2 of § 82 are satisfied here as well.

86. The functions $\beta(X)$ that satisfy the conditions of Theorem 2 of § 82 and Theorem 5 of § 85 are, of course, more special than the arbitrary monotonically increasing functions $\Omega(X)$. For example, if $\varphi(X)$ is a monotonically increasing soma function defined on $\mathfrak{A}$, if A and B are any two disjoint somas of $\mathfrak{A}$ for which $\varphi(A)$ and $\varphi(B)$ are finite numbers, and if we put

$$\Omega(X) = \begin{cases} \varphi(X) + 1 & \text{for } X(A+B) = A+B, \\ \varphi(X) & \text{for } X(A+B) \neq A+B, \end{cases} \tag{86.1}$$

then $\Omega(X)$ is a monotonically increasing soma function for which

$$\Omega(A+B) > \max\big(\Omega(A),\ \Omega(B)\big); \tag{86.2}$$

thus (84.12), with $\Omega(X)$ replacing $\beta(X)$, does not hold and therefore, by Theorem 4, $\Omega(X)$ can not be written in the form

$$\sup\big(\omega(Y);\ Y \subseteqq X\big).$$

Consequently, $\Omega(X)$ is not the supremum of a place function. As we shall see, however, in the remainder of the present section and in § 87, for each

[4] Cf. A. Bischof, *Schr. Math. Inst. u. Inst. angew. Math. Univ.* Berlin 5, pp. 237-262 (1941) = Diss., Berlin, 1941.

monotonically increasing soma function $\Omega(X)$, there is a largest monotonically decreasing function $\omega(X) \leqq \Omega(X)$, and this function, upon substitution in (85.1), yields the largest soma function $\tilde{\beta}(X) \leqq \Omega(X)$ having such a representation; this function plays an important rôle in many investigations.

We consider an arbitrary monotonically decreasing soma function $\omega(X)$ and an arbitrary monotonically increasing soma function $\Omega(X)$, each of which has as domain of definition the set $\mathfrak{A}$ of all non-empty subsomas of M, and we assume furthermore that

$$\omega(X) \leqq \Omega(X) \tag{86.3}$$

for each soma X of $\mathfrak{A}$.

With each soma X of $\mathfrak{A}$, moreover, we associate the least upper bound of the set of numbers $\omega(Y)$, where Y ranges over all the non-empty subsomas of X; and we denote this least upper bound by $\underline{\beta}(X)$.

The soma function

$$\underline{\beta}(X) = \sup\big(\omega(Y);\ Y \subseteqq X\big) \tag{86.4}$$

that is thus defined is monotonically increasing (cf. the first paragraph of § 84). On the other hand, we have by (86.3) that

$$\omega(Y) \leqq \Omega(Y) \leqq \Omega(X)$$

for every soma $Y \subseteqq X$, and from this it follows, by (86.4), that

$$\underline{\beta}(X) \leqq \Omega(X). \tag{86.5}$$

In addition, it follows from the defining equation (86.4) of $\underline{\beta}(X)$ that the relation

$$\omega(X) \leqq \underline{\beta}(X) \tag{86.6}$$

holds. But $\Omega(X)$ is an arbitrary monotonically increasing soma function larger than $\omega(X)$. By (86.5) and (86.6), therefore, $\underline{\beta}(X)$ is the smallest monotonically increasing function with this property, and the following theorem holds, the second half of which is proved in similar fashion.

THEOREM 6: *Consider an arbitrary monotonically decreasing function $\omega(X)$ defined on the set $\mathfrak{A}$ of all non-empty subsomas of a soma M. Among all the monotonically increasing functions $\Omega(X)$ that have the same domain of definition $\mathfrak{A}$ for which $\Omega(X) \geqq \omega(X)$, there is a smallest, $\underline{\beta}(X)$, which is determined by the equation*

$$\underline{\beta}(X) = \sup\big(\omega(Y);\ Y \subseteqq X\big). \tag{86.7}$$

In the same way, $\Omega(X)$ being held fixed, among all the monotonically decreasing functions $\omega(X)$ defined on $\mathfrak{A}$ and $\leqq \Omega(X)$, there is a largest, $\alpha(X)$, which is defined by the equation

$$\bar{\alpha}(X) = \inf(\Omega(Y);\ Y \subseteqq X). \tag{86.8}$$

The above result is supplemented by the following theorem.

THEOREM 7: *Retaining the hypotheses and notation of the preceding theorem, we define two new functions $\underline{\alpha}(X)$ and $\bar{\beta}(X)$ by the equations*

$$\underline{\alpha}(X) = \inf(\underline{\beta}(Y);\ Y \subseteqq X), \tag{86.9}$$

$$\bar{\beta}(X) = \sup(\bar{\alpha}(Y);\ Y \subseteqq X). \tag{86.10}$$

Then the inequalities

$$\omega(X) \leqq \underline{\alpha}(X) \leqq \underline{\beta}(X) \leqq \Omega(X), \tag{86.11}$$

$$\omega(X) \leqq \bar{\alpha}(X) \leqq \bar{\beta}(X) \leqq \Omega(X), \tag{86.12}$$

as well as the identities

$$\underline{\beta}(X) = \sup(\underline{\alpha}(Y);\ Y \subseteqq X), \tag{86.13}$$

$$\bar{\alpha}(X) = \inf(\bar{\beta}(Y);\ Y \subseteqq X) \tag{86.14}$$

hold.

Proof: By Theorem 6, we have the relations

$$\omega(X) \leqq \underline{\beta}(X) \leqq \Omega(X);$$

equation (86.9) indicates that $\underline{\alpha}(X)$ is the largest monotonically decreasing soma function that is $\leqq \underline{\beta}(X)$; consequently, we must also have

$$\omega(X) \leqq \underline{\alpha}(X) \leqq \underline{\beta}(X).$$

This verifies (86.11); and (86.12) can be confirmed in the same way.

Since $\omega(X) \leqq \underline{\alpha}(X)$, every monotonically increasing soma function $\Phi(X)$ that is $\geqq \underline{\alpha}(X)$ is also $\geqq \omega(X)$; by Theorem 6, it must therefore also be $\geqq \underline{\beta}(X)$. But then $\underline{\beta}(X)$ is the smallest monotonically increasing soma function that is $\geqq \underline{\alpha}(X)$ and it is therefore given by equation (86.13). The equation (86.14) is proved similarly.

87. We again consider a monotonically increasing soma function $\Omega(X)$ and a monotonically decreasing soma function $\omega(X) \leqq \Omega(X)$ both defined on the set of somas $\mathfrak{A}$, and we investigate the pairs of soma functions $\alpha(X)$ and $\beta(X)$ that satisfy all the following conditions:

$$\left.\begin{aligned} &\omega(X) \leqq \alpha(X) \leqq \beta(X) \leqq \Omega(X), \\ &\alpha(X) = \inf(\beta(Y);\ Y \subseteqq X), \\ &\beta(X) = \sup(\alpha(Y);\ Y \subseteqq X). \end{aligned}\right\} \tag{87.1}$$

Each of the two pairs of functions $\underline{\alpha}(X)$, $\underline{\beta}(X)$ and $\bar{\alpha}(X)$, $\bar{\beta}(X)$ that occur in the theorems of § 86 satisfies the conditions (87.1).

Now, since $\underline{\beta}(X)$ is the smallest monotonically increasing soma function that is $\geqq \omega(X)$, we have

$$\underline{\beta}(X) \leqq \beta(X) \qquad (X \in \mathfrak{A}), \qquad (87.2)$$

and similarly, we obtain the inequality

$$\alpha(X) \leqq \bar{\alpha}(X) \qquad (X \in \mathfrak{A}). \qquad (87.3)$$

A comparison of (87.2) with the equations

$$\underline{\alpha}(X) = \inf\big(\underline{\beta}(Y);\ Y \subseteqq X\big), \quad \alpha(X) = \inf\big(\beta(Y);\ Y \subseteqq X\big)$$

yields the relation $\underline{\alpha}(X) \leqq \alpha(X)$, which in conjunction with (87.3) we write:

$$\underline{\alpha}(X) \leqq \alpha(X) \leqq \bar{\alpha}(X) \qquad (X \in \mathfrak{A}). \qquad (87.4)$$

Similar reasoning yields the relation

$$\underline{\beta}(X) \leqq \beta(X) \leqq \bar{\beta}(X) \qquad (X \in \mathfrak{A}). \qquad (87.5)$$

If there is even a single non-empty soma $X_0 \subseteqq M$ for which

$$\bar{\alpha}(X_0) > \underline{\beta}(X_0) \geqq \underline{\alpha}(X_0), \qquad (87.6)$$

then the two functions $\underline{\alpha}(X)$ and $\bar{\alpha}(X)$ are distinct, and so there are at least two different pairs of functions $\alpha(X)$ and $\beta(X)$ that satisfy the conditions (87.1).

In the contrary case, the inequality

$$\bar{\alpha}(X) \leqq \underline{\beta}(X) \qquad (X \in \mathfrak{A}) \qquad (87.7)$$

must hold throughout, and it, together with (87.4) and (87.5), implies that

$$\alpha(X) \leqq \bar{\alpha}(X) \leqq \underline{\beta}(X) \leqq \beta(X) \qquad (X \in \mathfrak{A}). \qquad (87.8)$$

Now, according to (87.1), the soma function $\alpha(X)$ is the largest monotonically decreasing soma function that is $\leqq \beta(X)$, and $\beta(X)$ is the smallest monotonically increasing soma function that is $\geqq \alpha(X)$. Hence, we must have

$$\alpha(X) = \bar{\alpha}(X), \quad \beta(X) = \underline{\beta}(X), \qquad (87.9)$$

and this means that the functions $\alpha(X)$ and $\beta(X)$ are uniquely determined and, in particular, that the equations

$$\underline{\alpha}(X) = \bar{\alpha}(X), \quad \underline{\beta}(X) = \bar{\beta}(X) \qquad (87.10)$$

hold.

88. By (86.7) and (86.8), we may write the condition (87.7) in the form

$$\inf\bigl(\Omega(Y);\ Y \subseteqq X\bigr) \leqq \sup\bigl(\omega(Y);\ Y \subseteqq X\bigr). \tag{88.1}$$

In the case that $\bar{\alpha}(X)$ and $\underline{\beta}(X)$ are finite numbers, for any preassigned positive ε, there are two non-empty somas $Y \subseteqq X$ and $Z \subseteqq X$ for which

$$\Omega(Y) \leqq \bar{\alpha}(X) + \frac{\varepsilon}{2}, \quad \underline{\beta}(X) - \frac{\varepsilon}{2} \leqq \omega(Z). \tag{88.2}$$

It then follows from $\bar{\alpha}(X) \leqq \underline{\beta}(X)$ that

$$\Omega(Y) \leqq \omega(Z) + \varepsilon; \tag{88.3}$$

moreover, the two numbers $\Omega(Y)$ and $\omega(Z)$ are finite, by (88.2), since $\bar{\alpha}(X) \leqq \Omega(Y)$ and $\omega(Z) \leqq \underline{\beta}(X)$.

Assume, conversely, that we can assign to each soma X in $\mathfrak{A}$ and to each number $\varepsilon > 0$ two non-empty subsomas Y and Z of X in such a way that, first, the numbers $\Omega(Y)$ and $\omega(Z)$ are finite, and second, the relation (88.3) holds. The relations

$$\bar{\alpha}(X) < +\infty, \quad \underline{\beta}(X) > -\infty \tag{88.4}$$

follow from the finiteness of $\Omega(Y)$ and $\omega(Z)$, and from formula (88.3) it follows that

$$\bar{\alpha}(X) \leqq \underline{\beta}(X) + \varepsilon. \tag{88.5}$$

Thus, if $\bar{\alpha}(X)$ and $\underline{\beta}(X)$ are both finite, we obtain the relation (87.7) by letting ε in (88.5) tend to zero. If $\bar{\alpha}(X) = -\infty$ or if $\underline{\beta}(X) = +\infty$, (87.7) is automatically satisfied.

We combine the above results in the two following theorems.

THEOREM 8: *We consider a monotonically increasing soma function $\Omega(X)$ and a monotonically decreasing soma function $\omega(X)$ defined on the set of somas $\mathfrak{A}$ and we assume that $\omega(X) \leqq \Omega(X)$ for all X in $\mathfrak{A}$. Then the validity of the relation*

$$\inf\bigl(\Omega(Y); Y \subseteqq X\bigr) \leqq \sup\bigl(\omega(Y); Y \subseteqq X\bigr) \tag{88.6}$$

for all X of $\mathfrak{A}$ is necessary and sufficient for the existence of precisely one pair of soma functions $\alpha(X)$ and $\beta(X)$ for which the relations

$$\left.\begin{aligned} &\omega(X) \leqq \alpha(X) \leqq \beta(X) \leqq \Omega(X), \\ &\alpha(X) = \inf\bigl(\beta(Y); Y \subseteqq X\bigr), \\ &\beta(X) = \sup\bigl(\alpha(Y); Y \subseteqq X\bigr) \end{aligned}\right\} \tag{88.7}$$

hold throughout. These soma functions can be computed from $\omega(X)$ *and* $\Omega(X)$ *by means of the equations*

$$\alpha(X) = \inf(\Omega(Y); Y \subseteqq X), \tag{88.8}$$

$$\beta(X) = \sup(\omega(Y); Y \subseteqq X). \tag{88.9}$$

THEOREM 9: *Condition* (88.6) *of Theorem* 8 *can be replaced by the requirement that there can be assigned to each soma* X *of* $\mathfrak{A}$ *and to each positive number* ε *a pair of non-empty subsomas* Y *and* Z *of* X *such that the numbers* $\Omega(Y)$ *and* $\omega(Z)$ *are finite and the relation*

$$\Omega(Y) \leqq \omega(Z) + \varepsilon \tag{88.10}$$

holds.

These two theorems will often come in very handy. We shall have occasion again and again to use them for comparing, or identifying with each other, place functions that had been computed by different means. For such applications, it is convenient to have the following theorem also at our disposal.

THEOREM 10: *If the soma functions* $\omega(X)$ *and* $\Omega(X)$ *satisfy the hypotheses of Theorem* 8, *including* (88.6) *or the equivalent condition of Theorem* 9, *and if* f *is a place function with infinum and supremum* $\alpha(X)$ *and* $\beta(X)$, *respectively, then, if one of the relations*

$$\omega(X) \leqq \alpha(X) \leqq \Omega(X), \quad \omega(X) \leqq \beta(X) \leqq \Omega(X) \tag{88.11}$$

is valid throughout, so is the other, and f *is uniquely determined thereby.*

Proof: To see that this is true, it suffices to note that each of the relations (88.11) implies the formula (88.7), which in turn implies the two equations (88.8) and (88.9).

CHAPTER FOUR

CALCULATION WITH PLACE FUNCTIONS

§§ 89-94. Limit Processes

89. Let $\alpha_1(X)$, $\beta_1(X)$ and $\alpha_2(X)$, $\beta_2(X)$ denote the infimum and supremum of the two place functions f_1 and f_2, respectively, that have the same domain of definition M and are assumed to satisfy

$$f_1 \leqq f_2 . \tag{89.1}$$

As in the preceding chapter, let $\mathfrak{A}$ be the set of all non-empty subsomas X of M. If X is a soma of $\mathfrak{A}$ and if $\alpha_1(X) > -\infty$, then there are on X place functions c that are constant and $\leqq f_1$. But every such function is also $\leqq f_2$, and it follows that

$$\alpha_1(X) \leqq \alpha_2(X).$$

This relation holds even in the hitherto excluded case $\alpha_1(X) = -\infty$ and it is therefore true in general. The relation

$$\beta_1(X) \leqq \beta_2(X)$$

is proved in the same way.

In the contrary case, in which (89.1) does not hold, there is, by Theorem 6 of § 74, at least one finitely-valued function $f_1' \leqq f_1$ and at least one finitely-valued function $f_2'' \geqq f_2$ such that $f_1' \leqq f_2''$ does not hold. But then there is a non-empty subsoma Z of M on which f_1' and f_2'' are both constant and for which we have

$$\alpha_1'(Z) = \beta_1'(Z) > \alpha_2''(Z) = \beta_2''(Z).$$

Now since $f_1 \geqq f_1'$, we have $\alpha_1(Z) \geqq \alpha_1'(Z)$, and since $f_2'' \geqq f_2$, we have $\beta_2''(Z) \geqq \beta_2(Z)$; and consequently, for this soma Z, we have

$$\alpha_1(Z) > \beta_2(Z),$$

and we may therefore state the following theorem.

THEOREM 1: *If two place functions f_1 and f_2 having the same domain of definition M satisfy the relation*

$$f_1 \leqq f_2, \tag{89.2}$$

then we have the relations

$$\alpha_1(X) \leqq \alpha_2(X), \quad \beta_1(X) \leqq \beta_2(X) \qquad (X \in \mathfrak{A}). \quad (89.3)$$

Furthermore, for (89.2) *to hold, it is sufficient that the weaker condition*

$$\alpha_1(X) \leqq \beta_2(X) \quad (89.4)$$

be satisfied by every non-empty subsoma X of M.

An immediate corollary of this result is the following theorem.

THEOREM 2: *Two functions f_1 and f_2 are identical with each other if and only if both the relations*

$$\alpha_1(X) \leqq \beta_2(X), \quad \alpha_2(X) \leqq \beta_1(X) \quad (89.5)$$

hold for every soma X of $\mathfrak{A}$.

Proof: By Theorem 1, we have both $f_1 \leqq f_2$ and $f_2 \leqq f_1$.

In particular, the two relations (89.5) must hold if one of the relations

$$\alpha_1(X) = \alpha_2(X) \quad \text{or} \quad \beta_1(X) = \beta_2(X)$$

always holds for all X in $\mathfrak{A}$. Thus, by a very simple argument, we obtain explicitly a result that was contained implicitly in Theorem 3 of § 83.

90. We now denote by $\alpha_\nu(X)$ and $\beta_\nu(X)$ the infima and suprema of the place functions f_ν of a sequence $\{f_\nu\}$ and we introduce the following notation:

$$g = \sup(f_1, f_2, \ldots), \quad (90.1)$$

$$\omega(X) = \sup(\alpha_1(X), \alpha_2(X), \ldots), \quad (90.2)$$

$$\Omega(X) = \sup(\beta_1(X), \beta_2(X), \ldots). \quad (90.3)$$

It is clear that $\omega(X)$ is a monotonically decreasing and $\Omega(X)$ a monotonically increasing soma function and that, moreover, $\omega(X) \leqq \Omega(X)$ for all X in $\mathfrak{A}$. By § 89, it follows from $g \geqq f_\nu$ $(\nu = 1, 2, \ldots)$ that

$$\alpha_g(X) \geqq \alpha_\nu(X), \quad \beta_g(X) \geqq \beta_\nu(X) \quad (\nu = 1, 2, \ldots),$$

and hence also that

$$\alpha_g(X) \geqq \omega(X), \quad \beta_g(X) \geqq \Omega(X). \quad (90.4)$$

Now if $\Omega(X) < +\infty$ for a given soma X and if y is a number satisfying

$$\Omega(X) < y, \quad (90.5)$$

then, for $\nu = 1, 2, \ldots$, we also have $\beta_\nu(X) < y$. Then, by (80.2),

$$X \subseteqq S_\nu(y) \qquad (\nu = 1, 2, \ldots),$$

where $[S_\nu(y)]$ denotes a nest of somas of f_ν, and consequently

$$X \subseteqq \prod_\nu S_\nu(y) = T(y).$$

By §§ 71 ff., however, $[T(y)]$ is a nest of somas of g; hence $\beta_g(X) \leqq y$ for all values of y satisfying (90.5), and therefore

$$\beta_g(X) \leqq \Omega(X). \tag{90.6}$$

Taking (90.4) into account, we conclude that

$$\beta_g(X) = \Omega(X). \tag{90.7}$$

Hence, by Theorem 3 of § 83, it follows that

$$\alpha_g(X) = \inf\big(\Omega(Y);\ Y \subseteqq X\big). \tag{90.8}$$

On the other hand, the relations

$$\beta_\nu(X) = \sup\big(\alpha_\nu(Y);\ Y \subseteqq X\big) \leqq \sup\big(\omega(Y);\ Y \subseteqq X\big),$$

for $\nu = 1, 2, \ldots$ follow from $\alpha_\nu(X) \leqq \omega(X)$, and from these relations it follows that

$$\Omega(X) \leqq \sup\big(\omega(Y);\ Y \subseteqq X\big). \tag{90.9}$$

The right-hand side of this last relation represents the smallest monotonically increasing soma function that is $\geqq \omega(X)$ (Theorem 6 of § 86), and so must be $\leqq \Omega(X)$. All these relations yield the following theorem.

THEOREM 3: *Denoting by g the least upper bound of a sequence $\{f_\nu\}$ of place functions and writing*

$$\omega(X) = \sup\big(\alpha_1(X), \alpha_2(X), \ldots\big), \tag{90.10}$$

$$\Omega(X) = \sup\big(\beta_1(X), \beta_2(X), \ldots\big), \tag{90.11}$$

we have the identities

$$\alpha_g(X) = \inf\big(\Omega(Y);\ Y \subseteqq X\big), \tag{90.12}$$

$$\beta_g(X) = \Omega(X) = \sup\big(\omega(Y);\ Y \subseteqq X\big). \tag{90.13}$$

The place function g is the only place function for which the relations

$$\omega(X) \leqq \alpha_g(X) \leqq \beta_g(X) \leqq \Omega(X) \tag{90.14}$$

are satisfied throughout.

Proof: The last assertion, namely that the place function g is uniquely determined by (90.14), follows from the fact that the hypotheses of Theorem 8 of § 88 are satisfied, as we see by using equations (90.12) and (90.13).

The proof of the following theorem is similar to that of Theorem 3.

THEOREM 4: *Denoting the greatest lower bound of the sequence $\{f_\nu\}$ by h, and writing*

$$\left.\begin{aligned} \omega'(X) &= \inf(\alpha_1(X), \alpha_2(X), \ldots), \\ \Omega'(X) &= \inf(\beta_1(X), \beta_2(X), \ldots), \end{aligned}\right\} \tag{90.15}$$

h is uniquely determined by the relations

$$\omega'(X) \leqq \alpha_h(X) \leqq \beta_h(X) \leqq \Omega'(X); \tag{90.16}$$

and, in addition, we have

$$\left.\begin{aligned} \alpha_h(X) &= \omega'(X) = \inf(\Omega'(Y);\ Y \subseteqq X), \\ \beta_h(X) &= \sup(\omega'(Y);\ Y \subseteqq X). \end{aligned}\right\} \tag{90.17}$$

91. There is no reason why, under the right conditions, the equation $\alpha_g(X) = \omega(X)$ should not hold in addition to the equation $\beta_g(X) = \Omega(X)$ (which, by Theorem 6 of § 90, always holds).

Let g be a *bounded* place function defined on M and let $\{\varepsilon_\nu\}$ be a sequence of positive numbers converging to zero. By Theorem 1 of § 79, a decomposition of M

$$M = M_1^{(\nu)} + M_2^{(\nu)} + \cdots + M_{p_\nu}^{(\nu)} \tag{91.1}$$

can be assigned to each number ε_ν in such a way that the oscillation of g on each of the somas $M_j^{(\nu)}$ is less than or equal to ε_ν. We define a finitely-valued place function f_ν by assigning it the value $\alpha_g(M_j^{(\nu)})$ on the soma $M_j^{(\nu)}$. Then, for every soma $X \subseteqq M$, we have

$$\left.\begin{aligned} \alpha_\nu(X) &\leqq \alpha_g(X) \leqq \alpha_\nu(X) + \varepsilon_\nu, \\ \beta_\nu(X) &\leqq \beta_g(X) \leqq \beta_\nu(X) + \varepsilon_\nu. \end{aligned}\right\} \tag{91.2}$$

From this, it follows not only that $\alpha_g(X)$ is identical with the least upper bound $\omega(X)$ of the $\alpha_\nu(X)$, but also, using the fact that $\lim_{\nu=\infty} \varepsilon_\nu = 0$, that

$$\lim_{\nu=\infty} \alpha_\nu(X) = \alpha_g(X), \quad \lim_{\nu=\infty} \beta_\nu(X) = \beta_g(X).$$

Thus, we have proved the following theorem.

THEOREM 5: *Every bounded place function g defined on the soma M is the least upper bound of a sequence $\{f_\nu\}$ of finitely-valued place functions f_ν which can be chosen to satisfy the relations*

$$\lim_{\nu=\infty} \alpha_\nu(X) = \alpha_g(X), \quad \lim_{\nu=\infty} \beta_\nu(X) = \beta_g(X) \tag{91.3}$$

for every X in $\mathfrak{A}$.

Likewise, every bounded place function h can be represented as the greatest lower bound of a sequence $\{f_\nu'\}$ of finitely-valued place functions f_ν' in such a way that the conditions

$$\lim_{\nu=\infty} \alpha_\nu'(X) = \alpha_h(X), \quad \lim_{\nu=\infty} \beta_\nu'(X) = \beta_h(X) \tag{91.4}$$

are satisfied.

92. We now wish to establish the concept of the *upper limit* and *lower limit* of a sequence $\{f_\nu\}$ of arbitrary place functions.

To this end, and in analogy with § 25, we consider the least upper bounds g_ν of the subsequences

$$f_\nu, f_{\nu+1}, f_{\nu+2}, \dots \tag{92.1}$$

of the given sequence $\{f_\nu\}$. We obtain a monotonically decreasing sequence

$$g_1 \geqq g_2 \geqq g_3 \geqq \cdots \tag{92.2}$$

of new functions, whose greatest lower bound is denoted by

$$\bar{f} = \overline{\lim_{\nu=\infty}} f_\nu \tag{92.3}$$

and is called the *upper limit* of the sequence $\{f_\nu\}$.

By the results of §§ 71-73, a nest of somas $[\underline{S}(y)]$ of $\bar{f}$ can be obtained by putting

$$\underline{S}(y) = \underline{\lim_{\nu=\infty}} S_\nu(y), \tag{92.4}$$

as in § 25.

Similarly, let h_ν denote the greatest lower bounds of the sequences (92.1), and let

$$\underline{f} = \underline{\lim_{\nu=\infty}} f_\nu \tag{92.5}$$

denote the least upper bound of the monotonically increasing sequence

$$h_1 \leqq h_2 \leqq h_3 \leqq \dots. \tag{92.6}$$

This least upper bound is called the *lower limit* of the sequence $\{f_\nu\}$.

A nest of somas $[\bar{S}(y)]$ of the place function $\underline{f}$ is then given by the formula

$$\bar{S}(y) = \overline{\lim_{\nu=\infty}} S_\nu(y). \tag{92.7}$$

By § 25, we have the relation

$$\underline{S}(y) \subseteqq \bar{S}(y) \qquad (-\infty < y < +\infty), \quad (92.8)$$

from which it follows that

$$\underline{f} \leqq \bar{f}. \quad (92.9)$$

The sequence $\{f_\nu\}$ is said to be *convergent* if

$$\underline{f} = \bar{f} = f; \quad (92.10)$$

if this is the case, then we call f simply the *limit*, we say that the sequence *converges to* f, and we write

$$\lim_{\nu=\infty} f_\nu = f. \quad (92.11)$$

These considerations yield the following theorem.

THEOREM 6: *The upper limit $\bar{f}$ of a sequence of place functions $f_1, f_2, \ldots$ that have nests of somas $[S_1(y)], [S_2(y)], \ldots$ is a place function that has the nest of somas $[\underline{S}(y)]$ whose somas are given by*

$$\underline{S}(y) = \underline{\lim}_{\nu=\infty} S_\nu(y). \quad (92.12)$$

Likewise, $[\bar{S}(y)]$, where

$$\bar{S}(y) = \overline{\lim}_{\nu=\infty} S_\nu(y) \quad (92.13)$$

is a nest of somas of the lower limit $\underline{f}$ of $f_1, f_2, \ldots$ and we always have

$$\underline{f} \leqq \bar{f}. \quad (92.14)$$

The sequence $\{f_\nu\}$ converges to a function f if and only if

$$\underline{f} = \bar{f} = f. \quad (92.15)$$

A necessary and sufficient condition for this to occur is that whenever $y < z$,

$$\bar{S}(y) \subseteqq \underline{S}(z). \quad (92.16)$$

93. We now wish to use the infima and suprema $\alpha_\nu(X)$ and $\beta_\nu(X)$ of the functions f_ν, to find their analogues for $\bar{f}$ and $\underline{f}$. To this end, we introduce the soma function

$$\bar{\Omega}(X) = \overline{\lim}_{\nu=\infty} \beta_\nu(X). \quad (93.1)$$

Furthermore, we denote the infima and suprema of the functions

$$g_\nu = \sup (f_\nu, f_{\nu+1}, \ldots) \quad (93.2)$$

by $\bar{\alpha}_\nu(X)$ and $\bar{\beta}_\nu(X)$, respectively. We then have, by Theorem 3 of § 90,

$$\bar{\beta}_\nu(X) = \sup\left(\beta_\nu(X), \beta_{\nu+1}(X), \ldots\right); \tag{93.3}$$

and we obtain from (93.1), by the definition of the upper limit,

$$\bar{\Omega}(X) = \inf\,(\bar{\beta}_1(X), \bar{\beta}_2(X), \ldots). \tag{93.4}$$

If we denote by $\bar{\alpha}(X)$ the infimum of the place function

$$\bar{f} = \inf\,(g_1, g_2, \ldots) \tag{93.5}$$

on the soma X, and apply Theorem 4 of § 90 to this place function $\bar{f}$, then (93.4) plays the rôle of the second equation of (90.15), and so the first line of (90.17) becomes

$$\bar{\alpha}(X) = \inf\left(\bar{\Omega}(Y);\ Y \subseteqq X\right). \tag{93.6}$$

Finally, it follows from (93.5) that the supremum $\bar{\beta}(X)$ of $\bar{f}$ satisfies

$$\bar{\beta}(X) \leqq \bar{\beta}_\nu(X) \qquad (\nu = 1, 2, \ldots), \tag{93.7}$$

and therefore, by (93.4), satisfies

$$\bar{\beta}(X) \leqq \bar{\Omega}(X). \tag{93.8}$$

Thus, we can state the following theorem, that part of the theorem dealing with $\underline{f}$ being provable in a similar way.

THEOREM 7: *Let $\bar{f}$ and $\underline{f}$ denote the upper and lower limits of a sequence $\{f_\nu\}$ of place functions; let $\bar{\alpha}(X)$, $\bar{\beta}(X)$ and $\underline{\alpha}(X)$, $\underline{\beta}(X)$ denote the infimum and supremum of $\bar{f}$ and $\underline{f}$, respectively. Then, if we write*

$$\bar{\Omega}(X) = \overline{\lim_{\nu=\infty}}\, \beta_\nu(X), \quad \underline{\omega}(X) = \underline{\lim_{\nu=\infty}}\, \alpha_\nu(X), \tag{93.9}$$

we have the relations

$$\bar{\alpha}(X) = \inf\left(\bar{\Omega}(Y);\ Y \subseteqq X\right), \tag{93.10}$$

$$\underline{\beta}(X) = \sup\left(\underline{\omega}(Y);\ Y \subseteqq X\right), \tag{93.11}$$

$$\underline{\omega}(X) \leqq \underline{\alpha}(X) \leqq \frac{\underline{\beta}(X)}{\bar{\alpha}(X)} \leqq \bar{\beta}(X) \leqq \bar{\Omega}(X). \tag{93.12}$$

According to this result, $\bar{f}$ is the largest place function for which $\bar{\alpha}(X) \leqq \bar{\Omega}(X)$, and $\underline{f}$ is the smallest place function for which $\underline{\beta}(X) \geqq \underline{\omega}(X)$. From this, we obtain the following theorem.

THEOREM 8: *Using the notation of the preceding theorem, convergence occurs if and only if* $\bar{\alpha}(X)$ *and* $\underline{\beta}(X)$ *are the infimum and supremum, respectively, of one and the same place function* f, *i.e., if and only if the soma functions* $\underline{\omega}(X)$ *and* $\bar{\Omega}(X)$ *satisfy the hypotheses, including* (88.6), *of Theorem 8 of* § 88.

94. If the lower and upper limits $\underline{f}$ and $\bar{f}$ of a sequence $\{f_\nu\}$ are bounded place functions, then there are at least two finite numbers a and b for which

$$a < \underline{\alpha}(M) \leqq \bar{\beta}(M) < b. \tag{94.1}$$

Now, every soma X of $\mathfrak{A}$ satisfies the relations

$$\underline{\alpha}(M) \leqq \underline{\alpha}(X) \leqq \underline{\beta}(X) \leqq \bar{\beta}(X) \leqq \bar{\beta}(M),$$

$$\underline{\alpha}(M) \leqq \underline{\alpha}(X) \leqq \bar{\alpha}(X) \leqq \bar{\beta}(X) \leqq \bar{\beta}(M),$$

and consequently we also have

$$a < \underline{\beta}(X) < b, \quad a < \bar{\alpha}(X) < b. \tag{94.2}$$

In view of the relations (93.10) and (93.11), to each non-empty soma $X \subseteqq M$ there can be assigned a non-empty soma $Y \subseteqq X$ that satisfies

$$a < \underline{\omega}(Y) \leqq \bar{\Omega}(Y) < b. \tag{94.3}$$

Conversely, if the latter condition is fulfilled, we conclude from the same two relations that

$$\underline{\beta}(X) > a, \quad \bar{\alpha}(X) < b \tag{94.4}$$

for every soma X in $\mathfrak{A}$. It follows from this, by (83.6) and (83.7), that

$$a \leqq \underline{\alpha}(X) \leqq \bar{\beta}(X) \leqq b, \tag{94.5}$$

and this is a condition from which the boundedness of $\underline{f}$ and $\bar{f}$ can be deduced.

THEOREM 9: *A necessary and sufficient condition for the boundedness of the lower and upper limits* $\underline{f}$ *and* $\bar{f}$ *of a sequence* $\{f_\nu\}$ *of place functions is that there exist finite numbers* a *and* b *such that with every soma* X *in* $\mathfrak{A}$ *there can be associated a non-empty subsoma* $Y \subseteqq X$ *for which*

$$a < \underline{\omega}(Y) \leqq \bar{\Omega}(Y) < b. \tag{94.6}$$

§§ 95-106. Elementary Operations on Place Functions

95. Finitely-valued place functions

$$f' = \sum_j y'_j M_j, \quad f'' = \sum_j y''_j M_j \tag{95.1}$$

can be combined by treating them as a sort of hypercomplex number system, whose "units" are the somas M_j.

Thus, for example, the *sum*

$$f = f' + f'' \tag{95.2}$$

of the two place functions (95.1) is defined by the equation

$$f = \sum_j (y_j' + y_j'') M_j. \tag{95.3}$$

Let X be any soma of $\mathfrak{A}$; let $\alpha'(X)$ and $\alpha''(X)$ be the minima of the sets of y_j' and y_j'', respectively, where j runs through all the indices for which the somas XM_j are non-empty; and let $\beta'(X)$ and $\beta''(X)$ be the corresponding maxima; then for these values of j we have the inequalities

$$\alpha'(X) + \alpha''(X) \leqq y_j' + y_j'' \leqq \beta'(X) + \beta''(X).$$

Hence it follows that the relations

$$\alpha'(X) + \alpha''(X) \leqq \alpha(X) \leqq \beta(X) \leqq \beta'(X) + \beta''(X) \quad (X \in \mathfrak{A}) \tag{95.4}$$

hold.

We now assume that the functions f' and f'' are any bounded place functions. We represent each of these functions as the least upper bound of the monotonically increasing sequences of finitely-valued place functions

$$f_1' \leqq f_2' \leqq f_3' \leqq \ldots, \quad f_1'' \leqq f_2'' \leqq f_3'' \leqq \ldots, \tag{95.5}$$

respectively, and we suppose that each of these sequences satisfies Theorem 5 of § 91. Putting

$$f_\nu = f_\nu' + f_\nu'' \qquad (\nu = 1, 2, \ldots), \tag{95.6}$$

and making use of the definition (95.3) of the sum, we see from (95.5) that the relations

$$f_1 \leqq f_2 \leqq f_3 \leqq \ldots$$

must also hold. We shall now define the sum $f = f' + f''$ of the two original place functions to be the least upper bound

$$f = \sup(f_1, f_2, \ldots). \tag{95.7}$$

We shall see that this definition is not self-contradictory and that it is a sensible one, as well: that is, not only is the function f independent of the particular choice of approximating sequences $\{f_\nu'\}$ and $\{f_\nu''\}$, but also the operation $f = f' + f''$ has all the characteristic properties of ordinary addition. In what follows, all of this will be shown.

96. Applying Theorem 3 of § 90 to (95.7), we find that the supremum $\beta(X)$ of f is given by

$$\beta(X) = \sup(\beta_1(X), \beta_2(X), \ldots) = \lim_{\nu=\infty} \beta_\nu(X). \tag{96.1}$$

Moreover, we have, by Theorem 5 of § 91,

$$\left.\begin{array}{ll} \alpha'(X) = \lim\limits_{\nu=\infty} \alpha'_\nu(X), & \beta'(X) = \lim\limits_{\nu=\infty} \beta'_\nu(X), \\ \alpha''(X) = \lim\limits_{\nu=\infty} \alpha''_\nu(X), & \beta''(X) = \lim\limits_{\nu=\infty} \beta''_\nu(X). \end{array}\right\} \tag{96.2}$$

Now, by (95.4), we see

$$\alpha'_\nu(X) + \alpha''_\nu(X) \leqq \beta_\nu(X) \leqq \beta'_\nu(X) + \beta''_\nu(X),$$

or, taking (96.1) and (96.2) into consideration and passing to the limit,

$$\alpha'(X) + \alpha''(X) \leqq \beta(X) \leqq \beta'(X) + \beta''(X). \tag{96.3}$$

We now put

$$\omega(X) = \alpha'(X) + \alpha''(X), \quad \Omega(X) = \beta'(X) + \beta''(X). \tag{96.4}$$

If ε is an arbitrary positive number, then by Theorem 1 of § 79, there is at least one non-empty soma $Y \subseteqq X$ and at least one non-empty soma $Z \subseteqq Y$ such that

$$\beta'(Y) \leqq \alpha'(Y) + \frac{\varepsilon}{2}, \quad \beta''(Z) \leqq \alpha''(Z) + \frac{\varepsilon}{2}.$$

Using the relations

$$\alpha'(Y) \leqq \alpha'(Z) \leqq \beta'(Z) \leqq \beta'(Y),$$

we see that then

$$\Omega(Z) \leqq \omega(Z) + \varepsilon. \tag{96.5}$$

Then, by Theorem 9 of § 88, there is at most one place function for which

$$\omega(X) \leqq \alpha(X) \leqq \beta(X) \leqq \Omega(X) \tag{96.6}$$

holds throughout, and by Theorem 10 of § 88, together with (96.3) and (96.4), such a function always exists and is identical with $f = f' + f''$. Moreover, the inequalities (96.6) represent a criterion for $f' + f''$ that is independent of the particular choice of the sequences $\{f'_\nu\}$ and $\{f''_\nu\}$.

This result is easily extended to the case that the place functions f' and f'' are no longer bounded but merely finite. For the domain of definition

M common to f' and f'' can be decomposed into an at most countable number of subsomas M_j on each of which the given functions are bounded. Under these circumstances, Theorem 4 of § 92 gives a technique for extending the above result, valid in each soma M_j, to arbitrary subsomas X of M.

The sum of three or more finite place functions can also be defined in this way. Finally, we obtain the following theorem.

THEOREM 1: *If the place functions $f_1, f_2, \ldots, f_p$ are all finite, then a unique place function f is assigned to them by means of the relations*

$$\left.\begin{aligned} &\omega(X) \leqq \alpha(X) \leqq \beta(X) \leqq \Omega(X) \qquad (X \in \mathfrak{A}), \\ &\omega(X) = \alpha_1(X) + \alpha_2(X) + \cdots + \alpha_p(X), \\ &\Omega(X) = \beta_1(X) + \beta_2(X) + \cdots + \beta_p(X). \end{aligned}\right\} \tag{96.7}$$

This function f is called the sum of $f_1, \ldots, f_p$, and is denoted by

$$f = f_1 + f_2 + \cdots + f_p. \tag{96.8}$$

Further, f is the largest place function h for which

$$\alpha_h(X) \leqq \Omega(X) \qquad (X \in \mathfrak{A}) \tag{96.9}$$

and the smallest place function g for which

$$\beta_g(X) \geqq \omega(X). \tag{96.10}$$

97. In particular, if $p = 2$, the relations

$$\alpha_h(X) \leqq \beta_1(X) + \beta_2(X) \qquad (X \in \mathfrak{A}) \tag{97.1}$$

and

$$h \leqq f_1 + f_2 \tag{97.2}$$

are equivalent. Under the assumption of (97.1), moreover, every non-empty soma $Y \subseteqq X$ satisfies

$$\alpha_h(X) \leqq \alpha_h(Y) \leqq \beta_1(Y) + \beta_2(Y) \leqq \beta_1(Y) + \beta_2(X); \tag{97.3}$$

however,

$$\alpha_1(X) = \inf\left(\beta_1(Y);\ Y \subseteqq X\right),$$

and therefore, from (97.3), it follows that

$$\alpha_h(X) \leqq \alpha_1(X) + \beta_2(X). \tag{97.4}$$

Conversely, (97.1) follows from (97.4), so that the two conditions (97.1) and (97.4) are equivalent.

If we combine all these results, we obtain the first part of the theorem below; the remainder of the theorem is proved in a similar way.

THEOREM 2: *A necessary and sufficient condition that a place function h be less than or equal to the sum $f = f_1 + f_2$ of two finite place functions is that, for every soma X in $\mathfrak{A}$, at least one of the three equivalent inequalities*

$$\left.\begin{array}{ll} \alpha_h(X) \leqq \alpha_1(X) + \beta_2(X), & \alpha_h(X) \leqq \beta_1(X) + \beta_2(X), \\ \beta_h(X) \leqq \beta_1(X) + \beta_2(X) & \end{array}\right\} \tag{97.5}$$

holds.

A necessary and sufficient condition that a place function g be greater than or equal to the sum $f = f_1 + f_2$ is that at least one of the three equivalent inequalities

$$\left.\begin{array}{ll} \alpha_g(X) \geqq \alpha_1(X) + \alpha_2(X), & \\ \beta_g(X) \geqq \alpha_1(X) + \beta_2(X), & \beta_g(X) \geqq \alpha_1(X) + \alpha_2(X) \end{array}\right\} \tag{97.6}$$

holds for all X in $\mathfrak{A}$.

The function $f = f_1 + f_2$ itself is characterized not only by the conditions of Theorem 1 *of* § 96, *but also by the relations*

$$\alpha(X) \leqq \alpha_1(X) + \beta_2(X) \leqq \beta(X) \qquad (X \in \mathfrak{A}). \tag{97.7}$$

By the last two theorems, the sum $s = f + \varepsilon$ of a place function f and a constant function ε satisfies

$$\alpha_s(X) = \alpha(X) + \varepsilon, \quad \beta_s(X) = \beta(X) + \varepsilon. \tag{97.8}$$

Thus, if $[S(y)]$ is a nest of somas of f, $[S(y - \varepsilon)]$ is a nest of somas of $f + \varepsilon$.

98. The operation of addition defined by Theorem 1 of § 96 clearly satisfies all the axioms of addition. The relations

$$f_1 + f_2 = f_2 + f_1, \tag{98.1}$$

$$f_1 + (f_2 + f_3) = (f_1 + f_2) + f_3, \tag{98.2}$$

$$\text{if} \quad f_1 \leqq f_1', \ f_2 \leqq f_2' \quad \text{then} \quad f_1 + f_2 \leqq f_1' + f_2' \tag{98.3}$$

can be verified immediately.

99. Let f be an arbitrary place function. We put

$$\alpha'(X) = -\beta(X), \quad \beta'(X) = -\alpha(X). \tag{99.1}$$

Then $\alpha'(X)$ is a monotonically decreasing soma function, $\beta'(X)$ is a monotonically increasing soma function, and there exist between them relations analogous to (83.6) and (83.7). Moreover, for each real number y, the union of all the somas X in $\mathfrak{A}$ for which $\beta'(X) \leqq y$ exists, since this set of somas coincides with that for which $\alpha(X) \geqq -y$. By the Bischof Theorem (Theorem 5 of § 85), then, there exists a place function f' whose infimum and supremum are given by (99.1). If we put $g = f + f'$, the relations

$$\alpha(X) - \beta(X) \leqq \alpha_g(X) \leqq \beta_g(X) \leqq \beta(X) - \alpha(X) \tag{99.2}$$

determine g uniquely, by Theorem 1 of § 96. But since

$$\alpha(X) - \beta(X) \leqq 0 \leqq \beta(X) - \alpha(X)$$

also holds, we must have $g = 0$; and f' is a place function that we denote by $-f$.

It should be remarked that if $[S(y)]$ denotes a nest of somas of f, then the family of somas

$$S'(y) = M \dotplus S(-y) \tag{99.3}$$

is a nest of somas of $-f$.

We can now define the *difference*

$$f = f' - f'' \tag{99.4}$$

of finite place functions by means of the equation

$$f = f' + (-f'').$$

By Theorem 1 of § 96, and Theorem 2 of § 97, this difference is obtained by requiring that one of the following systems of inequalities hold for all X in $\mathfrak{A}$:

$$\alpha'(X) - \beta''(X) \leqq \alpha(X) \leqq \beta(X) \leqq \beta'(X) - \alpha''(X), \tag{99.5}$$

$$\alpha(X) \leqq \alpha'(X) - \alpha''(X) \leqq \beta(X), \tag{99.6}$$

$$\alpha(X) \leqq \beta'(X) - \beta''(X) \leqq \beta(X). \tag{99.7}$$

100. Let f be an arbitrary place function. We introduce the notation

$$p = \max(0, f), \quad n = \max(0, -f) \tag{100.1}$$

and observe that p and n are *non-negative* place functions.

If $[S(y)]$ is any nest of somas of f, then $p = 0$ on the soma $S(0)$, and $p = f$ on the soma $M \dotplus S(0)$; likewise, $n = -f$ on the soma $S(0)$, and $n = 0$ on the soma $M \dotplus S(0)$. Thus the equation

$$f = p - n \tag{100.2}$$

holds. Every place function can thus be written as the difference of non-negative place functions. Let

$$f = p_1 - n_1$$

be a second such representation of f. It follows from $f \leqq p_1$ and $0 \leqq p_1$ that $p \leqq p_1$, and we can prove by similar reasoning that $n \leqq n_1$. The place functions p and n defined by (100.1) are therefore the smallest non-negative place functions whose difference is equal to the given place function f.

By Theorem 3 of § 90, the suprema $\beta_p(X)$ and $\beta_n(X)$ of p and n are given by the equations

$$\beta_p(X) = \max\bigl(0, \beta(X)\bigr), \tag{100.3}$$

$$\beta_n(X) = \max\bigl(0, -\alpha(X)\bigr) = -\min\bigl(0, \alpha(X)\bigr). \tag{100.4}$$

101. By the absolute value $|f|$ of the function f we mean the non-negative place function

$$|f| = p + n. \tag{101.1}$$

On the soma $M \dotplus S(0)$, we have $p = f$ and $n = 0$; in addition, $f \geqq -f$ on the same soma. Thus, on this soma, we have

$$p + n = \max(p, n) = \max(f, -f). \tag{101.2}$$

But these equations hold also on $S(0)$ and hence hold everywhere. The absolute value can thus be represented by either of the equations

$$|f| = \max(p, n), \quad |f| = \max(f, -f). \tag{101.3}$$

By (99.3), $[M \dotplus S(y)]$ is a nest of somas of $-f$. Therefore, a nest of somas $[T(y)]$ of f is obtained by letting

$$T(y) = S(y)\bigl(M + S(-y)\bigr) = S(y) + S(y)\,S(-y). \tag{101.4}$$

Now, if f_1 and f_2 are two place functions, there follow from $f_1 \leqq |f_1|$ and $f_2 \leqq |f_2|$ on the one hand and from $-f_1 \leqq |f_1|$ and $-f_2 \leqq |f_2|$ on the other, the relations

$$f_1 + f_2 \leqq |f_1| + |f_2|, \quad -(f_1 + f_2) \leqq |f_1| + |f_2|,$$

respectively, from which we deduce that

$$|f_1 + f_2| \leqq |f_1| + |f_2|. \tag{101.5}$$

Since $f_1 = (f_1 + f_2) - f_2$, however, we have then

$$|f_1| \leqq |f_1 + f_2| + |f_2|,$$

so that we can write, similarly,

$$||f_1| - |f_2|| \leqq |f_1 + f_2|. \tag{101.6}$$

102. Let $\{f'_\nu\}$ and $\{f''_\nu\}$ be two sequences of finite place functions, and let the principal limits $\underline{f}'$ and $\overline{f}'$ of the first sequence be bounded. We construct a third sequence of finite place functions by putting

$$f_\nu = f'_\nu + f''_\nu \qquad (\nu = 1, 2, \ldots), \tag{102.1}$$

and we consider three non-empty subsomas X, Y, and Z of M which satisfy

$$Z \subseteqq Y \subseteqq X. \tag{102.2}$$

In fact, if only Y and X are given, for the moment, Z can always be so chosen, by Theorem 9 of § 94, that $\overline{\Omega}'(Z)$ is finite.

Now, by § 96,

$$\beta_\nu(Z) \leqq \beta'_\nu(Z) + \beta''_\nu(Z),$$

and by definition (93.1)

$$\overline{\Omega}(Z) = \overline{\lim_{\nu=\infty}}\, \beta_\nu(Z), \quad \overline{\Omega}'(Z) = \overline{\lim_{\nu=\infty}}\, \beta'_\nu(Z), \quad \overline{\Omega}''(Z) = \overline{\lim_{\nu=\infty}}\, \beta''_\nu(Z).$$

Thus,

$$\overline{\Omega}(Z) \leqq \overline{\Omega}'(Z) + \overline{\Omega}''(Z). \tag{102.3}$$

On the other hand, we have the inequalities

$$\overline{\alpha}(X) \leqq \overline{\alpha}(Z) \leqq \overline{\Omega}(Z), \quad \overline{\Omega}''(Z) \leqq \Omega''(Y),$$

so that from (102.3) we obtain the relation

$$\overline{\alpha}(X) \leqq \overline{\Omega}'(Z) + \overline{\Omega}''(Y). \tag{102.4}$$

Moreover, $\overline{\alpha}'(Y)$ is finite and, by (93.10), equal to the greatest lower bound of the set of numbers $\overline{\Omega}'(Z)$, where Z runs through those subsomas of Y for which $\overline{\Omega}'(Z)$ is finite. We therefore conclude from (102.4) that

$$\overline{\alpha}(X) \leqq \overline{\alpha}'(Y) + \overline{\Omega}''(Y),$$

and it follows, since $\overline{\alpha}'(Y) \leqq \overline{\beta}'(Y) \leqq \overline{\beta}'(X)$, that

$$\overline{\alpha}(X) \leqq \overline{\beta}'(X) + \overline{\Omega}''(Y). \tag{102.5}$$

The relation (102.5) holds for all $Y \subseteqq X$, and hence

$$\overline{\alpha}(X) \leqq \overline{\beta}'(X) + \overline{\alpha}''(X) \leqq \overline{\beta}'(X) + \overline{\beta}''(X).$$

The right-hand side of the latter inequality, being a monotonically increasing soma function, cannot be smaller than $\bar{\beta}(X)$, i.e., than the smallest monotonically increasing soma function that is $\geqq \bar{\alpha}(X)$. Thus, we finally obtain, for all X in $\mathfrak{A}$, the relation

$$\bar{\beta}(X) \leqq \bar{\beta}'(X) + \bar{\beta}''(X), \tag{102.6}$$

which, by Theorem 2 of § 97, implies

$$\bar{f} \leqq \bar{f}' + \bar{f}''. \tag{102.7}$$

103. We again take from $\mathfrak{A}$ an arbitrary soma $X \subseteqq M$, a second, $Y \subseteqq X$, and a third, $Z \subseteqq Y$ subject to the condition that $\underline{\omega}'(Z)$ be finite.

From $f_\nu' + f_\nu'' = f_\nu$ there follows by Theorem 2 of § 97, the relation

$$\alpha_\nu'(Z) + \beta_\nu''(Z) \leqq \beta_\nu(Z), \tag{103.1}$$

from which we deduce further that

$$\varliminf_{\nu=\infty} \alpha_\nu'(Z) + \varlimsup_{\nu=\infty} \beta_\nu''(Z) \leqq \varlimsup_{\nu=\infty} \beta_\nu(Z),$$

or, written another way,

$$\underline{\omega}'(Z) + \bar{\Omega}''(Z) \leqq \bar{\Omega}(Z). \tag{103.2}$$

But the relations

$$\bar{\alpha}''(X) \leqq \bar{\alpha}''(Z) \leqq \bar{\Omega}''(Z), \quad \bar{\Omega}(Z) \leqq \bar{\Omega}(Y)$$

hold, so that we may write

$$\underline{\omega}'(Z) + \bar{\alpha}''(X) \leqq \bar{\Omega}(Y). \tag{103.3}$$

If we hold X and Y fixed and allow Z to run through all somas $Z \subseteqq Y$ for which $\underline{\omega}'(Z)$ is finite, then the least upper bound of this set of numbers is, by (93.11), the number $\underline{\beta}'(Y)$, which is finite by hypothesis, and so we have

$$\underline{\beta}'(Y) + \bar{\alpha}''(X) \leqq \bar{\Omega}(Y). \tag{103.4}$$

But $\underline{\alpha}'(X) \leqq \underline{\alpha}'(Y) \leqq \underline{\beta}'(Y)$, and therefore

$$\underline{\alpha}'(X) + \bar{\alpha}''(X) \leqq \bar{\Omega}(Y) \tag{103.5}$$

for all $Y \subseteqq X$. Replacing the right-hand side of this last inequality by its greatest lower bound $\bar{\alpha}(X)$, we have, finally, that for all X in $\mathfrak{A}$

$$\underline{\alpha}'(X) + \bar{\alpha}''(X) \leqq \bar{\alpha}(X). \tag{103.6}$$

The last relation implies that

$$\underline{f}' + \bar{f}'' \leqq \bar{f}. \tag{103.7}$$

Each of the inequalities

$$\underline{f}' + \underline{f}'' \leqq \underline{f}, \quad \underline{f} \leqq \underline{f}' + \bar{f}'' \tag{103.8}$$

is obtained by an entirely similar train of reasoning. The relations (102.7), (103.7), and (103.8) were proved under the assumption that the principal limits $\underline{f}'$ and $\bar{f}'$ were bounded place functions. They are obviously also valid, however, under the assumption that these place functions are finite, and so we obtain the following theorem.

THEOREM 3: *We consider two sequences $\{f_\nu'\}$ and $\{f_\nu''\}$ of finite place functions and the sequence of their sums,*

$$f_\nu = f_\nu' + f_\nu'' \qquad (\nu = 1, 2, \ldots). \tag{103.9}$$

Moreover, the lower and upper limits of at least one of the sequences $\{f_\nu'\}$ and $\{f_\nu''\}$ are assumed to be finite place functions. Then the relations

$$\underline{f}' + \underline{f}'' \leqq \underline{f} \leqq \begin{matrix} \underline{f}' + \bar{f}'' \\ \bar{f}' + \underline{f}'' \end{matrix} \leqq \bar{f} \leqq \bar{f}' + \bar{f}'' \tag{103.10}$$

hold between the lower and upper limits of all these sequences.

If in addition $\{f_\nu'\}$, say, is convergent, then the equations

$$\underline{f} = f' + \underline{f}'', \quad \bar{f} = f' + \bar{f}'' \tag{103.11}$$

also hold.

104. Besides the two sequences $\{f_\nu'\}$ and $\{f_\nu''\}$, we now consider the sequence of functions

$$g_\nu = \max(f_\nu', f_\nu'') \qquad (\nu = 1, 2, \ldots) \tag{104.1}$$

and denote the somas of representative nests of somas of f_ν', f_ν'', and g_ν by $S_\nu'(y)$, $S_\nu''(y)$, and

$$T_\nu(y) = S_\nu'(y)\, S_\nu''(y), \tag{104.2}$$

respectively. If we then put

$$\underline{S}'(y) = \varliminf_{\nu=\infty} S_\nu'(y), \quad \ldots, \quad \bar{T}(y) = \varlimsup_{\nu=\infty} T_\nu(y),$$

we obtain, by (30.11), the relations

$$\underline{T}(y) = \underline{S}'(y)\, \underline{S}''(y) \subseteqq \underline{S}'(y)\, \bar{S}''(y) \subseteqq \bar{T}(y) \subseteqq \bar{S}'(y)\, \bar{S}''(y). \tag{104.3}$$

Taking the results of § 92 into consideration, we obtain from (104.3) that

$$\max(\underline{f}', \underline{f}'') \leqq \underline{g} \leqq \begin{matrix} \max(\underline{f}', \overline{f}'') \\ \max(\overline{f}', \underline{f}'') \end{matrix} \leqq \overline{g} = \max(\overline{f}', \overline{f}'').$$

Applying similar reasoning to the sequence $\{\min(f_\nu', f_\nu'')\}$, we finally obtain the following theorem.

THEOREM 4: *Given two sequences $\{f_\nu'\}$ and $\{f_\nu''\}$ of place functions, let*

$$g_\nu = \max(f_\nu', f_\nu''), \quad h_\nu = \min(f_\nu', f_\nu''). \tag{104.4}$$

The following relations then hold:

$$\max(\underline{f}', \underline{f}'') \leqq \underline{g} \leqq \begin{matrix} \max(\underline{f}', \overline{f}'') \\ \max(\overline{f}', \underline{f}'') \end{matrix} \leqq \overline{g} = \max(\overline{f}', \overline{f}''), \tag{104.5}$$

$$\min(\underline{f}', \underline{f}'') = \underline{h} \leqq \begin{matrix} \min(\underline{f}', \overline{f}'') \\ \min(\overline{f}', \underline{f}'') \end{matrix} \leqq \overline{h} \leqq \min(\overline{f}', \overline{f}''). \tag{104.6}$$

If at least one of the sequences, say $\{f_\nu'\}$, is convergent, then we have, in addition, the equations

$$\underline{g} = \max(f', \underline{f}''), \quad \overline{g} = \max(f', \overline{f}''), \tag{104.7}$$

$$\underline{h} = \min(f', \underline{f}''), \quad \overline{h} = \min(f', \overline{f}''). \tag{104.8}$$

Now let $\{f_\nu\}$ be an arbitrary sequence of functions with lower and upper limits $\underline{f}$ and $\overline{f}$. As in § 100, let

$$p_\nu = \max(0, f_\nu), \quad n_\nu = \max(0, -f_\nu). \tag{104.9}$$

Now observe that, writing $g_\nu = -f_\nu$, we have the formulas

$$\underline{g} = -\overline{f}, \quad \overline{g} = -\underline{f}, \tag{104.10}$$

which are an immediate consequence of Theorem 3 of § 103, when this theorem is applied to the sum $g_\nu + f_\nu = 0$. In accordance with (104.7), then, we have

$$\left.\begin{aligned} \underline{p} &= \max(0, \underline{f}), & \overline{p} &= \max(0, \overline{f}), \\ \underline{n} &= \max(0, -\overline{f}), & \overline{n} &= \max(0, -\underline{f}). \end{aligned}\right\} \tag{104.11}$$

From this it follows, in addition, that

$$\bar{p} + \underline{n} = |\bar{f}|, \quad \underline{p} + \bar{n} = |\underline{f}|. \tag{104.12}$$

We now apply the relations (103.10) to the sums

$$|f_\nu| = p_\nu + n_\nu \tag{104.13}$$

and, taking (104.12) into consideration, we obtain

$$\max(0, f) + \max(0, -\bar{f}) \leqq \underline{\lim}_{\nu=\infty} |f_\nu| \leqq \begin{matrix} |\bar{f}| \\ \\ |\underline{f}| \end{matrix} \leqq \lim_{\nu=\infty} |f_\nu| \tag{104.14}$$

$$\leqq \max(0, \bar{f}) + \max(0, -\underline{f}).$$

In particular, these relations yield the following theorem.

THEOREM 5: *If a sequence $\{f_\nu\}$ of place functions converges, so does the sequence $\{|f_\nu|\}$ of absolute values of the f_ν, and the equation*

$$\lim_{\nu=\infty} |f_\nu| = \left|\lim_{\nu=\infty} f_\nu\right| \tag{104.15}$$

holds. Conversely, if the sequence of $|f_\nu|$ converges, then at the very least, we can write

$$\lim_{\nu=\infty} |f_\nu| = \left|\overline{\lim_{\nu=\infty}} f_\nu\right| = \left|\underline{\lim}_{\nu=\infty} f_\nu\right|. \tag{104.16}$$

105. The formation of the *product* of place functions can be treated, with some slight modification, in much the same way as that of the sum.

To begin with, if two finitely-valued place functions are given,

$$f' = \sum_j y_j' M_j, \quad f'' = \sum_j y_j'' M_j, \tag{105.1}$$

we write

$$f' f'' = \sum_j (y_j' y_j'') M_j. \tag{105.2}$$

For *non-negative* place functions, that is, under the assumption that all the y_j' and all the y_j'' are $\geqq 0$, it follows from $f = f' f''$ that

$$\left.\begin{aligned} &\omega(X) \leqq \alpha(X) \leqq \beta(X) \leqq \Omega(X) \qquad (X \in \mathfrak{A}), \\ &\omega(X) = \alpha'(X)\, \alpha''(X), \quad \Omega(X) = \beta'(X)\, \beta''(X). \end{aligned}\right\} \tag{105.3}$$

As in §§ 95 and 96, we then show that the formulas (105.3) lead to a suitable definition of the product, provided f' and f'' are any non-negative, finite place functions, and we obtain the following theorem.

THEOREM 6: *If the place functions $f_1, f_2, \ldots, f_p$ are all finite and non-negative, there is a uniquely defined place function f associated with them by virtue of the relations*

$$\left.\begin{aligned} &\omega(X) \leqq \alpha(X) \leqq \beta(X) \leqq \Omega(X) && (X \in \mathfrak{A}), \\ &\omega(X) = \alpha_1(X)\,\alpha_2(X)\ldots\alpha_p(X), \quad \Omega(X) = \beta_1(X)\,\beta_2(X)\ldots\beta_p(X). \end{aligned}\right\} \quad (105.4)$$

This function f is called the product of $f_1, \ldots, f_p$, and is denoted by

$$f = f_1\, f_2 \cdots f_p\,. \quad (105.5)$$

Moreover, f is the smallest place function h for which

$$\alpha_h(X) \leqq \Omega(X), \qquad (X \in \mathfrak{A}) \quad (105.6)$$

and it is also the largest place function g for which

$$\beta_g(X) \geqq \omega(X). \quad (105.7)$$

Using this theorem in conjunction with Theorem 1 of § 96, we obtain the formulas

$$\left.\begin{aligned} &f_1 f_2 = f_2 f_1, \quad f_1 (f_2 f_3) = (f_1 f_2)\, f_3, \quad f_1 (f_2 + f_3) = f_1 f_2 + f_1 f_3, \\ &\text{if} \quad f_1 \geqq 0 \quad \text{and} \quad f_2 \leqq f_3 \quad \text{then} \quad f_1 f_2 \leqq f_1 f_3, \end{aligned}\right\} \quad (105.8)$$

under the assumption, which we shall shortly be able to dispense with, that $f_1 \geqq 0$, $f_2 \geqq 0$, and $f_3 \geqq 0$.

In order to obtain the product of place functions of arbitrary sign, we now, as in § 100, represent the functions f_1 and f_2 as differences

$$f_1 = p_1 - n_1, \quad f_2 = p_2 - n_2 \quad (105.9)$$

of non-negative place functions and define $f_1 f_2$ by the equation

$$f_1 f_2 = (p_1 p_2 + n_1 n_2) - (p_1 n_2 + p_2 n_1)\,. \quad (105.10)$$

With this extended definition of the product, not only are conditions (105.8) preserved, but there also holds, in addition, the equation

$$|f_1 f_2| = |f_1|\,|f_2|\,. \quad (105.11)$$

Furthermore, equation (105.2) remains valid for the product of finitely-valued place functions.

Finally, considerations of the same sort as in §§ 102 and 103 yield the following theorem.

THEOREM 7: *Let $\{f_\nu'\}$ and $\{f_\nu''\}$ be two sequences of finite, non-negative place functions, whose lower and upper limits are likewise finite functions. Then, putting*

$$f_\nu = f_\nu' f_\nu'' \qquad (\nu = 1, 2, \ldots), \qquad (105.12)$$

we have the relations

$$\underline{f}'\underline{f}'' \leqq \underline{f} \leqq \frac{\underline{f}'\bar{f}''}{\bar{f}'\underline{f}''} \leqq \bar{f} \leqq \bar{f}'\bar{f}'' \qquad (105.13)$$

This result can be extended, for convergent sequences, to functions of arbitrary sign, by use of the defining equation (105.10) and the earlier theorems of the present section. We have the following theorem.

THEOREM 8: *If the sequences $\{f_\nu'\}$ and $\{f_\nu''\}$ converge to functions f' and f'' that are both finite, then we have the identity*

$$\lim_{\nu=\infty} (f_\nu' f_\nu'') = f' f''. \qquad (105.14)$$

106. If f is a bounded place function whose infimum $\alpha(M)$ is > 0, then there are two positive numbers a and b satisfying

$$0 < a < \alpha(X) \leqq \beta(X) < b < +\infty \qquad (X \in \mathfrak{A}). \qquad (106.1)$$

The soma functions

$$\alpha'(X) = \frac{1}{\beta(X)}, \quad \beta'(X) = \frac{1}{\alpha(X)} \qquad (X \in \mathfrak{A}) \qquad (106.2)$$

are then, by the Bischof Theorem (Theorem 5 of § 85), which can be applied here in the same way as in § 99, the infimum and supremum of some function f'. Putting $g = ff'$, we obtain the relations

$$\frac{\alpha(X)}{\beta(X)} \leqq \alpha_g(X) \leqq \beta_g(X) \leqq \frac{\beta(X)}{\alpha(X)}, \qquad (106.3)$$

from which we conclude, by Theorem 6 of § 105, that $g = 1$. Thus the function f' can be considered as the *quotient* of 1 by f, i.e., as the inverse of f under multiplication, and can be represented by the symbol

$$f' = \frac{1}{f}. \qquad (106.4)$$

This symbol has meaning also for every finite place function that does not take the value zero, provided that on the soma $S_0(0)$, on which $f < 0$, we use the defining equation

$$\frac{1}{f} = -\frac{1}{(-f)}. \qquad (106.5)$$

Under the same hypothesis about f, we define the *quotient* g/f by means of the equation

$$\frac{g}{f} = g\,\frac{1}{f}\,. \tag{106.6}$$

We have thus shown that one can calculate with place functions in the same way as with real numbers and, moreover, we have stated explicitly those theorems about place functions that are used most frequently.

§§ 107-110. Uniform and Absolute Convergence

107. Uniformly convergent sequences of place functions arise from the following considerations.

Let a sequence $\{f_\nu\}$ of place functions be given; we assume that for some sequence of positive numbers $\varepsilon_1, \varepsilon_2, \ldots$ that converges to zero, and for all pairs k, p of positive integers, the relations

$$f_k - \varepsilon_k \leqq f_{k+p} \leqq f_k + \varepsilon_k \quad (k, p = 1, 2, \ldots) \tag{107.1}$$

hold.

If, as in § 92, we put

$$\left.\begin{aligned} h_\nu &= \inf(f_\nu, f_{\nu+1}, \ldots), & \underline{f} &= \sup(h_1, h_2, \ldots), \\ g_\nu &= \sup(f_\nu, f_{\nu+1}, \ldots), & \overline{f} &= \inf(g_1, g_2, \ldots), \end{aligned}\right\} \tag{107.2}$$

we obtain

$$f_k - \varepsilon_k \leqq h_{k+1} \leqq \underline{f}, \quad \overline{f} \leqq g_{k+1} \leqq f_k + \varepsilon_k. \tag{107.3}$$

Consequently,

$$\overline{f} \leqq \underline{f} + 2\,\varepsilon_k \qquad (k = 1, 2, \ldots), \tag{107.4}$$

and, since

$$\lim_{k=\infty} \varepsilon_k = 0, \tag{107.5}$$

we then have $\overline{f} \leqq \underline{f}$. But, in view of (92.9), this is a relation that can occur only if

$$\underline{f} = \overline{f} = f = \lim_{\nu=\infty} f_\nu, \tag{107.6}$$

i.e., only if the sequence $\{f_\nu\}$ converges. Uniformity of convergence is thereupon to be inferred from the relations

$$f - \varepsilon_k \leqq f_k \leqq f + \varepsilon_k, \tag{107.7}$$

which follow from (107.3) and (107.6) and which can also be written

$$|f_\nu - f| \leqq \varepsilon_\nu \qquad (\nu = 1, 2, \ldots). \tag{107.8}$$

The infima $\alpha(X)$ and $\alpha_\nu(X)$ on the soma X of the place functions f and f_ν, respectively, satisfy

$$\alpha(X) - \varepsilon_\nu \leqq \alpha_\nu(X) \leqq \alpha(X) + \varepsilon_\nu \quad (\nu = 1, 2, \ldots); \qquad (107.9)$$

and likewise, the suprema of these place functions satisfy

$$\beta(X) - \varepsilon_\nu \leqq \beta_\nu(X) \leqq \beta(X) + \varepsilon_\nu \quad (\nu = 1, 2, \ldots). \qquad (107.10)$$

The error of approximation ε_ν does not depend upon the choice of the soma X, so that the sequences of functions $\{\alpha_\nu(X)\}$ and $\{\beta_\nu(X)\}$ *converge to their limits uniformly for all somas of* $\mathfrak{A}$.

Conversely, the relations (107.9) and (107.10), or indeed only one of these relations, are a sufficient condition for the corresponding place functions to satisfy inequalities of the form (107.1).

Thus, if we define uniform convergence of place functions by the simultaneous subsistence of the conditions (107.1) and (107.5), the following theorem is valid.

THEOREM 1: *A necessary and sufficient condition for the uniform convergence to f of a sequence* $\{f_\nu\}$ *of place functions is that the infima* $\alpha_\nu(X)$ *converge to* $\alpha(X)$ *uniformly with respect to all non-empty* $X \subseteqq M$ *or that the suprema* $\beta_\nu(X)$ *converge to* $\beta(X)$ *uniformly with respect to all non-empty* $X \subseteqq M$.

108. If we examine the reasoning in § 91 that led to Theorem 5 of that section, we discover that the sequences of bounded, finitely-valued place functions that occur there converge uniformly. From this we deduce that every bounded function can be represented as the limit of a uniformly convergent sequence of finitely-valued functions.

Now since, by the last paragraph of § 78, every finite function can be represented by means of at most countably many bounded functions, it is convenient to introduce the concept of *countably-valued place function*, so as to be able to set up the following theorem. The definition of this term is the obvious one (cf. § 65).

THEOREM 2: *Every finite place function can be represented as the limit of a uniformly convergent sequence of at most countably-valued place functions.*

109. We consider an arbitrary sequence $\{f_\nu\}$ of non-negative place functions and put

$$s_1 = f_1, \quad s_k = s_{k-1} + f_k = f_1 + f_2 + \cdots + f_k \quad (k = 2, 3, \ldots). \qquad (109.1)$$

The sequence of functions $s_1, s_2, \ldots$ is monotonically increasing and converges to its least upper bound,

$$s = \lim_{\nu=\infty} s_\nu, \tag{109.2}$$

which is *by definition* the sum

$$s = f_1 + f_2 + f_3 + \cdots \tag{109.3}$$

of the series of the f_ν; this series is called *absolutely convergent* if its sum s is a *finite* place function.

A series (109.3) of place functions with *arbitrary* sign is said to be *absolutely convergent* if the sum

$$|f_1| + |f_2| + |f_3| + \cdots \tag{109.4}$$

of the absolute values of the f_ν is a finite place function. To determine s, consider the functions

$$p_\nu = \max(0, f_\nu), \quad n_\nu = \max(0, -f_\nu) \quad (\nu = 1, 2, \ldots) \tag{109.5}$$

and put

$$p = p_1 + p_2 + p_3 + \cdots, \quad n = n_1 + n_2 + n_3 + \cdots. \tag{109.6}$$

We define s by

$$s = p - n, \tag{109.7}$$

and then prove that we can also write

$$s = \lim_{\nu=\infty} (f_1 + f_2 + \cdots + f_\nu).$$

110. All those theorems that are usually derived for sums of countably many numbers are valid for absolutely convergent series of place functions, and the proofs of these theorems depend, in both cases, on the same reasoning.

For example, we can assign to each finite system $k_1, k_2, \ldots, k_p$ of distinct positive integers the place function

$$t(k_1, k_2, \ldots, k_p) = |f_{k_1}| + |f_{k_2}| + \cdots + |f_{k_p}|, \tag{110.1}$$

and the sum of the series (109.4) is identical with the least upper bound of all possible $t(k_1, k_2, \ldots, k_p)$.

Second, if the sequence of positive integers is ordered in such a way as to obtain a scheme

$$\left.\begin{array}{l} \nu_{11}, \nu_{12}, \nu_{13}, \cdots \\ \nu_{21}, \nu_{22}, \nu_{23}, \cdots \\ \ldots\ldots\ldots\ldots\ldots, \end{array}\right\} \tag{110.2}$$

then each of the series

$$\sigma_j = f_{\nu_{j1}} + f_{\nu_{j2}} + \cdots \qquad (j = 1, 2, \ldots), \quad (110.3)$$

as well as the series

$$s = \sigma_1 + \sigma_2 + \cdots, \quad (110.4)$$

is absolutely convergent, and the sum of the latter series coincides with the place function (109.7).

§§ 111-117. Composition of Place Functions

111. The elementary operations, which we met in §§ 95ff., can be viewed as special cases of much more general combinatory operations.

Let us consider a finite real-valued function

$$\chi(u_1, u_2, \ldots, u_m) \quad (111.1)$$

of m real variables that is defined for every point of the m-dimensional (u_j)-space. We also take two sets of finite real numbers $v_1, v_2, \ldots, v_m$ and $w_1, w_2, \ldots, w_m$ satisfying

$$v_j \leqq w_j \qquad (j = 1, 2, \ldots, m). \quad (111.2)$$

The inequalities

$$v_j \leqq u_j \leqq w_j \qquad (j = 1, 2, \ldots, m) \quad (111.3)$$

define a closed, bounded set of points in the (u_j)-space, which consists of at least a single point. Let the infimum of $\chi(u_1, \ldots, u_m)$ on that set of points be denoted by

$$\psi(v_1, \ldots, v_m; w_1, \ldots, w_m) \text{ or, for brevity, by } \psi(v_j, w_j) \quad (111.4)$$

and the supremum of the same function on that set of points by

$$\Psi(v_1, \ldots, v_m; w_1, \ldots, w_m) \text{ or, for brevity, by } \Psi(v_j, w_j)\,; \quad (111.5)$$

$\psi(v_j, w_j)$ is then monotonically increasing in each of the variables v_j and $\Psi(v_j, w_j)$ monotonically decreasing. In each of the variables w_j, however, $\Psi(v_j, w_j)$ is monotonically increasing and $\psi(v_j, w_j)$ monotonically decreasing.

Now, if $f_1(P), \ldots, f_m(P)$ are any ordinary point functions with a space M as domain of definition, we can replace the u_j in (111.1) by these functions to obtain the composite function

$$g(P) = \chi(f_1(P), f_2(P), \ldots, f_m(P)). \quad (111.6)$$

We denote by $\alpha_j(X)$ and $\beta_j(X)$, respectively, the infimum and the supremum of the set of numbers $f_j(P)$ obtained by letting P describe a subset X of M. For every such value of P, we then have

$$\psi(\alpha_j(X), \beta_j(X)) \leqq g(P) \leqq \Psi(\alpha_j(X), \beta_j(X)). \qquad (111.7)$$

Denoting the infimum and the supremum of $g(P)$ on X by $\alpha(X)$ and $\beta(X)$, respectively, we obtain the relations

$$\psi(\alpha_j(X), \beta_j(X)) \leqq \alpha(X) \leqq \beta(X) \leqq \Psi(\alpha_j(X), \beta_j(X)). \qquad (111.8)$$

Next, we consider finitely or countably-valued place functions $f_1, f_2, \ldots, f_m$ that have a soma M as common domain of definition. Then there is at least one decomposition

$$M = M_1 + M_2 + M_3 + \cdots \qquad (111.9)$$

of M into pairwise disjoint, non-empty somas such that each of the functions f_j is a constant on each of the somas M_k, the value of this constant being denoted by z_{jk}. We compute the numbers

$$y_k = \chi(z_{1k}, z_{2k}, \ldots, z_{mk}) \qquad (111.10)$$

and let

$$g = \sum_k y_k M_k \qquad (111.11)$$

denote the at most countably-valued place function that is constant on each of the somas M_k and that takes the value y_k on M_k. This function g is characterized by the fact that

$$\alpha(M_k) = \beta(M_k) = y_k \qquad (111.12)$$

on each of the somas M_k. But now, by hypothesis,

$$\alpha_j(M_k) = \beta_j(M_k) = z_{jk}; \qquad (111.13)$$

hence, if X is any soma of $\mathfrak{A}$ and if $X_k = XM_k$ is non-empty, then we have

$$\psi(\alpha_j(X_k), \beta_j(X_k)) = \alpha(X_k) = \beta(X_k) = \Psi(\alpha_j(X_k), \beta_j(X_k)). \qquad (111.14)$$

From this it follows, when the relations $\alpha_j(X) \leqq \alpha_j(X_k)$ and $\beta_j(X) \geqq \beta_j(X_k)$ are taken into consideration, that

$$\psi(\alpha_j(X), \beta_j(X)) \leqq \alpha(X_k) \leqq \beta(X_k) \leqq \Psi(\alpha_j(X), \beta_j(X)). \qquad (111.15)$$

But now, by Theorem 4 of § 84,

$$\alpha(X) = \inf(\alpha(X_1), \alpha(X_2), \ldots), \quad \beta(X) = \sup(\beta(X_1), \beta(X_2), \ldots), \qquad (111.16)$$

so that the relations (111.8) hold here, as well.

112. In general, let $f_1, f_2, \ldots, f_m$ be finite place functions; and let $\alpha_j(X)$ and $\beta_j(X)$ $(j = 1, 2, \ldots, m)$ be their infima and suprema, respectively. Then the soma function

$$\omega(X) = \psi(\alpha_j(X), \beta_j(X)) \tag{112.1}$$

is monotonically decreasing and the soma function

$$\Omega(X) = \Psi(\alpha_j(X), \beta_j(X)) \tag{112.2}$$

is monotonically increasing; furthermore, we have $\omega(X) \leqq \Omega(X)$.

Now, in each instance that the hypotheses of either Theorem 8 or Theorem 9 of § 88 are satisfied, there is *at most one* place function g which has infimum $\alpha(X)$ and supremum $\beta(X)$ and satisfies the relations

$$\omega(X) \leqq \alpha(X) \leqq \beta(X) \leqq \Omega(X) \qquad (X \in \mathfrak{A}). \tag{112.3}$$

If it is possible to demonstrate the existence of such a function, then we shall say that it is determined by the equation

$$g = \chi(f_1, f_2, \ldots, f_m). \tag{112.4}$$

In view of the discussion of § 111, a function (112.4) exists whenever the f_j are point functions or countably-valued place functions, and it should be observed that in both these cases the composite function g is uniquely defined by the conditions (112.3).

Moreover, if we let

$$\chi(u_1, u_2, \ldots, u_m) = u_1 + u_2 + \cdots + u_m, \tag{112.5}$$

we find that

$$\psi(v_j, w_j) = v_1 + v_2 + \cdots + v_m, \tag{112.6}$$

and

$$\Psi(v_j, w_j) = w_1 + w_2 + \cdots + w_m, \tag{112.7}$$

consequently,

$$\left.\begin{aligned} \omega(X) &= \alpha_1(X) + \alpha_2(X) + \cdots + \alpha_m(X), \\ \Omega(X) &= \beta_1(X) + \beta_2(X) + \cdots + \beta_m(X), \end{aligned}\right\} \tag{112.8}$$

and therefore, by Theorem 1 of § 96,

$$\chi(f_1, f_2, \ldots, f_m) = f_1 + f_2 + \cdots + f_m. \tag{112.9}$$

113. We shall now show that the place function (112.4) exists whenever the function $\chi(u_1, \ldots, u_m)$ is finite and continuous throughout the (u_j)-space. In this case, the functions $\psi(v_j, w_j)$ and $\Psi(v_j, w_j)$ are continuous as well.

Let δ and n_0 be any two positive numbers. Let the least upper bound of the differences

$$\Psi(v_j, w_j) - \psi(v_j, w_j)$$

for all pairs of numbers v_j and w_j $(j = 1, 2, \ldots, m)$ that satisfy the relations

$$|v_j| \leqq n_0, \quad |w_j| \leqq n_0, \quad 0 \leqq w_j - v_j \leqq \delta \quad (j = 1, 2, \ldots, m) \tag{113.1}$$

be denoted by

$$\varepsilon(\delta, n_0). \tag{113.2}$$

Because of the uniform continuity of $\chi(u_1, \ldots, u_m)$ on every closed cube in the (u_j)-space, we infer the relation

$$\lim_{\delta=0} \varepsilon(\delta, n_0) = 0. \tag{113.3}$$

Now let $f_1, f_2, \ldots, f_m$ be finite place functions and let X be an arbitrary soma of $\mathfrak{A}$. Then there is at least one non-empty soma $Y \subseteqq X$ and a positive number n_0 such that the conditions

$$|f_j| \leqq n_0 \qquad (j = 1, 2, \ldots, m) \tag{113.4}$$

are all fulfilled on Y. Now we choose a number $\varepsilon > 0$ and determine a number $\delta > 0$ such that

$$\varepsilon(\delta, n_0) \leqq \varepsilon. \tag{113.5}$$

Then, by § 79, there is a non-empty soma $Z \subseteqq Y$ such that the oscillation of each place function f_j on Z is less than or equal to δ. Then, defining $\omega(X)$ and $\Omega(X)$ by (112.1) and (112.2), we obtain

$$\Omega(Z) - \omega(Z) \leqq \varepsilon. \tag{113.6}$$

Thus, the hypotheses of Theorem 9 of § 88 are fulfilled, and thus, by § 112, there is at most one place function g whose infimum $\alpha(X)$ and supremum $\beta(X)$ satisfy the conditions (112.3).

114. We now express all the functions f_j as limits of uniformly convergent sequences of countably-valued place functions $f_j^{(\nu)}$ and introduce the composite functions

$$g^{(\nu)} = \chi(f_1^{(\nu)}, f_2^{(\nu)}, \ldots, f_m^{(\nu)}), \tag{114.1}$$

which, as we saw in § 111, exist. By Theorem 1 of § 107, we then have

$$\lim_{\nu=\infty} \alpha_j^{(\nu)}(X) = \alpha_j(X), \quad \lim_{\nu=\infty} \beta_j^{(\nu)}(X) = \beta_j(X) \quad (j = 1, 2, \ldots, m), \tag{114.2}$$

and, introducing the notation

$$\omega^{(\nu)}(X) = \psi(\alpha_j^{(\nu)}(X), \beta_j^{(\nu)}(X)), \quad \Omega^{(\nu)}(X) = \Psi(\alpha_j^{(\nu)}(X), \beta_j^{(\nu)}(X)), \tag{114.3}$$

the continuity of $\psi(v_j, w_j)$ and $\Psi(v_j, w_j)$ implies that the equations

$$\lim_{\nu=\infty} \omega^{(\nu)}(X) = \omega(X), \quad \lim_{\nu=\infty} \Omega^{(\nu)}(X) = \Omega(X) \tag{114.4}$$

must also hold.

We now denote the infimum and supremum of $g^{(\nu)}$ by $\alpha^{(\nu)}(X)$ and $\beta^{(\nu)}(X)$, respectively, and as in Theorem 7 of § 93, we put

$$\underline{\omega}(X) = \underline{\lim}_{\nu=\infty} \alpha^{(\nu)}(X), \quad \overline{\Omega}(X) = \overline{\lim}_{\nu=\infty} \beta^{(\nu)}(X). \tag{114.5}$$

A comparison of the relations (114.4) and (114.5) with the inequalities

$$\omega^{(\nu)}(X) \leqq \alpha^{(\nu)}(X) \leqq \beta^{(\nu)}(X) \leqq \Omega^{(\nu)}(X)$$

which, by § 111, follow from (114.1)—yields

$$\omega(X) \leqq \underline{\omega}(X) \leqq \overline{\Omega}(X) \leqq \Omega(X). \tag{114.6}$$

On the other hand, Theorem 7 of § 93, together with (92.14), indicates that the infima and suprema of both the lower limit $\underline{g}$ and the upper limit $\overline{g}$ of the sequence $\{g^{(\nu)}\}$ lie between $\underline{\omega}(X)$ and $\overline{\Omega}(X)$, and hence between $\omega(X)$ and $\Omega(X)$. And since by § 113 there is at most one place function g that satisfies these conditions, we must have

$$\underline{g} = \overline{g} = g,$$

in other words, we have the equation

$$g = \lim_{\nu=\infty} g^{(\nu)}. \tag{114.7}$$

Thus, we can enunciate the following theorem.

THEOREM 1: *Let the function $\chi(u_1, u_2, \ldots, u_m)$ be finite and continuous throughout the (u_j)-space. We denote the infimum and supremum of $\chi(u_1, \ldots, u_m)$ on the closed point set*

$$v_j \leqq u_j \leqq w_j \qquad (j = 1, 2, \ldots, m) \tag{114.8}$$

by $\psi(v_j, w_j)$ and $\Psi(v_j, w_j)$, respectively. Then, if $f_1, f_2, \ldots, f_m$ are finite place functions having the common domain of definition M with infima

$\alpha_j(X)$ and suprema $\beta_j(X)$, there is one and only one place function g whose infimum $\alpha(X)$ and supremum $\beta(X)$ satisfy the inequalities

$$\psi(\alpha_j(X), \beta_j(X)) \leqq \alpha(X) \leqq \beta(X) \leqq \Psi(\alpha_j(X), \beta_j(X)) \tag{114.9}$$

throughout. We denote this function g by the symbol

$$g = \chi(f_1, f_2, \ldots, f_m). \tag{114.10}$$

115. The utility of the notation $\chi(f_1, f_2, \ldots, f_m)$ is due to the fact that this expression can be looked upon as an iterable operation on $f_1, f_2, \ldots, f_m$. This is the content of the following theorem.

THEOREM 2: *We consider p functions*

$$\chi_j(u_1, \ldots, u_m) \qquad (j = 1, 2, \ldots, p), \tag{115.1}$$

as well as an additional function

$$\lambda(\bar{u}_1, \bar{u}_2, \ldots, \bar{u}_p), \tag{115.2}$$

that are finite and continuous at all values of u_k and $\bar{u}_j$, respectively, and we form the composite function

$$\tilde{\omega}(u_1, \ldots, u_m) = \lambda(\chi_1(u_1, \ldots, u_m), \ldots, \chi_p(u_1, \ldots, u_m)). \tag{115.3}$$

By Theorem 1, *if $f_1, f_2, \ldots, f_m$ are finite place functions, then there exist finite place functions*

$$\left.\begin{aligned} g_j &= \chi_j(f_1, \ldots, f_m) \qquad (j = 1, 2, \ldots, p), \\ h^* &= \lambda(g_1, g_2, \ldots, g_p), \\ h &= \tilde{\omega}(f_1, f_2, \ldots, f_m). \end{aligned}\right\} \tag{115.4}$$

Under these assumptions, the equality $h^* = h$ holds, i.e.,

$$\lambda(g_1, g_2, \ldots, g_p) = \tilde{\omega}(f_1, f_2, \ldots, f_m). \tag{115.5}$$

Proof: We denote the infima and suprema of the functions $\chi_j(u_1, \ldots, u_m)$, $\lambda(u_1, \ldots, u_p)$, and $\tilde{\omega}(u_1, \ldots, u_m)$ on the point sets $v_k \leqq u_k \leqq w_k$ ($k = 1, 2, 3, \ldots, m$) and $\bar{v}_j \leqq \bar{u}_j \leqq \bar{w}_j$ ($j = 1, 2, \ldots, p$), respectively, by

$$\left.\begin{aligned} &\psi_j(v_k, w_k), \quad \Psi_j(v_k, w_k) \qquad (j = 1, 2, \ldots, p), \\ &\psi^*(\bar{v}_j, w_j), \quad \Psi^*(\bar{v}_j, \bar{w}_j), \\ &\psi(v_k, w_k), \quad \Psi(v_k, w_k). \end{aligned}\right\} \tag{115.6}$$

Moreover, we denote the infima and suprema

of the functions f_k by $\alpha_k(X), \beta_k(X)$,
of the functions g_j by $\bar{\alpha}_j(X), \bar{\beta}_j(X)$,
of the function h^* by $\alpha^*(X), \beta^*(X)$,
of the function h by $\alpha(X), \beta(X)$.

Then, by Theorem 1 of § 114, we have the relations

$$\psi_j(\alpha_k(X), \beta_k(X)) \leqq \bar{\alpha}_j(X) \leqq \bar{\beta}_j(X) \leqq \Psi_j(\alpha_k(X), \beta_k(X)), \qquad (115.7)$$

$$\psi^*(\bar{\alpha}_j(X), \bar{\beta}_j(X)) \leqq \alpha^*(X) \leqq \beta^*(X) \leqq \Psi^*(\bar{\alpha}_j(X), \bar{\beta}_j(X)), \qquad (115.8)$$

$$\psi(\alpha_k(X), \beta_k(X)) \leqq \alpha(X) \leqq \beta(X) \leqq \Psi(\alpha_k(X), \beta_k(X)). \qquad (115.9)$$

Finally, we introduce the notation

$$\omega_j(X) = \psi_j(\alpha_k(X), \beta_k(X)), \ \Omega_j(X) = \Psi_j(\alpha_k(X), \beta_k(X)) \ (j=1,2,\ldots,p) \qquad (115.10)$$

$$\omega^*(X) = \psi^*(\omega_j(X), \Omega_j(X)), \ \Omega^*(X) = \Psi^*(\omega_j(X), \Omega_j(X)). \qquad (115.11)$$

By (115.10) and (115.7), we have

$$\omega_j(X) \leqq \bar{\alpha}_j(X) \leqq \bar{\beta}_j(X) \leqq \Omega_j(X),$$

and therefore, by (115.11),

$$\omega^*(X) \leqq \psi^*(\bar{\alpha}_j(X), \bar{\beta}_j(X)), \quad \Omega^*(X) \geqq \Psi^*(\bar{\alpha}_j(X), \bar{\beta}_j(X)),$$

so that, by (115.8), we obtain

$$\omega^*(X) \leqq \alpha^*(X) \leqq \beta^*(X) \leqq \Omega^*(X). \qquad (115.12)$$

Conversely, the inequalities

$$\alpha_k(X) \leqq u_k \leqq \beta_k(X) \quad (k = 1, 2, \ldots, m) \qquad (115.13)$$

yield, by means of (115.10), the further inequalities

$$\omega_j(X) \leqq \chi_j(u_1, \ldots, u_m) \leqq \Omega_j(X) \quad (j = 1, 2, \ldots, p).$$

Now, because of equations (115.3), we obtain bounds for $\tilde{\omega}(u_1, \ldots, u_m)$ as the u_k describe the point set (115.13) by obtaining bounds for $\lambda(\bar{u}_1, \ldots, \bar{u}_p)$ as the $\bar{u}_j$ describe the point set

$$\omega_j(X) \leqq \bar{u}_j \leqq \Omega_j(X) \qquad (j = 1, 2, \ldots, p).$$

Taking (115.6) and (115.11) into consideration, we obtain

$$\omega^*(X) \leqq \alpha(X) \leqq \beta(X) \leqq \Omega^*(X). \tag{115.14}$$

Our theorem, however, is equivalent to the identities $\alpha(X) = \alpha^*(X)$ or $\beta(X) = \beta^*(X)$, which in turn, according to (115.12) and (115.14), always hold whenever the pair of functions $\omega^*(X)$ and $\Omega^*(X)$ satisfy the condition of Theorem 9 of § 88. But this condition can be verified immediately: To each soma X of $\mathfrak{A}$ and to each number $\varepsilon > 0$, we can assign a non-empty subsoma Y of X such that

$$\Omega^*(Y) - \omega^*(Y) < \varepsilon$$

For this, we need only make sure that none of the p numbers $\Omega_j(Y) - \omega_j(Y)$ for $j = 1, 2, \ldots, p$ be larger than some suitable number δ^*, and this, according to § 113, is always possible. Thus, we have established our theorem.

116. In conclusion, we should like to supplement the result of § 114 by defining the functions $g^{(\nu)}$ by the equations

$$g^{(\nu)} = \chi^{(\nu)}(f_1^{(\nu)}, \ldots, f_m^{(\nu)}) \qquad (\nu = 1, 2, \ldots)$$

rather than by (114.1), where the substitution functions $\chi^{(\nu)}(u_1, \ldots, u_m)$ are assumed to converge uniformly to a continuous function $\chi(u_1, \ldots, u_m)$ on every bounded domain of the (u_j)-space. By the properties of continuous convergence,[1] the last condition is equivalent to the requirement that the sequence of functions

$$\chi^{(\nu)}(u_1, u_2, \ldots, u_m) \qquad (\nu = 1, 2, \ldots) \tag{116.1}$$

be continuously convergent at every point of the (u_j)-space, i.e., we must postulate the existence of a function $\chi(u_1, \ldots, u_m)$ such that, whenever the equations

$$\lim_{\nu=\infty} u_j^{(\nu)} = u_j^* \qquad (j = 1, 2, \ldots, m) \tag{116.2}$$

hold, the equations

$$\lim_{\nu=\infty} \chi^{(\nu)}(u_1^{(\nu)}, u_2^{(\nu)}, \ldots, u_m^{(\nu)}) = \chi(u_1^*, u_2^*, \ldots, u_m^*) \tag{116.3}$$

also hold. From this requirement it follows easily that the limit function $\chi(u_1, \ldots, u_m)$ is continuous.

As in § 111, to each of the functions $\chi^{(\nu)}(u_1, \ldots, u_m)$ we assign the pair of functions $\psi^{(\nu)}(v_j, w_j)$, $\Psi^{(\nu)}(v_j, w_j)$ and to the limit function $\chi(u_1, \ldots, u_m)$ we assign the pair of functions $\psi(v_j, w_j)$, $\Psi(v_j, w_j)$. We shall show that

[1] A short exposition of the theory of continuous convergence can be found in C. Carathéodory, *Reelle Funktionen,* Vol. I (Leipzig and Berlin, 1939; repr., New York, 1946), pp. 172-80.

the sequences of functions $\{\psi^{(\nu)}(v_j, w_j)\}$, $\{\Psi^{(\nu)}(v_j, w_j)\}$ are themselves continuously convergent to $\psi(v_j, w_j)$ and $\Psi(v_j, w_j)$, respectively.

To this end, we consider sequences $\{v_j^{(\nu)}\}$ and $\{w_j^{(\nu)}\}$ of finite real numbers, where $j = 1, 2, \ldots, m$, that satisfy the conditions

$$v_j^{(\nu)} \leqq w_j^{(\nu)} \quad (\nu = 1, 2, \ldots), \quad \lim_{\nu=\infty} v_j^{(\nu)} = v_j, \quad \lim_{\nu=\infty} w_j^{(\nu)} = w_j, \quad (116.4)$$

and we assume that the limits v_j and w_j are all finite.

In the closed point set $v_j \leqq u_j \leqq w_j$ $(j = 1, 2, \ldots, m)$ there is, in virtue of the continuity of $\chi(u_1, \ldots, u_m)$, at least one point, with coordinates $u_1^*, u_2^*, \ldots, u_m^*$, for which the equality

$$\psi(v_j, w_j) = \chi(u_1^*, u_2^*, \ldots, u_m^*) \quad (116.5)$$

holds. Within the point set $v_j^{(\nu)} \leqq u_j \leqq w_j^{(\nu)}$, we choose a point with coordinates $u_1^{(\nu)}, u_2^{(\nu)}, \ldots, u_m^{(\nu)}$, for each value of ν, in such a way that the equations (116.2) are all satisfied and that the limits $u_1^*, u_2^*, \ldots, u_m^*$ satisfy equation (116.5).

From

$$\psi^{(\nu)}(v_j^{(\nu)}, w_j^{(\nu)}) \leqq \chi^{(\nu)}(u_1^{(\nu)}, u_2^{(\nu)}, \ldots, u_m^{(\nu)})$$

we then obtain, in conjunction with (116.3) and (116.5),

$$\lim_{\nu=\infty} \psi^{(\nu)}(v_j^{(\nu)}, w_j^{(\nu)}) \leqq \psi(v_j, w_j). \quad (116.6)$$

On the other hand, there exist convergent subsequences $\{\psi^{(\nu_k)}(v_j^{(\nu_k)}, w_j^{(\nu_k)})\}$ of the sequence of numbers $\{\psi^{(\nu)}(v_j^{(\nu)}, w_j^{(\nu)})\}$, for which we can write

$$\underline{\lim}_{\nu=\infty} \psi^{(\nu)}(v_j^{(\nu)}, w_j^{(\nu)}) = \lim_{k=\infty} \psi^{(\nu_k)}(v_j^{(\nu_k)}, w_j^{(\nu_k)}), \quad (116.7)$$

and within each of the sets of points $v_j^{(\nu_k)} \leqq u_j \leqq w_j^{(\nu_k)}$ there is at least one point, with coordinates $u_1^{(\nu_k)}, u_2^{(\nu_k)}, \ldots, u_m^{(\nu_k)}$, such that

$$\psi^{(\nu_k)}(v_j^{(\nu_k)}, w_j^{(\nu_k)}) \geqq \chi^{(\nu_k)}(u_1^{(\nu_k)}, u_2^{(\nu_k)}, \ldots, u_m^{(\nu_k)}) - \frac{1}{\nu_k}. \quad (116.8)$$

We may assume without loss of generality that our subsequence has been chosen in such a way that the equations

$$\lim_{k=\infty} u_j^{(\nu_k)} = u_j' \qquad (j = 1, 2, \ldots, m)$$

hold. Then, recalling that $v_j \leqq u_j' \leqq w_j$, we have

$$\lim_{k=\infty} \chi^{(\nu_k)}(u_1^{(\nu_k)}, u_2^{(\nu_k)}, \ldots, u_m^{(\nu_k)}) = \chi(u_1', u_2', \ldots, u_m') \geqq \psi(v_j, w_j). \quad (116.9)$$

A comparison of (116.7) through (116.9) next yields the relation

$$\varliminf_{\nu=\infty} \psi^{(\nu)}(v_j^{(\nu)}, w_j^{(\nu)}) \geqq \psi(v_j, w_j),$$

from which, in conjunction with (116.6), it finally follows that

$$\lim_{\nu=\infty} \psi^{(\nu)}(v_j^{(\nu)}, w_j^{(\nu)}) = \psi(v_j, w_j). \tag{116.10}$$

The equation

$$\lim_{\nu=\infty} \Psi^{(\nu)}(v_j^{(\nu)}, w_j^{(\nu)}) = \Psi(v_j, w_j) \tag{116.11}$$

can be proved similarly.

The last two equations were proved under the single hypothesis that (116.4) holds; they state that the sequences of functions $\{\psi^{(\nu)}(v_j, w_j)\}$ and $\{\Psi^{(\nu)}(v_j, w_j)\}$ are continuously convergent in the (v_j, w_j)-space.

117. By the properties of continuous convergence, the sequences of functions $\psi^{(\nu)}(v_j, w_j)$ and $\Psi^{(\nu)}(v_j, w_j)$ converge uniformly to $\psi(v_j, w_j)$ and $\Psi(v_j, w_j)$, respectively, on every closed and bounded subset of the (v_j, w_j)-space. In fact, the following theorem[2] holds: *Given a pair of numbers $n_0 > 0$ and $\varepsilon > 0$, a positive integer ν_0 and a positive number δ can be determined in such a way that, under the assumptions*

$$\left.\begin{array}{cccc} & & \nu \geqq \nu_0, & \\ |v_j'| \leqq n_0, & |w_j'| \leqq n_0, & |v_j| \leqq n_0, & |w_j| \leqq n_0, \\ v_j' \leqq w_j', & v_j \leqq w_j, & |v_j' - v_j| \leqq \delta, & |w_j' - w_j| \leqq \delta, \end{array}\right\} \tag{117.1}$$

we have the relations

$$|\psi^{(\nu)}(v_j', w_j') - \psi(v_j, w_j)| < \varepsilon, \quad |\Psi^{(\nu)}(v_j', w_j') - \Psi(v_j, w_j)| < \varepsilon. \tag{117.2}$$

We now consider uniformly convergent sequences $\{f_j^{(\nu)}\}$ $(j = 1, 2, \ldots, m)$ of finite place functions whose limits f_j must of course also be finite place functions. We assume, moreover, that the composite functions

$$g^{(\nu)} = \chi^{(\nu)}(f_1^{(\nu)}, f_2^{(\nu)}, \ldots, f_m^{(\nu)}) \qquad (\nu = 1, 2, \ldots) \tag{117.3}$$

all exist; this assumption must be made explicitly, because we have not postulated continuity of the $\chi^{(\nu)}(u_1, \ldots, u_m)$. These functions $g^{(\nu)}$ are to be compared with the function

$$g = \chi(f_1, f_2, \ldots, f_m). \tag{117.4}$$

[2] C. Carathéodory, *op. cit.*, (Theorem 7 of § 195, p. 178).

Let

$$\alpha_j^{(\nu)}(Y),\ \beta_j^{(\nu)}(Y);\quad \alpha_j(Y),\ \beta_j(Y);\quad \alpha^{(\nu)}(Y),\ \beta^{(\nu)}(Y);\quad \alpha(Y),\ \beta(Y)$$

be the infima and suprema of the place functions

$$f_j^{(\nu)},\quad f_j,\quad g^{(\nu)},\quad g$$

on any non-empty soma Y in their common domain of definition. Further, let X be a soma on which each of the functions f_j is bounded. Then there is a number n_0 such that the relations

$$|\alpha_j(Y)| \leqq n_0,\quad |\beta_j(Y)| \leqq n_0 \qquad (O \subset Y \subseteqq X) \qquad (117.5)$$

hold for $j = 1, 2, \ldots, m$. In view of the uniform convergence to f_j of the *functions* $f_j^{(\nu)}$, there is a positive integer ν_1 such that for all $\nu \geqq \nu_1$, the inequalities

$$|\alpha_j^{(\nu)}(Y) - \alpha_j(Y)| \leqq \delta,\quad |\beta_j^{(\nu)}(Y) - \beta_j(Y)| \leqq \delta \quad (O \subset Y \subseteqq X) \qquad (117.6)$$

hold, where δ has the same meaning as in (117.1). By (117.6), the number n_0 in (117.5) can be chosen so large that for $\nu \geqq \nu_1$, the further inequalities

$$|\alpha_j^{(\nu)}(Y)| \leqq n_0,\quad |\beta_j^{(\nu)}(Y)| \leqq n_0 \quad (O \subset Y \subseteqq X) \qquad (117.7)$$

hold.

Thus, if

$$\nu \geqq \max(\nu_0, \nu_1),\quad O \subset Y \subseteqq X,$$

$$v_j' = \alpha_j^{(\nu)}(Y),\quad v_j = \alpha_j(Y),\quad w_j' = \beta_j^{(\nu)}(Y),\quad w_j = \beta_j(Y),$$

all the assumptions of (117.1) are satisfied. Hence (117.2) holds and, if we put

$$\omega^{(\nu)}(Y) = \psi^{(\nu)}(\alpha_j^{(\nu)}(Y),\ \beta_j^{(\nu)}(Y)),\quad \Omega^{(\nu)}(Y) = \Psi^{(\nu)}(\alpha_j^{(\nu)}(Y),\ \beta_j^{(\nu)}(Y)),$$

$$\omega(Y) = \psi(\alpha_j(Y),\ \beta_j(Y)),\qquad \Omega(Y) = \Psi(\alpha_j(Y),\ \beta_j(Y))$$

becomes

$$\left.\begin{array}{c} |\omega^{(\nu)}(Y) - \omega(Y)| < \varepsilon,\ |\Omega^{(\nu)}(Y) - \Omega(Y)| < \varepsilon \\ (\nu \geqq \max(\nu_0, \nu_1);\ O \subset Y \subseteqq X). \end{array}\right\} \qquad (117.8)$$

Since we are ensured of the existence of the place functions $g^{(\nu)}$ and g, their infima and suprema satisfy equations (88.8) and (88.9). From these equations and (117.8) it follows that

$$|\alpha^{(\nu)}(Y) - \alpha(Y)| \leqq \varepsilon,\quad |\beta^{(\nu)}(Y) - \beta(Y)| \leqq \varepsilon\ (\nu \geqq \max(\nu_0, \nu_1);\ O \subset Y \subseteqq X),$$

and by Theorem 1 of § 107, these relations indicate that the sequence $\{g^{(\nu)}\}$ converges uniformly to g on the soma X.

From this, we have the following theorem.

THEOREM 3: *Let* $\{\chi^{(\nu)}(u_1, u_2, \ldots, u_m)\}$ *denote a sequence of substitution functions that converge continuously to the function* $\chi(u_1, u_2, \ldots, u_m)$ *at every point of the* (u_j)*-space. Moreover, let the sequences* $\{f_j^{(\nu)}\}$ *of place functions converge uniformly to* f_j $(j = 1, 2, \ldots, m)$ *and let all these place functions be finite. The individual functions* $\chi^{(\nu)}(u_1, \ldots, u_m)$ *need not be continuous; but let the composite function*

$$g^{(\nu)} = \chi^{(\nu)}(f_1^{(\nu)}, f_2^{(\nu)}, \ldots, f_m^{(\nu)})$$

exist for each value of ν. *Then the sequence* $\{g^{(\nu)}\}$ *converges uniformly to*

$$g = \chi(f_1, f_2, \ldots, f_m)$$

on every soma X *on which all the* f_j *are bounded.*

§§ 118-125. Homomorphisms of Place Functions

118. Let $\mathfrak{A}$ and $\mathfrak{A}'$ be two complete rings of somas that are related by the homomorphism (§ 56)

$$A' = \sigma A. \tag{118.1}$$

The totality $\mathfrak{N}$ of somas U of $\mathfrak{A}$ that are mapped onto the empty soma O' is a complete ring hereditary with respect to $\mathfrak{A}$ (Theorem 3 of § 58).

If the somas $S(y)$ of any given nest of somas belong to $\mathfrak{A}$, the homomorphism maps them onto somas

$$S'(y) = \sigma S(y) \tag{118.2}$$

of $\mathfrak{A}'$ which in turn, if they are not all empty, form a nest of somas.

If $[S(y)]$ and $[T(y)]$ are two nests of somas, and if $y < z$ implies

$$S(y) \subseteqq T(z), \tag{118.3}$$

then we also have

$$\sigma S(y) \subseteqq \sigma T(z). \tag{118.4}$$

Let f be a place function whose domain of definition M is in $\mathfrak{A}$ but is not a soma of $\mathfrak{N}$. The soma

$$M' = \sigma M \tag{118.5}$$

is then distinct from the empty soma. From the result of the preceding paragraph, it follows that any two nests $[S(y)]$ and $[T(y)]$ of somas of f are mapped by the homomorphism onto two nests $[S'(y)]$ and $[T'(y)]$ of somas for which

$$S'(y) = \sigma\, S(y)\,, \quad T'(y) = \sigma\, T(y)\,, \tag{118.6}$$

which give rise to one and the same place function

$$f' = \sigma f \tag{118.7}$$

with domain of definition M'. Thus every place function whose domain of definition lies in $\mathfrak{A}$ but not in $\mathfrak{N}$ is mapped by our homomorphism onto a well-defined place function whose domain of definition lies in $\mathfrak{A}'$. We see at the same time that the upper and lower nests of somas of f are mapped onto the corresponding nests of somas of f'.

119. The function f', defined by equation (118.7), will be called the *homomorphic image* of the place function f. Two distinct functions f_1 and f_2 can have the same homomorphic image; then they are called *equivalent* with respect to that homomorphism. We denote the upper nests of somas of the two equivalent functions f_1 and f_2 by $[S_1^0(y)]$ and $[S_2^0(y)]$. Then, whenever $y < z$, we have

$$\sigma\, S_2^0(y) \subseteqq \sigma\, S_1^0(z)\,, \quad \sigma\, S_1^0(y) \subseteqq \sigma\, S_2^0(z)\,, \tag{119.1}$$

which, by (57.5), can also be written as

$$\sigma\left(S_2^0(y) \dotplus S_2^0(y)\, S_1^0(z)\right) = O', \quad \sigma\left(S_1^0(y) \dotplus S_1^0(y)\, S_2^0(z)\right) = O'. \tag{119.2}$$

In this form, these relations are equivalent with

$$S_2^0(y) \dotplus S_2^0(y)\, S_1^0(z) \in \mathfrak{N}, \quad S_1^0(y) \dotplus S_1^0(y)\, S_2^0(z) \in \mathfrak{N}. \tag{119.3}$$

If, in these last relations, we replace z successively by the values $z_1 > z_2 > z_3 \ldots$ of a monotone sequence of numbers that converges to y, we obtain the relations

$$S_2^0(y) \dotplus S_2^0(y)\, S_1^0(y) \in \mathfrak{N}, \quad S_1^0(y) \dotplus S_1^0(y)\, S_2^0(y) \in \mathfrak{N}\,, \tag{119.4}$$

since $\mathfrak{N}$ is a complete ring.

Now, for any two somas A and B, we have

$$(A \dotplus AB)\,(B \dotplus AB) = O\,,$$

and consequently the relation

$$(A \dotplus AB) \dotplus (B \dotplus AB) = A \dotplus B \tag{119.5}$$

also holds.

Hence, the two relations (119.4) both hold if and only if, for all values of y,

$$S_1^0(y) \dotplus S_2^0(y) \in \mathfrak{N}.$$

Conversely, by taking note, for example, of the relations

$$\begin{aligned} S_1^0(y) \dotplus S_2^0(y) &\supseteqq S_2^0(y) \dotplus S_2^0(y)\, S_1^0(y) \\ &\supseteqq S_2^0(y) \dotplus S_2^0(y)\, S_1^0(z), \end{aligned} \qquad (y < z)$$

we conclude that the relations (119.3), (119.2), and (119.1) hold, and we finally obtain the following theorem.

THEOREM 1: *Two place functions f_1 and f_2 are equivalent with respect to a homomorphism $A' = \sigma A$ that takes the ring $\mathfrak{N}$ onto the empty soma O' if and only if the somas of the upper nests of somas $[S_1^0(y)]$ and $[S_2^0(y)]$ of both these functions satisfy the relations*

$$S_1^0(y) \dotplus S_2^0(y) \in \mathfrak{N} \qquad (-\infty < y < +\infty). \quad (119.6)$$

A completely analogous theorem holds for the lower nests of somas; to prove this, we make use of a monotonically increasing sequence $y_1 < y_2 < \dots$ that converges to z.

120. Let A be a subsoma of M that is not a soma of $\mathfrak{N}$, i.e., one whose image $A' = \sigma A$ is non-empty. We denote the infimum and supremum of $f' = \sigma f$ on A' by $\alpha'(A')$ and $\beta'(A')$, respectively; and those of f on A by $\alpha(A)$ and $\beta(A)$, respectively.

Then, if $[S(y)]$ is any nest of somas of f, the relation

$$A \circ S(y),$$

by (80.1) and (69.4), and therefore the relation

$$\sigma A \circ \sigma S(y)$$

must hold for every $y < \alpha(A)$. Consequently, we have

$$y \leqq \alpha'(\sigma A) = \alpha'(A'),$$

and, finally, we obtain the inequality

$$\alpha(A) \leqq \alpha'(A'). \qquad (120.1)$$

The relation

$$\beta(A) \geqq \beta'(A') \qquad (120.2)$$

is proved quite similarly.

Next, we take two fixed monotone sequences of numbers

$$y_1 < y_2 < y_3 < \dots, \quad z_1 > z_2 > z_3 > \dots \tag{120.3}$$

that satisfy the conditions

$$\lim_{n=\infty} y_n = \alpha'(A'), \quad \lim_{n=\infty} z_n = \beta'(A'). \tag{120.4}$$

By (80.1) and (80.2), we obtain from $y_n < \alpha'(A')$, $z_n > \beta'(A')$, and $A' = \sigma A$, the relations

$$\sigma A \circ \sigma S(y_n), \quad \sigma A \subseteqq \sigma S(z_n),$$

and these relations are equivalent with

$$\sigma\big(A\, S(y_n)\big) = O', \quad \sigma\big(A\, S(z_n)\big) = \sigma A. \tag{120.5}$$

We now introduce the somas

$$B_n = A\big(S(z_n) \dotplus S(y_n)\big) = A\big(S(z_n) \dotplus S(z_n)\, S(y_n)\big) \tag{120.6}$$

and put

$$B = \prod_n B_n. \tag{120.7}$$

Since the equalities

$$\sigma B_n = \sigma A \qquad (n = 1, 2, \dots)$$

follow from (120.5) and (120.6), Theorem 1 of § 57 implies

$$\sigma B = \prod_n \sigma B_n = \sigma A = A'. \tag{120.8}$$

From this it follows that none of the B_n nor B can be the empty soma.

From (120.6) we deduce the relations

$$B_n \circ S(y_n), \quad B_n \subseteqq S(z_n);$$

consequently we also have

$$B \circ S(y_n), \ B \subseteqq S(z_n),$$

and therefore

$$y_n \leqq \alpha(B), \quad z_n \geqq \beta(B) \quad (n = 1, 2, \dots).$$

By passage to the limit, we finally obtain

$$\alpha(B) \geqq \alpha'(A'), \quad \beta(B) \leqq \beta'(A'). \tag{120.9}$$

In view of (120.8), we can replace A by B in (120.1) and (120.2), thus obtaining

$$\alpha(B) \leqq \alpha'(A'), \quad \beta(B) \geqq \beta'(A'). \tag{120.10}$$

Finally, if we note that B is a subsoma of A, we can state the following theorem.

THEOREM 2: *Let A be a soma whose homomorphic image $A' = \sigma A$ is non-empty. Then the infima and suprema of a place function f on A and the place function $f' = \sigma f$ on A' are related by*

$$\alpha(A) \leqq \alpha'(A'), \quad \beta(A) \geqq \beta'(A'). \tag{120.11}$$

Moreover, there always exist somas $B \neq O$ that satisfy all the conditions

$$B \subseteqq A, \quad \sigma B = \sigma A = A', \quad \alpha(B) = \alpha'(A'), \quad \beta(B) = \beta'(A'). \tag{120.12}$$

121. All the operations on place functions are preserved when the functions undergo a homomorphism.

From the definition of a homomorphic mapping, it follows in the first place that the relation $f_1 \leqq f_2$ implies $\sigma f_1 \leqq \sigma f_2$.

Given a sequence of place functions f_k ($k = 1, 2, \ldots$) with homomorphic images denoted by $f_k' = \sigma f_k$, let us put

$$\left.\begin{aligned} g &= \sup(f_1, f_2, \ldots), \quad & g' &= \sup(f_1', f_2', \ldots), \\ h &= \inf(f_1, f_2, \ldots), \quad & h' &= \inf(f_1', f_2', \ldots). \end{aligned}\right\} \tag{121.1}$$

Then we obtain the equations

$$g' = \sigma g, \quad h' = \sigma h. \tag{121.2}$$

The first of these equations follows from the relation

$$\prod_k \sigma S_k(y) = \sigma\Big(\prod_k S_k(y)\Big), \tag{121.3}$$

which is valid for an arbitrary nest $[S_k(y)]$ of somas of the function f_k (Theorem 1 of § 57). The validity of the second equation of (121.2) is established quite similarly. We prove the relations

$$\overline{\lim_{k=\infty}} \sigma f_k = \sigma \Big(\overline{\lim_{k=\infty}} f_k\Big) \tag{121.4}$$

and

$$\underline{\lim_{k=\infty}} \sigma f_k = \sigma \Big(\underline{\lim_{k=\infty}} f_k\Big) \tag{121.5}$$

in the same way.

It follows in particular from these relations that every convergent sequence of place functions $f_1, f_2, \ldots$ is transformed by the homomorphism into a convergent sequence of place functions $\sigma f_1, \sigma f_2, \ldots$ and that moreover the limit functions correspond to each other.

If $[S(y)]$ is a nest of somas of the place function f, then $[S(y-\varepsilon)]$ is a nest of somas of $f+\varepsilon$, where ε denotes an arbitrary constant; it follows that

$$f'+\varepsilon=\sigma f+\varepsilon=\sigma\,(f+\varepsilon). \tag{121.6}$$

We deduce from this that a *uniformly* convergent sequence of place functions f_k is transformed by the homomorphism (118.1) into a uniformly convergent sequence of functions f_k'.

122. According to § 66, to obtain a finitely-valued place function f, we must decompose the soma M. To each of the somas M_j in the sum

$$M=M_0+M_1+M_2+\cdots+M_p, \tag{122.1}$$

there is assigned a constant y_j. Then Theorem 2 of § 120 shows that the homomorphic image $f'=\sigma f$ is obtained by determining the somas $M_j'=\sigma M_j$ and assigning to them the values y_j. From the equation

$$M'=\sigma\,M=\sigma\,M_0+\sigma\,M_1+\cdots+\sigma\,M_p, \tag{122.2}$$

it follows that not all the σM_j can be empty. This fact does not, however, exclude the possibility that some of these somas may indeed be empty. *If such is the case, the finitely-valued function $f'=\sigma f$ takes fewer values than the original function f.*

Let us now compare the construction given in §§ 111 ff. of the composite function

$$g=\chi(f_1,f_2,\ldots,f_m) \tag{122.3}$$

with the considerations of the preceding sections. It turns out that, for finitely-valued functions $f_1,\ldots,f_m$, we have the equation

$$g'=\chi(\sigma f_1,\ldots,\sigma f_m)=\sigma\,\chi(f_1,\ldots,f_m), \tag{122.4}$$

and since limit processes are preserved under homomorphism, this equation is valid in general.

In the same way we prove the important identity

$$\sigma\big(\max(f_1,f_2)\big)=\max(\sigma f_1,\sigma f_2) \tag{122.5}$$

first, for finitely-valued place functions, and then, by passage to the limit, for arbitrary place functions. A direct consequence is the positivity of our mapping, i.e., the fact that

$$\text{if}\quad f\geqq 0\quad\text{then}\quad \sigma f\geqq 0, \tag{122.6}$$

which, of course, can also be deduced from (120.1).

It should be observed that, as follows from (121.4) and (121.5), the symbol σ commutes with the symbols of limit processes.

All the other formulas that we make use of in computing with homomorphic images of place functions are obtained by specialization of (122.4) and (122.5). In this way are obtained, for example,

$$\sigma\,(f_1 + f_2) = \sigma\, f_1 + \sigma\, f_2, \quad \sigma\, f_1\, f_2 = \sigma\, f_1\, \sigma\, f_2, \quad \sigma\left(\frac{f}{g}\right) = \frac{\sigma\, f}{\sigma\, g}, \qquad (122.7)$$

$$\sigma(-f) = -\sigma\, f, \quad \sigma(|f|) = |\sigma\, f|, \qquad (122.8)$$

and many others, which there are no need to write down.

A value y that is taken by the homomorphic image f' of a place function f must also be taken by f. On the other hand, it can happen that f' fails to take values taken by f. An extreme case is that in which f' takes no values whatever. This happens whenever all the somas on which the place function f is constant, in other words, all the somas of the form $S^0(y) - S_0(y)$ are in the ring $\mathfrak{N}$ (compare § 78).

123. The results of the previous sections admit of a remarkable converse. On a complete ring $\mathfrak{A}$ of somas A that includes a non-empty maximal element M we consider a set $\mathfrak{F}$ of place functions f that are defined as follows: If $O \subset A \subset M$, let $e(A)$ be the two-valued place function that is 1 on the soma A and 0 on the soma $M \dotplus A$. Correspondingly, let $e(M)$ and $e(O)$ be the constant functions 1 and 0, respectively, on M. Let $\mathfrak{F}$ denote the totality of finitely-valued place functions

$$f = a_1\, e(A_1) + a_2\, e(A_2) + \cdots + a_m\, e(A_m) \qquad (123.1)$$

and all further place functions that arise from these by limit processes. Here $A_1, A_2, \ldots, A_m$ are arbitrary somas of $\mathfrak{A}$; however, it comes to the same thing if we require in addition that they be pairwise disjoint. For by repeated application of the identity

$$a\, e(A) + b\, e(B) = a\, e(A \dotplus AB) + (a + b)\, e(AB) + b\, e(B \dotplus AB),$$

every place function (123.1) can be brought into the required form.

We now suppose that to each place function f of $\mathfrak{F}$ there is associated a place function σf whose nests of somas are defined on a complete ring $\mathfrak{A}'$ of somas A' with the non-empty maximal element M'. We suppose the operator σ to enjoy the following properties:

a) each constant place function on M is transformed into itself:

$$\sigma\, a \equiv a; \qquad (123.2)$$

b) the operator σ is linear; thus, for all real numbers a and b, we must have

$$\sigma\,(a\, f_1 + b\, f_2) = a\, \sigma\, f_1 + b\, \sigma\, f_2; \qquad (123.3)$$

c) the operator σ is continuous, i.e.,

$$\text{if} \quad \lim_{\nu=\infty} f_\nu = f \quad \text{and} \quad \lim_{\nu=\infty} \sigma f_\nu = f' \quad \text{then} \quad f' = \sigma f; \tag{123.4}$$

d) the following relation always holds:

$$\sigma |f| = |\sigma f|. \tag{123.5}$$

124. We propose to demonstrate that under these circumstances there is assigned to each soma A of $\mathfrak{A}$ a soma A' of $\mathfrak{A}'$ in such a way as to give rise to a homomorphism by which the place function f is mapped into the place function σf.

To this end, we put

$$f = 2\,e(A) - 1, \tag{124.1}$$

where A denotes any soma of $\mathfrak{A}$, and we observe that if $A = M$, f is the constant 1; if $A = O$, f is the constant -1; and if $O \subset A \subset M$, f is a two-valued place function that takes the value $+1$ on A and the value -1 on $M \dotplus A$. Thus in every case, we have

$$|f| \equiv 1, \quad \sigma|f| \equiv 1, \tag{124.2}$$

and by (123.5),

$$|\sigma f| \equiv 1. \tag{124.3}$$

Thus the place function σf is itself an at most two-valued place function which, as can be verified from its nests of somas, can take only the values $+1$ and -1, and must take at least one of these values. We put $\sigma A = M'$ if σf is the constant 1; $\sigma A = O'$ if σf is the constant -1; and $\sigma A = A'$ if σf takes the value $+1$ on the soma A' and -1 on the soma $M' \dotplus A'$. Then we are justified in expressing the place function

$$\sigma\, e(A) = \frac{\sigma f + 1}{2} \tag{124.4}$$

in every case as

$$\sigma\, e(A) = e(\sigma A). \tag{124.5}$$

125. We must still show that the mapping $A' = \sigma A$ induces a homomorphism; by the definition given in § 56, this is the case if and only if the conditions

$$\text{if} \quad B \circ C \quad \text{then} \quad \sigma B \circ \sigma C, \tag{125.1}$$

$$\text{if} \quad A = \sum_j \dotplus A_j \quad \text{then} \quad \sigma A = \sum_j \dotplus \sigma A_j \tag{125.2}$$

are both satisfied.

If A denotes the sum of two disjoint somas B and C, we have

$$e(A) = e(B) + e(C) \qquad (A = B + C,\ B \circ C), \quad (125.3)$$

and therefore, by (123.3),

$$\sigma\, e(A) = \sigma\, e(B) + \sigma\, e(C). \qquad (125.4)$$

But by (124.5), this can be written

$$e(\sigma\, A) = e(\sigma\, B) + e(\sigma\, C). \qquad (125.5)$$

By the definition of the place function $e(\sigma X)$, a necessary and sufficient condition for the validity of this equation is that we have

$$\sigma\, B \circ \sigma\, C, \quad \sigma\, A = \sigma\, B + \sigma\, C. \qquad (125.6)$$

Thus, we have verified (125.1).

From (123.3) and (124.5) it follows, in addition, that if f represents a finitely-valued place function

$$f = \sum_{j=1}^{m} y_j\, e(A_j)$$

of $\mathfrak{F}$, then σf can be calculated by means of the mapping $A_j' = \sigma A_j$ $(j = 1, \ldots, m)$. This holds irrespective of the particular representation of f and it also holds for expressions of the form

$$e\left(\sum_{j=1}^{m} \dot{+}\, A_j\right),$$

since they can be written (cf. § 22) in the form

$$\sum_{k=1}^{n} y_k\, e(B_k),$$

where the somas B_k are pairwise disjoint; and it follows, corresponding to (125.6), that if $B_k' = \sigma B_k$ for all k, then $A_j' = \sigma A_j$ for all j.

Thus, if we put

$$f_\nu = e\left(\sum_{j=1}^{\nu} \dot{+}\, A_j\right) = e(V_\nu),$$

we obtain

$$\sigma f_\nu = e\left(\sum_{j=1}^{\nu} \dot{+}\, \sigma\, A_j\right) = e(\sigma\, V_\nu),$$

and accordingly

$$\sigma V_\nu = \sum_{j=1}^{\nu} \dot{+}\, \sigma\, A_j.$$

From this, it follows not only that

$$\lim_{\nu=\infty} e(V_\nu) = e\Big(\sum_j \dotplus A_j\Big) = e(A),$$

but also that

$$\lim_{\nu=\infty} e(\sigma V_\nu) = e\Big(\sum_j \dotplus \sigma A_j\Big).$$

By the continuity of the operator σ postulated in c) of § 123, and by (124.5), we have

$$e\Big(\sum_j \dotplus \sigma A_j\Big) = \sigma\, e(A) = e(\sigma A),$$

and from this it follows that

$$\sigma A = \sum_j \dotplus \sigma A_j,$$

i.e., (125.2) is verified.

Besides this, we see that the homomorphic mappings of place functions f induced by the homomorphisms $A' = \sigma A$ are identical with the mappings σf with which we started.

CHAPTER FIVE

MEASURE FUNCTIONS

§§ 126-128. Additive and Union-bounded Soma Functions

126. Having discussed the fundamental properties of place functions, we turn our attention to soma functions. In § 80 we have already defined *monotone soma functions.* Further classes of soma functions are defined as follows:

DEFINITION 1: *A soma function $\varphi(X)$ whose domain of definition is an arbitrary non-empty set $\mathfrak{A}$ of somas is called an additive function if for every pair of disjoint somas A and B whose sum $A + B$ belongs to $\mathfrak{A}$ we have the equation*

$$\varphi(A + B) = \varphi(A) + \varphi(B). \tag{126.1}$$

If, under the same assumptions,

$$\varphi(A + B) \geqq \varphi(A) + \varphi(B), \tag{126.2}$$

$\varphi(X)$ is called superadditive; similarly, $\varphi(X)$ is called subadditive if

$$\varphi(A + B) \leqq \varphi(A) + \varphi(B). \tag{126.3}$$

A function is called semi-additive if it is either superadditive or subadditive.

DEFINITION 2: *A soma function $\varphi(X)$ is called completely additive if for each at most countable sequence of pairwise disjoint somas A_j of $\mathfrak{A}$ whose sum*

$$A = A_1 + A_2 + A_3 + \cdots \tag{126.4}$$

also belongs to the domain of definition $\mathfrak{A}$ of $\varphi(X)$ we have the equation

$$\varphi(A) = \varphi(A_1) + \varphi(A_2) + \cdots. \tag{126.5}$$

DEFINITION 3: *A soma function $\varphi(X)$ is called union-bounded if for every at most countable sequence of arbitrary somas A_j of $\mathfrak{A}$ whose union*

$$V = A_1 \dotplus A_2 \dotplus A_3 \dotplus \cdots \tag{126.6}$$

likewise belongs to $\mathfrak{A}$ *we always have the relation*

$$\varphi(V) \leqq \varphi(A_1) + \varphi(A_2) + \cdots. \tag{126.7}$$

DEFINITION 4: *A soma function* $\varphi(X)$ *is called cover-bounded if whenever an at most countable number of somas* A_j *of* $\mathfrak{A}$ *and any other soma* B *of* $\mathfrak{A}$ *satisfy the relation*

$$B \subseteqq A_1 \dotplus A_2 \dotplus A_3 \dotplus \cdots, \tag{126.8}$$

then the relation

$$\varphi(B) \leqq \varphi(A_1) + \varphi(A_2) + \cdots \tag{126.9}$$

also holds.

In all these definitions it is tacitly assumed that the operations involved can all be carried out. Thus, we may not speak of an additive soma function if the number $\varphi(A)$ in (126.1) is $+\infty$ and the number $\varphi(B)$ is $-\infty$; neither may we speak of a completely additive or of a cover-bounded function if the series $\varphi(A_1) + \varphi(A_2) + \ldots$ does not represent a fixed finite or infinite number independent of the order of the terms of the series. All these difficulties vanish if the soma functions under consideration are non-negative.

A soma function $\varphi(X)$ can of course belong to several of the classes distinguished in Definitions 1 through 4. Thus, every additive soma function is both superadditive and subadditive; and a completely additive soma function is always additive. On the other hand, as can be shown by means of examples, there exist additive soma functions that are not completely additive, which is what justifies the introduction of the latter as a special class of functions.[1]

For semi-additive soma functions, however, it can be shown that under certain conditions they enjoy the analogous properties for sums of an infinite number of terms as well. In particular, we have the following theorem.

THEOREM 1: *Let the soma function* $\varphi(X)$ *be superadditive and non-negative. Moreover, let the domain of definition* $\mathfrak{A}$ *of* $\varphi(X)$ *be a subtractive set of somas. Given an at most countable number of pairwise disjoint somas* $A_1, A_2, \ldots$ *of* $\mathfrak{A}$ *and another soma* B *of* $\mathfrak{A}$ *which satisfy*

$$A_j \subseteqq B \qquad (j = 1, 2, \ldots), \tag{126.10}$$

[1] Let the somas A be subsets of a countable set $\{P_n\}$ of points. For each n, let the number $1/n^2$ be assigned to the point P_n. If A consists of a finite number of points $P_{n_1}, P_{n_2}, \ldots, P_{n_m}$, let $\varphi(A) = \sum_{j=1}^{m} 1/n_j^2$. If, however, A consists of an infinite number of points, let $\varphi(A) = +\infty$. This soma function $\varphi(A)$ is additive, but not countably additive.

then we have the relation

$$\varphi(B) \geqq \sum_j \varphi(A_j). \tag{126.11}$$

Proof: We introduce the notation

$$B_1 = A_1, \quad B_k = A_1 + A_2 + \cdots + A_k \quad (k = 2, 3, \ldots), \tag{126.12}$$

$$B'_k = B \dot{+} B_k. \tag{126.13}$$

All these somas are subsomas of B and, by Theorem 4 of § 34, must all belong to $\mathfrak{A}$. Since the somas A_j are pairwise disjoint, we have always $A_k \circ B_{k-1}$, and in place of the above equations we can write

$$B = B_k + B'_k, \quad B_k = A_k + B_{k-1} \quad (k = 2, 3, \ldots). \tag{126.14}$$

Now let the soma function $\varphi(X)$ be superadditive and non-negative. It follows from this that

$$\varphi(B) \geqq \varphi(B_k) + \varphi(B'_k) \geqq \varphi(B_k) \geqq \varphi(A_k) + \varphi(B_{k-1}), \tag{126.15}$$

and consequently also that

$$\varphi(B) \geqq \sum_{k=1}^{p} \varphi(A_k) \qquad (p = 1, 2, \ldots). \tag{126.16}$$

The relation (126.11), which we are to prove, follows from the last inequalities.

127. We now turn our attention to the class of union-bounded soma functions. This name does not in the least mean that a union-bounded function must itself be bounded. According to our definition, even the function $\varphi(X) \equiv +\infty$ is to be classed as a union-bounded function.

A non-negative soma function whose domain of definition $\mathfrak{A}$ is subtractive must be completely additive if it is both superadditive and union-bounded. Indeed, if $\mathfrak{A}$ contains the sum

$$A = A_1 + A_2 + \cdots \tag{127.1}$$

of at most countably many somas A_j that all belong to $\mathfrak{A}$, then by Theorem 1 of § 126, we have

$$\varphi(A) \geqq \sum_j \varphi(A_j),$$

and at the same time, since $\varphi(X)$ is union-bounded,

$$\varphi(A) \leqq \sum_j \varphi(A_j).$$

Conversely, let a completely additive and non-negative soma function $\varphi(X)$ be defined on a subtractive set $\mathfrak{A}$. Such a function is not only superadditive and (by Theorem 1 of § 126) monotonically increasing, but also union-bounded. Indeed, if each of the at most countable number of somas A_j as well as their union

$$V = A_1 \dot{+} A_2 \dot{+} \cdots \tag{127.2}$$

belongs to $\mathfrak{A}$, then there exist, by § 22, pairwise disjoint somas A_j' that satisfy

$$V = A_1' + A_2' + \cdots, \quad A_j' \subseteqq A_j \quad (j = 1, 2, \ldots), \tag{127.3}$$

and these somas all belong to $\mathfrak{A}$. Then we can write

$$\varphi(V) = \sum_j \varphi(A_j'), \quad \varphi(A_j') \leqq \varphi(A_j), \tag{127.4}$$

whence $\varphi(X)$ is union-bounded. Thus, we have:

THEOREM 2: *Non-negative soma functions that are defined on a subtractive set $\mathfrak{A}$ are completely additive if and only if they are superadditive and union-bounded.*

128. A non-negative soma function that is union-bounded need not be monotonically increasing: The four somas

$$O, A, B \ C = A + B \quad (O \neq A, B; A \circ B) \tag{128.1}$$

constitute a complete ring; the soma function defined on this ring by the equations

$$\psi_1(A) = 1, \quad \psi_1(O) = \psi_1(B) = \psi_1(C) = 0 \tag{128.2}$$

is not monotonically increasing but it is union-bounded.

Nor need a monotonically increasing non-negative soma function be union-bounded: For proof, it suffices to consider the soma function

$$\psi_2(A) = \psi_2(B) = \psi_2(O) = 0, \quad \psi_2(C) = 1 \tag{128.3}$$

defined on the above ring.

A cover-bounded soma function is monotonically increasing, because the condition (126.9) must hold even when the expression on the right-hand side of (126.8) consists of a single soma; moreover, it is obviously also union-bounded. In this connection, we have the following theorem.

TEOREM 3: *A monotonically increasing and union-bounded soma function whose domain of definition $\mathfrak{A}$ is multiplicative is cover-bounded.*

Proof: Let

$$B \in \mathfrak{A}, \quad A_j \in \mathfrak{A} \qquad (j = 1, 2, \ldots)$$

and

$$B \subseteqq A_1 \dot{+} A_2 \dot{+} \cdots. \tag{128.4}$$

Then we have first of all, by hypothesis,

$$A_j B \in \mathfrak{A} \qquad (j = 1, 2, \ldots), \quad (128.5)$$

and second,

$$B = A_1 B \dot{+} A_2 B \dot{+} \cdots. \quad (128.6)$$

Consequently, we see

$$\varphi(B) \leqq \varphi(A_1 B) + \varphi(A_2 B) + \cdots \leqq \varphi(A_1) + \varphi(A_2) + \cdots, \quad (128.7)$$

which proves our theorem.

§§ 129-130. Measurability

129. One of the most important concepts to play a role in our theory is the concept of measurability. This concept can be enunciated for entirely general soma functions $F(X)$, as follows:

DEFINITION: *A soma U in the domain of definition $\mathfrak{A}$ of a soma function $F(X)$ is said to be measurable for F, or F-measurable, if for every soma A which, together with AU and $A \dot{+} AU$, belongs to $\mathfrak{A}$ and for which in addition the numbers $F(A)$, $F(AU)$, and $F(A \dot{+} AU)$ are finite, the equality*

$$F(A) = F(AU) + F(A \dot{+} AU) \quad (129.1)$$

always holds.

Observe that in this definition we have not required that $F(U)$ be finite; a soma U that is F-measurable can very well have $F(U) = \pm\infty$. Using this definition, we have the following theorem.

THEOREM 1: *Let the domain of definition $\mathfrak{A}$ of a soma function $F(X)$ be a subtractive set of somas. Let the totality $\mathfrak{E}_F$ of those somas X of $\mathfrak{A}$ for which*

$$|F(X)| < +\infty \quad (129.2)$$

be $\mathfrak{A}$-hereditary. Furthermore let

$$F(O) = 0 \quad (129.3)$$

hold for the empty soma O.

Then the totality $\mathfrak{M}_F$ of F-measurable somas U forms a ring which contains at least the empty soma O. This ring is called the ring of measurability of $F(X)$.

Proof: Since the set of somas $\mathfrak{E}_F$ is hereditary for $\mathfrak{A}$ (§ 54), if X is in $\mathfrak{E}_F$ and Y in $\mathfrak{A}$, the somas XY and $X \dot{+} XY$ belong to $\mathfrak{E}_F$. Moreover, the empty soma O is F-measurable. For, taking (129.3) into consideration, we have

$$F(A \dotplus AO) = F(A), \quad F(AO) = F(O) = 0. \tag{129.4}$$

Now let U and V be two F-measurable somas and let A be a soma of $\mathfrak{E}_F$. By means of the somas U and V, the soma A can be decomposed (§ 21) into four pairwise disjoint somas S_1, S_2, S_3, and S_4 (see Fig. 8), for which we have

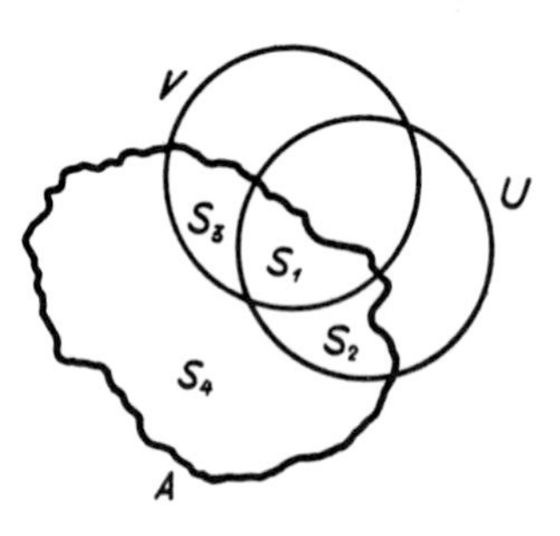

Fig. 8

$$A = S_1 + S_2 + S_3 + S_4, \tag{129.5}$$

$$AU = S_1 + S_2, \tag{129.6}$$

$$AV = S_1 + S_3. \tag{129.7}$$

By assumption, the somas $S_1 + S_3 + S_4$ and $S_1 + S_2 + S_3$ belong to $\mathfrak{E}_F$, since A does. Thus, the supposition that U is measurable yields the following three equations:

$$F(S_1 + S_2 + S_3 + S_4) = F(S_1 + S_2) + F(S_3 + S_4), \tag{129.8}$$

$$F(S_1 + S_3 + S_4) = F(S_1) + F(S_3 + S_4), \tag{129.9}$$

$$F(S_1 + S_2 + S_3) = F(S_1 + S_2) + F(S_3). \tag{129.10}$$

The following equations derive similarly from the measurability of V:

$$F(S_1 + S_2) = F(S_1) + F(S_2), \tag{129.11}$$

$$F(S_3 + S_4) = F(S_3) + F(S_4). \tag{129.12}$$

The above equations now yield:

$$F(S_1 + S_2 + S_3 + S_4) = F(S_1 + S_2 + S_3) + F(S_4), \tag{129.13}$$

$$F(S_1 + S_2 + S_3 + S_4) = F(S_2) + F(S_1 + S_3 + S_4), \tag{129.14}$$

which can also be written as

$$F(A) = F(A(U \dot{+} V)) + F(A \underset{\cdot}{+} A(U \dot{+} V)), \qquad (129.15)$$

$$F(A) = F(A(U \underset{\cdot}{+} UV)) + F(A \underset{\cdot}{+} A(U \underset{\cdot}{+} UV)). \qquad (129.16)$$

These last equations state that the measurability of $U \dot{+} V$ and of $U \underset{\cdot}{+} UV$, and hence that of $V \underset{\cdot}{+} UV$ as well, follows from the measurability of U and of V. Thus, the set of somas $\mathfrak{M}_F$ is additive and subtractive, and therefore, by Theorem 3 b) of § 34, it is a ring.

130. We retain the assumptions of the last theorem and let U and A denote two somas of $\mathfrak{A}$, the first of which belongs to the ring of measurability of $\mathfrak{M}_F$, which are so constituted that

$$|F(A \dot{+} U)| < +\infty. \qquad (130.1)$$

We then also have $|F(A)| < +\infty$ and $|F(U)| < +\infty$; by virtue of the measurability of U, we obtain the equations

$$\left.\begin{aligned} F(A \dot{+} U) &= F(U(A \dot{+} U)) + F((A \dot{+} U) \underset{\cdot}{+} U(A \dot{+} U)) \\ &= F(U) + F(A \underset{\cdot}{+} AU), \end{aligned}\right\} \qquad (130.2)$$

$$F(A) = F(AU) + F(A \underset{\cdot}{+} AU). \qquad (130.3)$$

A comparison of these two relations yields the following theorem.

THEOREM 2: *Under the same hypotheses as the last theorem, let a measurable soma U and a soma A satisfy the relation $|F(A \dot{+} U)| < +\infty$. Then we have the equation*

$$F(A \dot{+} U) = F(A) + F(U) - F(AU). \qquad (130.4)$$

If, in particular, A and U in the last formula are disjoint, then $AU = O$ and $F(AU) = 0$, and we have:

THEOREM 3: *Under the hypotheses of Theorem 1 of § 129, $F(X)$ is an additive soma function on the set of somas $\mathfrak{E}_F\mathfrak{M}_F$.*

§§ 131-135. Measure Functions

131. The assumptions that Euclid made about the surface area of planar figures and about the volume of solids can be expressed, in our terminology, by a single word: the assumption that the content of these figures be *cover-bounded.* A further examination of the matter leads to the following precise definition.

DEFINITION: *A soma function $\varphi(X)$ is called a measure function whenever it satisfies the following conditions:*

a) *its domain of definition $\mathfrak{A}$ is a complete ring;*

b) *it is cover-bounded;*

c) *for the empty soma O we have $\varphi(O) = 0$.*

We could, of course, speak of a measure function when the domain of definition $\mathfrak{A}$ of $\varphi(X)$ is merely *subtractive* and *countably multiplicative,* without necessarily being a complete ring; for, by Theorem 2 of § 43, the subsomas of a given soma M of $\mathfrak{A}$ which are contained in $\mathfrak{A}$ form a complete ring. In general, however, the above definition is more suitable, since the majority of theorems have a simpler wording with this definition.

Since a cover-bounded soma function is monotonically increasing, from the fact that $\varphi(O) = 0$ it follows that for every soma X of $\mathfrak{A}$ the measure function $\varphi(X)$ is non-negative. Indeed, this would be the case even if, instead of condition c), we had postulated merely that $\varphi(O)$ be different from $-\infty$. For in that case, if the number $\varphi(A_0)$ is $< +\infty$ for even only one soma A_0, we have, first,

$$-\infty < \varphi(O) \leqq \varphi(A_0) < +\infty, \tag{131.1}$$

and next,

$$\varphi(A_0) = \varphi(A_0 \dotplus O) \leqq \varphi(A_0) + \varphi(O), \tag{131.2}$$

whence we conclude that $\varphi(O) \geqq 0$. Our stipulation that $\varphi(O) > 0$ shall not hold but that $\varphi(O) = 0$ shall, is indispensable, however, since otherwise, as is shown in § 132 (in the paragraph immediately following Theorem 2), no soma of $\mathfrak{A}$ whatsoever would be φ-measurable in the sense of the definition of § 129.

To determine whether a given soma function $\varphi(X)$ is a measure function, one can also make use of the following easily proved theorem (cf. § 22 and Theorem 3 of § 128):

THEOREM 1: *A soma function $\varphi(X)$ that satisfies conditions* a) *and* c) *of the above definition is a measure function if it is monotonically increasing and union-bounded for sums of pairwise disjoint somas.*

132. Measure functions, being monotonically increasing, non-negative soma functions, satisfy the hypotheses of Theorem 1 of § 129; according to this theorem, the totality of φ-measurable somas forms a ring, the *ring of measurability* $\mathfrak{M}_\varphi$ of $\varphi(X)$.

In our present case, moreover, it follows from

$$X = AX \dotplus (X \dotplus AX) \tag{132.1}$$

that the relation

$$\varphi(X) \leqq \varphi(AX) + \varphi(X \dotplus AX) \tag{132.2}$$

holds for *every* pair of somas, i.e., even where $\varphi(X) = +\infty$. In consequence, we may reformulate the criterion for the measurability of a soma A as follows:

$$\varphi(X) \geqq \varphi(AX) + \varphi(X \dotplus AX) \tag{132.3}$$

must hold for *every* soma X in $\mathfrak{A}$. Furthermore, if the soma A does not belong to $\mathfrak{M}_\varphi$, there is at least one soma B for which

$$\varphi(B) < \varphi(AB) + \varphi(B \dotplus AB); \tag{132.4}$$

then, of necessity, $\varphi(B) < +\infty$.

Thus, putting $AB = V$, we obtain

$$\varphi(V) \leqq \varphi(B) < +\infty; \tag{132.5}$$

but (132.4) can now be written in the form

$$\varphi(B) < \varphi(VB) + \varphi(B \dotplus VB), \tag{132.6}$$

from which we conclude that V is not measurable. We have thus proved the following theorem.

THEOREM 2: *Every soma A that is not φ-measurable contains at least one subsoma V that is likewise not measurable and for which $\varphi(V) < +\infty$.*

If, in the definition of measure functions, we had not required that $\varphi(O) = 0$, the possibility would have remained that $\varphi(O)$ might be finite and positive. But then, it would follow from

$$\varphi(OX) + \varphi(O \dotplus OX) = 2\,\varphi(O) > \varphi(O)$$

that no soma of $\mathfrak{A}$ whatsoever is measurable. Condition c) in the definition of measure functions thus ensures that *at least the empty soma O is measurable for every measure function.*

If U is a soma measurable for the measure function $\varphi(X)$ and if $A \subseteqq U$ is a non-measurable subsoma of U, then there is at least one soma X that satisfies

$$\varphi(X) < \varphi(AX) + \varphi(X \dotplus AX) = \varphi(AUX) + \varphi(X \dotplus AUX). \tag{132.7}$$

However,

$$X \dotplus AUX = (X \dotplus UX) + (UX \dotplus AUX),$$

and consequently

$$\varphi(X \dotplus AUX) \leqq \varphi(X \dotplus UX) + \varphi(UX \dotplus AUX). \qquad (132.8)$$

A comparison of (132.7) with (132.8) yields

$$\varphi(X) - \varphi(X \dotplus UX) < \varphi(AUX) + \varphi(UX \dotplus AUX), \qquad (132.9)$$

however, and the measurability of U implies that the left-hand side of (132.9) is equal to $\varphi(UX)$. Thus, putting $UX = Y$, we obtain the relation

$$\varphi(Y) < \varphi(AY) + \varphi(Y \dotplus AY), \qquad (132.10)$$

so that we have the following theorem.

THEOREM 3: *If U is a soma of the ring of measurability of $\varphi(X)$, then a subsoma A of U necessarily belongs to $\mathfrak{M}_\varphi$ if the equality*

$$\varphi(Y) = \varphi(AY) + \varphi(Y \dotplus AY) \qquad (132.11)$$

holds for all somas $Y \subseteqq U$.

133. The somas N of $\mathfrak{A}$ for which

$$\varphi(N) = 0 \qquad (133.1)$$

are called the *null somas* of $\varphi(X)$, or the *somas of φ-measure zero.* For every soma B of $\mathfrak{A}$, then, we have

$$0 \leqq \varphi(BN) \leqq \varphi(N) = 0, \qquad (133.2)$$

$$\varphi(B \dotplus BN) \leqq \varphi(B) \leqq \varphi(BN) + \varphi(B \dotplus BN) = \varphi(B \dotplus BN). \qquad (133.3)$$

Now it follows from these relations that every null soma is φ-measurable. Letting N' denote any soma of $\mathfrak{A}$ that is a subsoma of a null soma and letting N'' denote the union of at most countably many null somas N_j, it follows from

$$0 \leqq \varphi(N') \leqq \varphi(N) = 0,$$

$$0 \leqq \varphi(N'') \leqq \sum_j \varphi(N_j) = 0$$

that the totality $\mathfrak{N}_\varphi$ of null somas forms a complete ring that is hereditary with respect to $\mathfrak{A}$ (cf. § 54).

THEOREM 4: *The null somas of $\varphi(X)$ all belong to the ring of measurability $\mathfrak{M}_\varphi$ of the measure function $\varphi(X)$. The totality $\mathfrak{N}_\varphi$ of these somas form a complete ring hereditary with respect to $\mathfrak{A}$. This ring is called the null ring of $\varphi(X)$.*

Let us also mention that if $B \in \mathfrak{A}$ and $N \in \mathfrak{N}_\varphi$, then

$$\varphi(B) = \varphi(B \dotplus BN) \leqq \varphi(B \dotplus N) \leqq \varphi(B \dot{+} N) \leqq \varphi(B) + \varphi(N) = \varphi(B),$$

whence

$$\varphi(B) = \varphi(B \dotplus N) = \varphi(B \dotplus N). \tag{133.4}$$

It is also easy to verify the following theorem.

THEOREM 5: *Let $\mathfrak{A}$ be a complete ring of somas and let $\mathfrak{N}$ be a complete subring of $\mathfrak{A}$ hereditary with respect to $\mathfrak{A}$. The soma function $\psi(X)$ that vanishes on every soma of $\mathfrak{N}$ and takes the value $+\infty$ on all the remaining somas of $\mathfrak{A}$ is a measure function. Every soma of $\mathfrak{A}$ is ψ-measurable.*

134. We now prove the following theorem.

THEOREM 6: *The ring of measurability $\mathfrak{M}_\varphi$ of a measure function $\varphi(X)$ is always a complete ring.*

Proof: It suffices to show that $\mathfrak{M}_\varphi$ is a countably additive set of somas. Denoting by U_1', U_2', . . . a sequence of measurable somas, let us investigate the measurability of the somas

$$U = U_1' \dotplus U_2' \dotplus U_3' \dotplus \cdots. \tag{134.1}$$

If we put

$$U_k = U_1' \dotplus U_2' \dotplus \cdots \dotplus U_k' \quad (k = 1, 2, \ldots), \tag{134.2}$$

then, by Theorem 1 of § 129, each of the somas U_k is measurable, and we have in addition

$$U_1 \subseteqq U_2 \subseteqq \ldots, \qquad \lim_{k=\infty} U_k = U. \tag{134.3}$$

Now let A be any soma for which $\varphi(A) < +\infty$. We put

$$V_k = A\,U_k, \quad W_k = A \dotplus A\,U_k, \tag{134.4}$$

$$V = A\,U, \qquad W = A \dotplus A\,U. \tag{134.5}$$

We then obtain $V_1 \subseteqq V_2 \subseteqq \ldots$ and $W_1 \supseteqq W_2 \supseteqq \ldots$, the two numerical sequences $\{\varphi(V_k)\}$ and $\{\varphi(W_k)\}$ are monotone and their terms are less than or equal to $\varphi(A)$. Thus, there exist finite limits

$$\lim_{k=\infty} \varphi(V_k) = \lambda, \quad \lim_{k=\infty} \varphi(W_k) = \mu; \tag{134.6}$$

the measurability of U_k, moreover, can be expressed by the formula

$$\varphi(A) = \varphi(V_k) + \varphi(W_k), \tag{134.7}$$

and, passing to the limit, we obtain

$$\varphi(A) = \lambda + \mu. \tag{134.8}$$

Observe next that, by Theorem 8 of § 31 and Theorem 5 of § 15, the soma V is identical with the union of all the somas V_k and that consequently we may write

$$V = V_1 \dotplus V_2 \dotplus \cdots = V_1 + (V_2 - V_1) + (V_3 - V_2) + \cdots. \qquad (134.9)$$

From this it follows that

$$\varphi(V) \leqq \varphi(V_1) + \varphi(V_2 \dotplus V_1) + \varphi(V_3 \dotplus V_2) + \cdots, \qquad (134.10)$$

since $\varphi(X)$ is union-bounded. On the other hand, the measurability of the somas U_k implies that

$$\left.\begin{aligned} \varphi(V_{k+1}) &= \varphi(V_{k+1}U_k) + \varphi(V_{k+1} \dotplus V_{k+1}U_k) \\ &= \varphi(V_k) + \varphi(V_{k+1} \dotplus V_k). \end{aligned}\right\} \qquad (134.11)$$

The last two relations now yield

$$\varphi(V) \leqq \lim_{k=\infty} \varphi(V_k) = \lambda.$$

Comparing this with the relation $\varphi(V_k) \leqq \varphi(V)$, which follows from $V_k \subseteqq V$, we finally obtain

$$\varphi(V) = \lambda. \qquad (134.12)$$

On the other hand, since $A = V + W$, we can write

$$\varphi(A) \leqq \varphi(V) + \varphi(W),$$

and from this, by (134.8) and (134.12), it follows that $\varphi(W) \geqq \mu$. From $W_k \supseteqq W$, however, we deduce first $\varphi(W_k) \geqq \varphi(W)$ and then $\mu \geqq \varphi(W)$, so that

$$\varphi(W) = \mu. \qquad (134.13)$$

A comparison of (134.12) and (134.13) with (134.8) allows us finally to deduce the equality

$$\varphi(A) = \varphi(AU) + \varphi(A \dotplus AU), \qquad (134.14)$$

which is thus proved for all somas A with $\varphi(A) < +\infty$ and which expresses the measurability of $U = \sum_j \dotplus U'_j$. Hence the ring of measurability must be a complete ring, and our theorem is proved.

135. It is very helpful to introduce, in addition to the null ring $\mathfrak{N}_\varphi$ and the ring of measurability $\mathfrak{M}_\varphi$ of a measure function $\varphi(X)$, other complete rings that will frequently be used in our theory.

As in § 129, we denote by $\mathfrak{E}_\varphi$ the totality of somas X in $\mathfrak{A}$ for which

$\varphi(X) < +\infty$. By the definition of § 131, $\mathfrak{A}$ is a complete ring. With the notation of §§ 42, 53, and 55, we then have

$$(\mathfrak{E}_\varphi)_\sigma = \overline{\mathfrak{E}}_\varphi = \mathfrak{E}^*_\varphi = \mathfrak{A}_{\mathfrak{E}_\varphi}.$$

For, first of all, it follows from the definitions that $(\mathfrak{E}_\varphi)_\sigma \prec \overline{\mathfrak{E}}_\varphi \prec \mathfrak{E}^*_\varphi$; second, according to Theorem 1 of § 55, $\mathfrak{E}^*_\varphi = \mathfrak{A}_{\mathfrak{E}_\varphi}$; and third, $\mathfrak{A}_{\mathfrak{E}_\varphi} = (\mathfrak{E}_\varphi)_\sigma$. This last equality follows from the fact that, since $\varphi(X)$ is a monotonically increasing soma function, $\mathfrak{E}_\varphi$ is $\mathfrak{A}$-hereditary (Definition 1 of § 54). The somas of $(\mathfrak{E}_\varphi)_\sigma$, i.e., the somas of $\mathfrak{A}$ that can be represented as the union of an at most countable number of somas of $\mathfrak{E}_\varphi$, are called the *normal somas* of $\varphi(X)$.

The *normal somas of the ring of measurability* $\mathfrak{M}_\varphi$ are defined similarly: they are the somas that can be represented as the union of an at most countable number of *measurable* somas U for which $\varphi(U)$ is a finite number. The totality of these somas is a complete ring, which can be obtained by forming the countably additive closure of $\mathfrak{M}_\varphi \mathfrak{E}_\varphi$.

If, for example, we consider the ring of all point sets on an x-axis, we obtain a measure function $\varphi(X)$ by putting $\varphi(A) = +\infty$ for all point sets A that consist of an infinite number of points and, for point sets B that consist of a finite number of points, putting $\varphi(B)$ equal to the number n of points in B. The at most countable point sets are normal for this measure function; the uncountable point sets, on the contrary, are not normal. Observe that in this example, the ring of measurability $\mathfrak{M}_\varphi$ and the domain of definition $\mathfrak{A}$ of $\varphi(X)$ coincide.

§§ 136-140. The Measure Function on its Ring of Measurability

136. Both theorems of § 130 hold for measure functions $\varphi(X)$. By Theorem 2 of § 127, then, $\varphi(X)$ is necessarily completely additive on $\mathfrak{M}_\varphi$, and we thus have the following basic theorem of the theory of measure functions.

THEOREM 1: *Every measure function is completely additive on its ring of measurability* $\mathfrak{M}_\varphi$.

This theorem admits the following generalization: Let $U_1, U_2, \ldots$ be *pairwise disjoint* somas that all belong to the ring of measurability $\mathfrak{M}_\varphi$ of a measure function $\varphi(X)$. Further, let A be a subsoma of the sum

$$U = U_1 + U_2 + \cdots; \tag{136.1}$$

we put

$$A_j = AU_j \qquad (j = 1, 2, \ldots) \tag{136.2}$$

and obtain

$$A = A_1 + A_2 + \cdots. \tag{136.3}$$

Using the notation

$$V_k = \sum_{j=1}^{k} U_j, \quad B_k = AV_k = \sum_{j=1}^{k} A_j \quad (k = 1, 2, \ldots), \quad (136.4)$$

we obtain

$$B_k = B_k U_k + B_{k-1} = B_{k-1} + A_k. \quad (136.5)$$

Because of the measurability of U_k, we deduce from this (cf. § 130) that

$$\varphi(B_k) = \varphi(B_{k-1}) + \varphi(A_k) \quad (136.6)$$

$$= \sum_{j=1}^{k} \varphi(A_j),$$

and consequently, taking into account that $A \supseteqq B_k$, we see that

$$\varphi(A) \geqq \varphi(B_k) = \sum_{j=1}^{k} \varphi(A_j). \quad (136.7)$$

We conclude from this and from the fact that $\varphi(A)$ is union-bounded that

$$\varphi(A) = \sum_j \varphi(A_j), \quad (136.8)$$

and we have thus proved the following theorem.

THEOREM 2: *If each of the at most countable number of pairwise disjoint somas $U_1, U_2, \ldots$ is φ-measurable, then the sum A of any somas A_j that are subject only to the conditions*

$$A_j \subseteqq U_j \qquad (j = 1, 2, \ldots) \quad (136.9)$$

satisfies the equality

$$\varphi(A) = \sum_j \varphi(A_j). \quad (136.10)$$

137. Now let the soma A be a subsoma of the union $\sum_j \dot{+}\, U_j$ of an at most countable number of somas U_j all of which are φ-measurable. By the construction of § 22, we obtain a sequence of pairwise disjoint somas U_j' which all belong to the ring of measurability $\mathfrak{M}_\varphi$ of $\varphi(X)$ and for which we have

$$U_j' \subseteqq U_j \quad (j = 1, 2, \ldots), \quad \sum_j \dot{+}\, U_j = \sum_j U_j'.$$

If we then put

$$A_j = AU_j' \qquad (j = 1, 2, \ldots),$$

the preceding theorem yields:

THEOREM 3: *Let the soma A be covered by the union of an at most countable number of φ-measurable somas U_j. Then A can be represented as the sum of pairwise disjoint somas A_j for which we have*

$$A_j \subseteqq U_j \quad (j = 1, 2, \ldots), \quad \varphi(A) = \sum_j \varphi(A_j). \tag{137.1}$$

138. Let A be the limit of a monotonically increasing sequence

$$A_1 \subseteqq A_2 \subseteqq A_3 \subseteqq \ldots \tag{138.1}$$

of somas of $\mathfrak{M}_\varphi$. If the number $\varphi(A_k) = +\infty$ for any value of k, then $\varphi(A) = +\infty$ as well, since $A_k \subseteqq A$. In every other case, by Theorem 1 of § 136, it follows from

$$A = A_1 + (A_2 - A_1) + \cdots \tag{138.2}$$

that

$$\varphi(A) = \varphi(A_1) + \varphi(A_2 - A_1) + \varphi(A_3 - A_2) + \cdots; \tag{138.3}$$

and, since all the somas A_k are assumed to be measurable, we have

$$\varphi(A_{k+1} - A_k) = \varphi(A_{k+1}) - \varphi(A_k).$$

From the last two equations it follows that

$$\varphi(A) = \lim_{k=\infty} \varphi(A_k).$$

Thus, we have proved the following theorem.

THEOREM 4: *If $\varphi(X)$ denotes a measure function, then the union A of a monotonically increasing sequence $A_1 \subseteqq A_2 \subseteqq \ldots$ of φ-measurable somas satisfies the equation*

$$\varphi(A) = \lim_{k=\infty} \varphi(A_k). \tag{138.4}$$

We now denote by B the intersection of all the somas of a monotonically decreasing sequence

$$B_1 \supseteqq B_2 \supseteqq B_3 \supseteqq \ldots, \tag{138.5}$$

all of which belong to the ring of measurability $\mathfrak{M}_\varphi$ of $\varphi(X)$, and we assume in addition that $\varphi(B_1) < +\infty$. Then, if we write

$$A_k = B_1 - B_k \quad (k = 1, 2, \ldots), \quad A = B_1 - B, \tag{138.6}$$

we obtain $A = \lim_{k=\infty} A_k$, and furthermore

$$\left.\begin{aligned} \varphi(A_k) = \varphi(B_1) - \varphi(B_k), \quad \varphi(A) = \varphi(B_1) - \varphi(B), \\ \varphi(A) = \lim_{k=\infty} \varphi(A_k). \end{aligned}\right\} \tag{138.7}$$

Thus, we also have the following theorem.

THEOREM 5: *The intersection B of a monotonically decreasing sequence $B_1 \supseteqq B_2 \supseteqq \ldots$ of somas of the ring of measurability $\mathfrak{M}_\varphi$ of a measure function $\varphi(X)$ satisfies the relation*

$$\varphi(B) = \lim_{k=\infty} \varphi(B_k), \tag{138.8}$$

provided that $\varphi(B_1) < +\infty$.

139. The restriction that $\varphi(B_1) < +\infty$, or more generally, that the right-hand side of (138.8) be finite, is essential. Even in the case that all the somas B_k are normal somas of the ring of measurability $\mathfrak{M}_\varphi$ (§ 135), equation (138.8) need not hold: Consider the example given in § 135 and take for B_k the totality of rational points contained in the interval $0 < x < 1/k$. Then $B = O$ and $\varphi(B) = 0$; but $\varphi(B_k) = +\infty$ for each value of k, and so $\lim_{k=\infty} \varphi(B_k) = +\infty$.

140. Let $A_1, A_2, \ldots$ be infinitely many somas of $\mathfrak{M}_\varphi$ and

$$\underline{A} = \varliminf_{n=\infty} A_n. \tag{140.1}$$

By § 25, we have

$$\underline{A} = D_1 \dot{+} D_2 \dot{+} \cdots, \tag{140.2}$$

where

$$D_k = A_k A_{k+1} \cdots. \tag{140.3}$$

By Theorem 4 of § 138, it follows from $D_1 \subseteqq D_2 \subseteqq \ldots$ that

$$\varphi(\underline{A}) = \lim_{k=\infty} \varphi(D_k). \tag{140.4}$$

On the other hand, it follows from (140.3) that

$$\varphi(D_k) \leqq \inf\,(\varphi(A_k), \varphi(A_{k+1}), \ldots), \tag{140.5}$$

and so we obtain the following theorem.

THEOREM 6: *Denoting the lower limit of a sequence of somas A_j of the ring of measurability $\mathfrak{M}_\varphi$ of a measure function $\varphi(X)$ by $\underline{A}$, we have*

$$\varphi(\underline{A}) \leqq \varliminf_{j=\infty} \varphi(A_j). \tag{140.6}$$

An analogous theorem holds for the soma

$$A = \lim_{n=\infty} A_n. \tag{140.7}$$

By § 25, we have here

$$\bar{A} = V_1 V_2 V_3 \dots, \tag{140.8}$$

where

$$V_k = A_k \dotplus A_{k+1} \dotplus \cdots. \tag{140.9}$$

In order to be able to apply Theorem 5 of § 138, we must assume that not all the numbers $\varphi(V_j)$ are $+\infty$. Taking this into account, we obtain the following theorem.

THEOREM 7: *If the somas A_j of the ring of measurability $\mathfrak{M}_\varphi$ are subsomas of a soma M for which $\varphi(M) < +\infty$, then the upper limit $\bar{A}$ of the sequence $A_1, A_2, \dots$ satisfies*

$$\varphi(A) \geqq \overline{\lim_{j=\infty}} \varphi(A_j). \tag{140.10}$$

Under the assumptions of the above theorem, then, we have in any case

$$\varphi(\underline{A}) \leqq \underline{\lim_{j=\infty}} \varphi(A_j) \leqq \overline{\lim_{j=\infty}} \varphi(A_j) \leqq \varphi(\bar{A}). \tag{140.11}$$

If the sequence of somas $A_1, A_2, \dots$ is convergent, then by definition, $\underline{A} = \bar{A} = A$ and we have:

THEOREM 8: *Let A be the limit of the convergent sequence of somas $A_1, A_2, \dots$ all of which are φ-measurable and in addition are subsomas of a soma M for which $\varphi(M) < +\infty$. Then the numbers $\varphi(A_j)$ converge to $\varphi(A)$, i.e., we have the equation*

$$\varphi(A) = \lim_{j=\infty} \varphi(A_j). \tag{140.12}$$

§§ 141-143. Sequences of Measure Functions and their Limits

141. We consider a set $\{\varphi_\lambda\}$ of measure functions $\varphi_\lambda(X)$, all of which have the same domain of definition $\mathfrak{A}$. This set $\{\varphi_\lambda\}$ need not be countable. We denote the least upper bound of the numbers $\varphi_\lambda(X)$ for each soma X of $\mathfrak{A}$ by $\varphi(X)$. The soma function $\varphi(X)$ is a measure function. In fact, if $X \subseteqq \sum_j \dotplus Y_j$, then

$$\varphi_\lambda(X) \leqq \sum_j \varphi_\lambda(Y_j) \leqq \sum_j \varphi(Y_j)$$

for each measure function of the set $\{\varphi_\lambda\}$, and so

$$\varphi(X) \leqq \sum_j \varphi(Y_j).$$

We assume in addition that given two measure functions $\varphi_{\lambda_1}(X)$ and $\varphi_{\lambda_2}(X)$ from $\{\varphi_\lambda\}$, this set contains a third function $\varphi_{\lambda_3}(X)$ for which the two inequalities $\varphi_{\lambda_3}(X) \geqq \varphi_{\lambda_1}(X)$ and $\varphi_{\lambda_3}(X) \geqq \varphi_{\lambda_2}(X)$ hold for all X in $\mathfrak{A}$. Then every soma U that is measurable for every $\varphi_\lambda(X)$ is measurable for $\varphi(X)$ as well. Indeed, if Y is a soma of $\mathfrak{A}$ for which $\varphi(Y) < +\infty$, then to every positive number ε there can be assigned two corresponding measure functions $\varphi_{\lambda_1}(X)$ and $\varphi_{\lambda_2}(X)$ in such a way that we have

$$\varphi_{\lambda_1}(UY) \geqq \varphi(UY) - \varepsilon, \quad \varphi_{\lambda_2}(Y \dotplus UY) \geqq \varphi(Y \dotplus UY) - \varepsilon. \qquad (141.1)$$

If we now choose

$$\varphi_{\lambda_3}(X) \geqq \max\left(\varphi_{\lambda_1}(X), \varphi_{\lambda_2}(X)\right), \qquad (141.2)$$

we obtain

$$\begin{aligned}\varphi(Y) \geqq \varphi_{\lambda_3}(Y) = \varphi_{\lambda_3}(UY) + \varphi_{\lambda_3}(Y \dotplus UY) \geqq \\ \geqq \varphi_{\lambda_1}(UY) + \varphi_{\lambda_2}(Y \dotplus UY),\end{aligned} \qquad (141.3)$$

and a comparison of (141.1) with (141.3) yields the relation

$$\varphi(Y) \geqq \varphi(UY) + \varphi(Y \dotplus UY) - 2\,\varepsilon, \qquad (141.4)$$

from which the φ-measurability of U can be deduced by passing to the limit. Thus we have the following theorem.

THEOREM 1: *The least upper bound*

$$\varphi(X) = \sup\left(\varphi_\lambda(X)\right)$$

of an arbitrary set $\{\varphi_\lambda\}$ of measure functions $\varphi_\lambda(X)$ all having the same domain of definition $\mathfrak{A}$ is itself a measure function.

If, for each two measure functions $\varphi_{\lambda_1}(X)$ and $\varphi_{\lambda_2}(X)$, the set $\{\varphi_\lambda\}$ always contains a third measure function satisfying

$$\varphi_{\lambda_3}(X) \geqq \max\left(\varphi_{\lambda_1}(X), \varphi_{\lambda_2}(X)\right), \qquad (X \in \mathfrak{A}),$$

then every soma U that is measurable for all the $\varphi_\lambda(X)$ is also φ-measurable.

142. The following theorem is an almost obvious consequence of the definition of a measure function (§ 131) and of the definition of measurability (§ 129).

THEOREM 2: *The limit*

$$\varphi(X) = \lim_{n=\infty} \varphi_n(X) \qquad (X \in \mathfrak{A}) \quad (142.1)$$

of a sequence of measure functions $\varphi_n(X)$ that converges for every soma of $\mathfrak{A}$ is itself a measure function provided that it is union-bounded. Every soma U that is measurable for all of the $\varphi_n(X)$ is measurable for $\varphi(X)$ as well.

By Theorem 1 above, the soma function $\varphi(X)$ represented by equation (142.1) is, in particular, a measure function whenever

$$\varphi(X) \geqq \varphi_n(X) \qquad (n = 1, 2, \ldots; X \in \mathfrak{A}). \quad (142.2)$$

If $\varphi_1(X)$ and $\varphi_2(X)$ are two measure functions with common domain of definition, then $\varphi_1(X) + \varphi_2(X)$ is also a measure function. If $\varphi(X)$ is a measure function and a is a positive number, then $a\varphi(X)$ is likewise a measure function. These remarks, in conjunction with Theorem 1 of § 141, yield the following theorem.

THEOREM 3: *For every sequence of measure functions $\varphi_1(X)$, $\varphi_2(X)$, ... all of which have the same domain of definition, and for every sequence of positive numbers a_1, a_2, ..., the soma function*

$$\varphi(X) = \sum_j a_j \, \varphi_j(X) \quad (142.3)$$

is a measure function. Every soma U that is measurable for every measure function $\varphi_j(X)$ is also measurable for $\varphi(X)$.

143. When a measure function $\varphi(X)$ is compared with another soma function $F(X)$, an essential role is played by the concepts embodied in the following definitions.

DEFINITION 1: *If all the somas U of the ring of measurability $\mathfrak{M}_\varphi$ of a given measure function $\varphi(X)$ are measurable for a soma function $F(X)$, $F(X)$ is called cometric to $\varphi(X)$.*

DEFINITION 2: *An arbitrary soma function $F(X)$ that vanishes on every soma N of the null ring $\mathfrak{N}_\varphi$ of a measure function $\varphi(X)$ is called absolutely continuous with respect to $\varphi(X)$.*

DEFINITION 3: *If a soma N_X of the null ring $\mathfrak{N}_\varphi$ of a measure function $\varphi(X)$ can be assigned to each soma X on which a given soma function $F(X)$ is defined, in such a way that the equation*

$$F(X) = F(X N_X) \quad (143.1)$$

holds, then $F(X)$ is called singular with respect to $\varphi(X)$.

§§ 144-147. Transformation of Measure Functions by Homomorphisms

144. Let the domain of definition $\mathfrak{A}$ of a measure function $\varphi(X)$ be mapped by a homomorphism

$$X' = \sigma X \quad (144.1)$$

onto the complete ring (§ 56)

$$\mathfrak{A}' = \sigma\,\mathfrak{A}. \tag{144.2}$$

To each soma X' of $\mathfrak{A}'$ we assign a number $\psi(X')$ by means of the equation

$$\psi(X') = \inf\big(\varphi(X);\, \sigma X = X'\big). \tag{144.3}$$

In other words, we form the set of numbers $\{\varphi(X)\}$ for all somas X that are mapped onto X' by the homomorphism, and we call the greatest lower bound of this set of numbers $\psi(X')$.

The soma function $\psi(X')$ is a measure function. For if X', Y_1', Y_2', ... are somas of $\mathfrak{A}'$ for which

$$X' \subseteqq \sum_j \dot{+}\, Y_j', \tag{144.4}$$

and if ε is a given positive number, then we can assign to each Y_k' a soma Y_k of $\mathfrak{A}$ for which the two relations

$$\sigma Y_k = Y_k', \quad \varphi(Y_k) \leqq \psi(Y_k') + \frac{\varepsilon}{2^k} \tag{144.5}$$

hold. Now, if X is any soma for which $\sigma X = X'$, the relation (144.4) guarantees the existence of a soma V in the ring $\mathfrak{N}$ that is mapped onto O' for which we can write (Theorem 5 of § 58)

$$X \subseteqq (\sum_j \dot{+}\, Y_j) \dot{+} V.$$

From this it follows, on the one hand, that

$$X \dot{+} XV \subseteqq \sum_j \dot{+}\, Y_j \tag{144.6}$$

and, on the other hand, that

$$\sigma(X \dot{+} XV) = \sigma X \dot{+} \sigma XV = \sigma X = X'. \tag{144.7}$$

From the last two relations, in conjunction with (144.5), it follows that

$$\psi(X') \leqq \varphi(X \dot{+} XV) \leqq \sum_j \varphi(Y_j) \leqq \sum_j \psi(Y_j') + \varepsilon, \tag{144.8}$$

and since the choice of ε was arbitrary, $\psi(X')$ must be cover-bounded. It follows, moreover, from

$$0 \leqq \psi(O') = \psi(\sigma\, O) \leqq \varphi(O) = 0,$$

that

$$\psi(O') = 0.$$

Next, let U be a soma of the ring of measurability $\mathfrak{M}_\varphi$ of $\varphi(X)$ and let $U' = \sigma U$; in addition, let X' be any soma of $\mathfrak{A}'$. Every representative X of X' then satisfies

$$\varphi(X) = \varphi(XU) + \varphi(X \dot{+} XU) \geqq \psi(X'U') + \psi(X' \dot{+} X'U'), \quad (144.9)$$

and we must therefore have

$$\psi(X') \geqq \psi(X'U') + \psi(X' \dot{+} X'U'). \quad (144.10)$$

On the other hand, since $\psi(X')$ is cover-bounded, it follows that U' is ψ-measurable. Combining all these results, we obtain the following theorem.

THEOREM 1: *For any homomorphic mapping $X' = \sigma X$ of the domain of definition $\mathfrak{A}$ of a measure function $\varphi(X)$, the soma function defined by the equation*

$$\psi(X') = \inf\left(\varphi(X); \sigma X = X'\right) \quad (144.11)$$

is a measure function. Denoting the rings of measurability of the measure functions $\varphi(X)$ and $\psi(X')$ by $\mathfrak{M}_\varphi$ and $\mathfrak{M}'_\psi$, respectively, we have the relation

$$\sigma\,\mathfrak{M}_\varphi \prec \mathfrak{M}'_\psi. \quad (144.12)$$

145. Conversely, to each measure function $\psi(X')$ with domain of definition $\mathfrak{A}' = \sigma\mathfrak{A}$ we can assign a soma function $\varphi^*(X)$ defined by the equation

$$\varphi^*(X) = \psi(\sigma X). \quad (145.1)$$

This soma function is also a measure function, since from

$$X \subseteqq \sum_j \dot{+}\, Y_j \quad (145.2)$$

it follows that

$$\sigma X \subseteqq \sum_j \dot{+}\, \sigma Y_j. \quad (145.3)$$

Moreover, if U' belongs to the ring of measurability $\mathfrak{M}'_\psi$ of $\psi(X')$ and if U denotes a soma for which $\sigma U = U'$, then U must be φ^*-measurable. This follows easily from the relations

$$\left.\begin{aligned} &\sigma(XU) = X'U', \quad \sigma(X \dot{+} XU) = X' \dot{+} X'U', \\ &\psi(X') = \psi(X'U') + \psi(X' \dot{+} X'U'). \end{aligned}\right\} \quad (145.4)$$

In particular, we have the following theorem.

THEOREM 2: *If the measure function $\psi(X')$ is defined by the equation* (144.11), *and if we put*

$$\varphi^*(X) = \psi(\sigma X) \quad (145.5)$$

for every soma X of $\mathfrak{A}$, then $\varphi^*(X)$ is a measure function that is $\leqq \varphi(X)$ and in addition is cometric to $\varphi(X)$.

The following theorem (which is best proved by direct verification) can be looked upon as a special case of the preceding theorem.

THEOREM 3: *If K is any soma in the domain of definition $\mathfrak{A}$ of a measure function $\varphi(X)$, then the soma function*

$$\varphi^*(X) = \varphi(KX) \tag{145.6}$$

is a measure function that is cometric to $\varphi(X)$.

146. An important special case of the results of the last sections is obtained when the ring $\mathfrak{N}$ that is mapped onto the empty soma O' by the homomorphism (144.1) is chosen to be a subset of the null ring $\mathfrak{N}_\varphi$ of $\varphi(X)$. We also obtain this special case, as a moment's thought will show, if we replace $\varphi(X)$ by the measure function $\varphi^*(X)$ defined above in Theorem 2.

Given two representatives X_1 and X_2 of a soma X', we can in this case write (Theorem 4 of § 58)

$$X_1 \dot{+} U_1 = X_2 \dot{+} U_2, \quad (U_1, U_2 \in \mathfrak{N}_\varphi)$$
$$\varphi(X_1) = \varphi(X_1 \dot{+} U_1), \quad \varphi(X_2) = \varphi(X_2 \dot{+} U_2),$$

and, accordingly, $\varphi(X)$ always takes the same value for each representative X of a soma X'. Thus equation (144.11), which defines $\psi(X')$, can be replaced by

$$\psi(X') = \psi(\sigma X) = \varphi(X). \tag{146.1}$$

The mapping of measure functions induced by the homomorphism $X' = \sigma X$ is thus *measure-preserving*.

In this case, the relation (144.12) is replaced by the more precise relation

$$\sigma \mathfrak{M}_\varphi = \mathfrak{M}'_\psi. \tag{146.2}$$

For if A denotes a soma that does not belong to $\mathfrak{M}_\varphi$, there is at least one soma X in $\mathfrak{A}$ that satisfies

$$\varphi(X) < \varphi(XA) + \varphi(X \dot{+} XA), \tag{146.3}$$

and so, if $X' = \sigma X$ and $A' = \sigma A$, we obtain

$$\psi(X') < \psi(X'A') + \psi(X' \dot{+} X'A'). \tag{146.4}$$

147. If, in particular, we choose $\mathfrak{N} = \mathfrak{N}_\varphi$, the null ring $\mathfrak{N}'_\psi$ of the transformed measure function $\psi(X')$ consists of a single soma, namely, the empty soma O'. We then have, for every non-empty soma A',

$$\psi(A') > 0. \tag{147.1}$$

Any measure function that enjoys this property is called a *reduced measure function.*

Hence we have the following theorem.

Theorem 4: *Every measure function can be mapped by a measure-preserving homomorphism onto a reduced measure function.*

For reduced measure functions, furthermore, we have the following theorem.

Theorem 5: *Let U be a soma measurable for a reduced measure function $\varphi(X)$. Moreover, let A be a soma for which $\varphi(A) < +\infty$. Then*

$$\varphi(AU) < \varphi(A) \tag{147.2}$$

always holds, except if

$$AU = A. \tag{147.3}$$

Proof: The measurability of U implies

$$\varphi(A) = \varphi(AU) + \varphi(A \dotplus AU)$$

and $\varphi(A \dotplus AU) > 0$ unless $A \dotplus AU = O$, i.e., $AU = A$.

§§ 148-153. The Borel-Lebesgue Content

148. The earliest known measure function, the one out of which the whole theory of measure developed, came about as a result of the effort to define for arbitrary point sets a generalization of the notion of the volume of a body in Euclidean space.

In an n-dimensional space $\mathfrak{R}_n$ with rectangular coordinates $x_1, x_2, \ldots, x_n$ we consider the interval

$$I: \; a_k < x_k < b_k \qquad (k = 1, 2, \ldots, n)$$

and denote the lengths of the edges of this interval by

$$h_k = b_k - a_k \qquad (k = 1, 2, \ldots, n).$$

To each such interval I of $\mathfrak{R}_n$ we assign a "weight" $p(I)$ computed by the formula

$$p(I) = h_1 h_2 \ldots h_n.$$

We now shall assign to each and every point set A in $\mathfrak{R}_n$ a number m^*A, called the (*outer*) *Borel-Lebesgue content*[2] of A and defined as follows:

[2] H. Lebesgue, *Bull. Soc. Math. France*, Vol. 36 (1908), p. 12.

We consider all possible sequences $\{I_j\}$ *of intervals whose unions all cover the point set* A, *i.e., for which we have*

$$A \subseteqq I_1 \dotplus I_2 \dotplus I_3 \dotplus \cdots,$$

and let m^*A *be the greatest lower bound of the set of sums*

$$\sum_j p(I_j)$$

of the weights of the intervals that constitute these various sequences. In addition, for the empty set O, *let* $m^*O = 0$.

We now have the following theorem.

THEOREM 1: *The Borel-Lebesgue content* m^*A *is a measure function.*

Proof: By the definition of measure function, it suffices to prove that m^*A is a cover-bounded soma function. Thus, let

$$B \subseteqq A_1 \dotplus A_2 \dotplus A_3 \dotplus \cdots.$$

Then, given any number $\varepsilon > 0$, each of the point sets A_k can, by assumption, be covered by at most countably many intervals $I_{k1}, I_{k2}, \ldots$ in such a way that

$$\sum_j p(I_{kj}) \leqq m^*A_k + \frac{\varepsilon}{2^k}.$$

Since the union of all the I_{kj} covers the point set B, we have

$$m^*B \leqq \sum_{k,j} p(I_{kj}) \leqq \sum_k m^*A_k + \varepsilon,$$

and from this we obtain the desired relation

$$m^*B \leqq \sum_k m^*A_k,$$

which implies the theorem.

149. The content m^*A is easy to compute for certain special point sets. To begin with, we have the following theorem.

THEOREM 2: *For* $n \geqq 2$, *every* $(n-1)$*-dimensional hyperplane that satisfies an equation of the form*

$$x_k = c_k \tag{149.1}$$

is a set of measure zero for the measure function m^*A.

Proof: We cover the hyperplane (149.1), which we shall denote by E, with countably many $(n-1)$-dimensional intervals J_m $(m = 1, 2, \ldots)$ and we denote the weight of these intervals by $p(J_m)$. The interval J_m is characterized by, say, the relations

$$a_{mj} < x_j < b_{mj} \qquad (j \neq k), \quad (149.2)$$

$$x_k = c_k. \quad (149.3)$$

We cover each of the $(n - 1)$-dimensional intervals J_m by an n-dimensional interval I_n which is defined by replacing relation (149.3) by

$$c_k - \frac{h_m}{2} < x_k < c_k + \frac{h_m}{2} \qquad (h_m > 0).$$

We then have

$$p(I_m) = h_m\, p(J_m).$$

We now specify the h_m by means of the equations

$$h_m\, p(J_m) = \frac{\varepsilon}{2^m},$$

where ε denotes an arbitrary positive number. Since E is contained in the union of all the I_m, we have

$$m^* E \leqq \sum_m p(I_m) = \varepsilon,$$

from which it follows, by passage to the limit, that $m^* E = 0$.

It is now easy to prove the following theorem

THEOREM 3: *If we denote an arbitrary interval of $\mathfrak{R}_n$ by I and its closure by $\bar{I}$, we always have*

$$m^* I = m^* \bar{I} = p(I). \quad (149.4)$$

Proof: To begin with, from the relations

$$I \subseteqq \bar{I}, \quad \bar{I} = I + (\bar{I} - I)$$

it follows that

$$m^* I \leqq m^* \bar{I} \leqq m^* I + m^* (\bar{I} - I).$$

The point set $\bar{I} - I$ consists of subsets of $(n - 1)$-dimensional hyperplanes, and therefore, by Theorem 2, we have

$$m^* (\bar{I} - I) = 0.$$

We thus obtain

$$m^* I = m^* I. \quad (149.5)$$

Next, let ε be any positive number. We can cover the closed interval I by an at most countable number of intervals I_1', I_2', ... in such a way that

$$\sum_k p(I_k') < m^* \bar{I} + \varepsilon. \quad (149.6)$$

By the Heine-Borel covering theorem, there is a finite number of these intervals I'_k, say

$$I'_1, I'_2, \ldots, I'_m, \tag{149.7}$$

whose union contains $\bar{I}$.

The projection on the x_k-axis of each of the $m + 1$ intervals

$$I, I'_1, I'_2, \ldots, I'_m \tag{149.8}$$

is a linear interval; through each end-point $\xi_k^{(l)}$ of each of the latter intervals we pass the orthogonal $(n - 1)$-dimensional hyperplane $x_k = \xi_k^{(l)}$ and we repeat this operation for $k = 1, 2, \ldots, n$. The totality of these orthogonal hyperplanes decomposes each interval (149.8) into a finite number of subintervals: say, I'_1 into $I'_{11}, I'_{12}, \ldots, I'_{1j_1}$; ... ; I'_m into $I'_{m1}, I'_{m2}, \ldots, I'_{mj_m}$, and I itself into $I_1, I_2, \ldots, I_k$. We then have

$$\begin{aligned}
p(I'_1) &= p(I'_{11}) + p(I'_{12}) + \cdots + p(I'_{1j_1}),\\
p(I'_2) &= p(I'_{21}) + p(I'_{22}) + \cdots + p(I'_{2j_2}),\\
&\cdots\cdots\cdots\cdots\cdots\cdots\\
p(I'_m) &= p(I'_{m1}) + p(I'_{m2}) + \cdots + p(I'_{mj_m}),\\
p(I) &= p(I_1) + p(I_2) + \cdots + p(I_j).
\end{aligned}$$

Now observe that any two subintervals I'_{rs} and I_t either coincide or else have no point in common. Since the I'_u cover the interval I, I_1 in particular must coincide with one of the subintervals of at least one of the I'_k : say, with a subinterval of I'_{k_1}. We remove from I all those I_t that are also contained in I'_{k_1}; the sum of their weights is less than or equal to $p(I'_{k_1})$. Suppose the first of the remaining I_k is contained in I'_{k_2}. We remove from I all those I_t that are contained in I'_{k_2}; the sum of their weights is less than or equal to $p(I'_{k_2})$. We continue in this way until we have exhausted the I_t. We then have

$$\begin{aligned}
p(I) &= p(I_1) + p(I_2) + \cdots + p(I_j)\\
&\leqq p(I'_{k_1}) + p(I'_{k_2}) + \cdots + p(I'_{kl})\\
&\leqq p(I'_1) + p(I'_2) + \cdots + p(I'_m),
\end{aligned}$$

and therefore, by (149.6),

$$p(I) < m^*\bar{I} + \varepsilon.$$

From this inequality, which holds for all $\varepsilon > 0$, we obtain

$$p(I) \leqq m^*\bar{I}. \tag{149.9}$$

On the other hand, we have by definition

$$m^*I \leqq p(I), \tag{149.10}$$

and the relations (149.4) follow from a comparison of (149.9) and (149.10) if we take (149.5) into account.

150. An $(n - 1)$-dimensional hyperplane

$$E\colon\ x_k = c_k \tag{150.1}$$

divides the space $\mathfrak{R}_n$ into two domains

$$U\colon\ x_k < c_k \quad \text{and} \quad V\colon\ x_k > c_k. \tag{150.2}$$

Let X be any point set of finite content m^*X. From the equation

$$X = XU + XE + XV$$

it follows that

$$X \dotplus XU = XE + XV,$$

and since XE, being a subset of E, is a set of measure zero, we conclude that

$$m^*(X \dotplus XU) = m^*XV. \tag{150.3}$$

Now let $I_1, I_2, \ldots$ be a sequence of intervals that covers X and satisfies

$$\sum_k p(I_k) < m^*X + \varepsilon, \tag{150.4}$$

where ε is a positive number specified in advance. The intervals $I_k' = I_k U$ cover XU, and the intervals $I_k'' = I_k V$ cover XV. Thus, the relations

$$m^*XU \leqq \sum_k p(I_k U), \quad m^*XV \leqq \sum_k p(I_k V) \tag{150.5}$$

hold. On the other hand,

$$p(I_k) = p(I_k U) + p(I_k V) \qquad (k = 1, 2, \ldots), \tag{150.6}$$

and a comparison of the relations (150.3) through (150.6) yields the inequality

$$m^*X + \varepsilon > m^*XU + m^*(X \dotplus XU). \tag{150.7}$$

Taking into account that (150.7) holds for all $\varepsilon > 0$ and that the set function m^*A is union-bounded, we obtain the equation

$$m^*X = m^*XU + m^*(X \dotplus XU),$$

which states that U is m^*-measurable. A similar proof shows that V is measurable.

Now, any interval I can be represented as the intersection of point sets

$$a_k < x_k, \quad b_k > x_k \qquad (k = 1, 2, \ldots, n).$$

Therefore I is also m^*-measurable.

151. By the result just proved, the ring of measurability $\mathfrak{M}_{m^*}$ of the Borel-Lebesgue content in $\mathfrak{R}_q$ must contain the complete ring of point sets $\mathfrak{M}_B$ that is generated by the totality of intervals I by means of transfinite induction, following the method of § 53. The elements of $\mathfrak{M}_B$ are called *Borel sets.* Among the Borel sets are included the open point sets, since they can be represented as a countable union of intervals, and likewise, the closed point sets. In addition, all point sets that can be obtained from these latter by passage to the limit are Borel sets.

We are now in a position to prove an important theorem about measurable point sets. Let A be an arbitrary point set that is measurable for the Borel-Lebesgue content. Let $\overline{W}_n$ $(n = 1, 2, \ldots)$ denote the closed cube of side n with center at the origin; we put

$$A_n = A\overline{W}_n \qquad (n = 1, 2, 3, \ldots) \quad (151.1)$$

and remark that $\overline{W}_n$, A_n, and $\overline{W}_n - A_n$ are all measurable point sets of finite content. We cover the last point set $\overline{W}_n - A_n$ by a sequence $\{I_k\}$ of intervals in such a way that the union $U_n = \sum_k \dot{+} I_k$ satisfies both of the relations

$$\overline{W}_n - A_n \subseteqq U_n, \quad m^* U_n < m^*(\overline{W}_n - A_n) + \frac{1}{2^n}. \qquad (151.2)$$

The first of the formulas (151.2) states that we have

$$\overline{W}_n - A_n = \overline{W}_n U_n - A_n U_n, \text{ i.e., } A_n U_n = \overline{W}_n U_n - (\overline{W}_n - A_n); \quad (151.3)$$

because of the measurability of all the point sets that appear in this latter equation, it follows from this, by use of the second equation of (151.3), that

$$m^* A_n U_n = m^* \overline{W}_n U_n - m^*(\overline{W}_n - A_n) \leqq m^* U_n - m^*(\overline{W}_n - A_n) < \frac{1}{2^n}. \quad (151.4)$$

Next, we introduce the notation

$$B_n = A_n - A_n U_n, \quad C_n = A_n U_n. \qquad (151.5)$$

The first equation of (151.3) allows us to write

$$B_n = \overline{W}_n - \overline{W}_n U_n,$$

and from this representation of B_n we deduce that this point set, being the intersection of the closed cube $\overline{W}_n$ with the closed complement of U_n, is itself closed. Thus,

$$A_n = B_n + C_n \qquad (n = 1, 2, \ldots) \quad (151.6)$$

is the sum of a closed point set B_n and a point set C_n which, by (151.4), satisfies

$$m^* C_n < \frac{1}{2^n}. \qquad (151.7)$$

But now it follows from (151.1) that

$$A_n \subseteqq A_{n+1}, \quad \lim_{n=\infty} A_n = A,$$

so that we can write, for every positive integer n,

$$A = A_n \dotplus A_{n+1} \dotplus A_{n+2} \dotplus \cdots. \qquad (151.8)$$

If we now put

$$B_n^* = B_n \dotplus B_{n+1} \dotplus B_{n+2} \dotplus \cdots, \quad C_n^* = C_n \dotplus C_{n+1} \dotplus C_{n+2} \dotplus \cdots, \quad (151.9)$$

it follows from (151.8) and (151.6) that

$$A = B_n^* \dotplus C_n^* \qquad (n = 1, 2, \ldots), \qquad (151.10)$$

and from (151.9) and (151.7) that

$$m^* C_n^* \leqq m^* C_n + m^* C_{n+1} + \cdots < \frac{1}{2^{n-1}}. \qquad (151.11)$$

Finally, we introduce the notation

$$B = B_1^*, \quad N = A - B. \qquad (151.12)$$

From $B_n^* \subseteqq B \subseteqq A$ and from (151.10), we now obtain

$$A = B \dotplus C_n^*;$$

and therefore, by (151.12),

$$N \subseteqq C_n^* \qquad (n = 1, 2, \ldots).$$

Hence, by (151.11),

$$m^* N < \frac{1}{2^{n-1}}$$

holds for every positive integer n, whence it follows that N is a set of measure zero.

Taking all the above results into account, we can now formulate the following theorem.

THEOREM 4: *The ring of measurability $\mathfrak{M}_{m^*}$ of the Borel-Lebesgue measure function m^*X contains, in addition to the complete ring $\mathfrak{N}_{m^*}$ of sets of measure zero for this measure function, the complete ring $\mathfrak{M}_B$ of all Borel sets as well.*

Every point set A of $\mathfrak{M}_{m^*}$ can be represented as the sum of a set N of measure zero and a Borel set B that is the union of at most countably many closed, bounded point sets B_j. Conversely, the union of an arbitrary Borel set with an arbitrary set N of measure zero is always a point set of $\mathfrak{M}_{m^*}$.

It is sometimes more convenient to apply the above theorem to the complement A' of a measurable point set A. A itself, in that case, is represented as the difference of a Borel set B that is the intersection of an at most countable number of open point sets and a set N_1 of measure zero.

Note 1: As is well known, every closed set B_j is the sum of an at most countable set and a perfect set. The point set B that is mentioned in the preceding theorem can therefore be represented as the sum of a point set B° that is the union of an at most countable number of perfect sets B_j° and an at most countable point set N° that must, of course, be of measure zero. The measurable point set A is thus also the sum of B° and the set $N^\circ + N$ of measure zero.

Note 2: There are sets of measure zero N that are not Borel sets, as is shown in § 251, pp. 256-257 of my *Vorlesungen über reelle Funktionen* (Leipzig and Berlin, 1918; 2nd edition, 1927; repr., New York, 1948). Hence, the wording of the preceding theorem cannot be altered to omit the set N of measure zero, even if B were allowed to be a completely arbitrary Borel set not having the special structure called for.

152. We prove a corollary to the preceding theorem.

THEOREM 5: *The outer Borel-Lebesgue content m^*U of an open point set U is equal to the least upper bound of the sums of weights of a finite number of pairwise disjoint intervals lying in U.*

Proof: By Theorem 4, U is the union of a countable number of closed bounded point sets B_n, to which there may have to be adjoined a set N of measure zero. The point sets

$$V_n = B_1 \dotplus B_2 \dotplus \cdots \dotplus B_n$$

are closed and bounded and, by Theorem 4 of § 138,

$$m^* U = \lim_{n=\infty} m^* V_n .$$

Hence, if p is any positive number $< m^* U$, a positive integer n_0 can be so chosen that

$$m^* V_{n_0} > p.$$

The closed bounded point set V_{n_0}, which lies in the open point set U, can be covered by a finite number of intervals all of which lie in U. Let us decompose these intervals as in § 149; in this way, we obtain a finite number of pairwise disjoint intervals whose closures cover V_{n_0} and the sum of whose weights is therefore $> p$. This proves Theorem 5.

153. We now consider (cf. Theorem 6 of § 59 and Theorem 7 of § 62) the homomorphism

$$A' = \sigma A, \tag{153.1}$$

by which all the null sets of the ring $\mathfrak{N}_{m^*}$ and only such sets are mapped into the empty soma O'. This homomorphism maps the measure function $m^* X$ onto a reduced measure function $m'X'$ (§ 147). The only non-empty somas that are measurable for $m'X'$ are, in this instance, the images $B' = \sigma B$ of point sets B that can be represented as the union of an at most countable number of perfect point sets (Note 1 of § 151).

Note: In the ring $\mathfrak{A}'$ of all somas (153.1) there are somas that have no non-empty subsomas measurable for the measure function $m'X'$; in § 334, pp. 352-354, of the book *Vorlesungen über reelle Funktionen* mentioned above, a point set Ω is explicitly constructed whose image $\Omega' = \sigma\Omega$ has this property.

For the invariance of the Borel-Lebesgue content under Euclidean motions, see Theorem 3 of § 277 below.

CHAPTER SIX

THE INTEGRAL

§ 154. Fields of Place Functions; Measurable Place Functions

154. In § 75, we computed the lower and upper nests of somas of a place function f using a countable set of somas $C_1, C_2, \ldots$ and carrying out certain passages to the limit. Consequently, in the case that all the somas C_k belong to a *complete ring* $\mathfrak{M}$ *of somas*, all the somas of the nests of somas $[S_0(y)]$ and $[S^0(y)]$ of f likewise belong to $\mathfrak{M}$. This is clearly the case also if all the somas of any one nest of somas $[S(y)]$ of f belong to $\mathfrak{M}$. The remark allows us to make the following definition.

DEFINITION: *The totality of all place functions f that have at least one nest of somas all of whose somas $S(y)$ belong to a complete ring $\mathfrak{M}$, is called a field of place functions. The ring $\mathfrak{M}$ is called the fundamental ring of the field.*

If the fundamental ring $\mathfrak{M}$ of a field of place functions coincides with the ring of measurability $\mathfrak{M}_\varphi$ of a measure function $\varphi(X)$, the place functions of this field are said to be φ-measurable, or measurable for $\varphi(X)$.

A field of place functions is a set of place functions that is closed under all the operations defined in Chapters Three and Four.

If, for example, all the functions $f_1, f_2, \ldots$ of a sequence belong to a field F, the discussion in § 71 and Theorem 4 of § 73 show that the functions

$$g = \sup(f_1, f_2, \ldots), \quad h = \inf(f_1, f_2, \ldots), \tag{154.1}$$

and, in particular, the functions

$$\max(f_1, f_2, \ldots, f_m), \quad \min(f_1, f_2, \ldots, f_m), \tag{154.2}$$

$$\bar{f} = \overline{\lim_{j=\infty}} f_j, \quad \underline{f} = \underline{\lim_{j=\infty}} f_j\ , \tag{154.3}$$

also belong to F. By Theorem 1 of § 79, every bounded place function that belongs to F can be approximated uniformly by finitely-valued place functions *that themselves belong to* F; and by Theorem 3 of § 117, under the hypotheses of that theorem the composite function $\chi(f_1, \ldots, f_m)$ belongs to the field if the functions $f_1, \ldots, f_m$ do.

In particular, whenever two functions f_1 and f_2 belong to a field of place functions, so do the functions

$$f_1 \pm f_2, \quad f_1 f_2, \quad \frac{f_1}{f_2}, \quad |f_1|, \quad \text{etc.} \tag{154.4}$$

§§ 155-162. The Notion of the Integral

155. In elementary geometry, the area of a rectangle is equal to the product bh of the length b of its base and its height h.

Similarly, the volume of a prism or of a cylinder is equal to the product bh of the area b of its base and its height h.

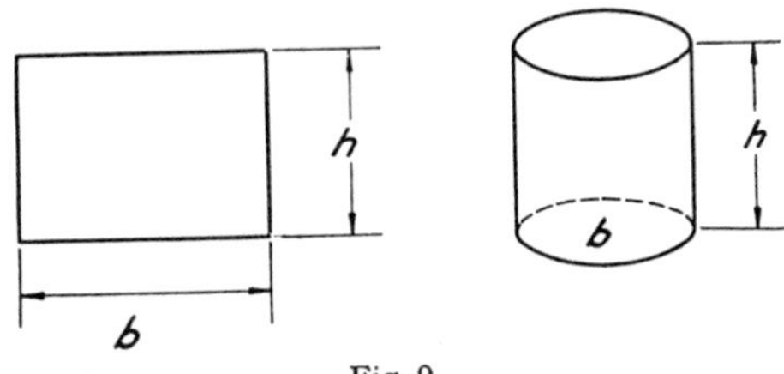

Fig. 9

Guided by these simple facts, we form the most general notion of an integral; and to do this only a few steps are necessary, each of which suggests itself in a natural fashion once the earlier steps are taken.

We must first develop the idea of an "abstract cylinder": we can take as the base, for example, a soma X of any complete ring of somas, and as the altitude, a segment of the real axis. We set the "area" of the base X of our cylinder equal to the value $\varphi(X)$ given it by any fixed measure function we please, and we define the volume of the cylinder to be equal to the product

$$y\, \varphi(X) \tag{155.1}$$

of the length of its altitude (its height) and the "area" of its base.

We now consider a bounded finitely-valued place function f, which, by § 66, can be represented by means of the formula

$$f = \sum_{j=1}^{p} y_j M_j \quad \left(M_j \neq 0, j = 1, \ldots, p; \sum_{j=1}^{p} M_j = M\right). \tag{155.2}$$

We assume that $f \geqq 0$, or, what comes to the same thing, that all the y_j are $\geqq 0$; we assume, furthermore, that the relation

$$\varphi(M) < +\infty \tag{155.3}$$

holds for the domain of definition M of f.

Let X be any subsoma of M; the formula

$$f = \sum_j{}' y_j (M_j X) \tag{155.4}$$

represents the place function f on the soma X. The prime on the summation sign indicates that the summation is carried out only for those indices

$$j_1, j_2, \ldots, j_q$$

for which $M_j X$ is non-empty. We now consider the configuration consisting of the q cylinders with base $M_{j_k} X$ and height y_{j_k} and define the volume $\psi(X)$ of this configuration to be the sum of the volumes of the individual cylinders. In this way, we obtain the equation

$$\psi(X) = \sum_{k=1}^{q} y_{j_k} \varphi(M_{j_k} X),$$

which we can also write as follows:

$$\psi(X) = \sum_j{}' y_j \varphi(M_j X). \tag{155.5}$$

In this second form of the expression, it can happen that certain values of the set of indices j are omitted; but for these indices $M_j X = O$, and thus $\varphi(M_j X) = 0$. Therefore we can just as well sum with respect to all the indices j and hence write

$$\psi(X) = \sum_{j=1}^{p} y_j \varphi(M_j X). \tag{155.6}$$

The "representation" of a finitely-valued place function is not unique (§ 66). For each decomposition

$$M = \sum_k M_k' \tag{155.7}$$

of the domain of definition M of f, we can write, instead of (155.2),

$$f = \sum_{j,k}{}' y_j (M_j M_k'). \tag{155.8}$$

For the volume $\psi(X)$ we would then have

$$\psi(X) = \sum_{j,k} y_j \varphi(M_j M_k' X). \tag{155.9}$$

We now require that the volume $\psi(X)$ be independent of the representation of f, i.e., that the expressions on the right-hand sides of (155.6) and

(155.9) denote the same number. But by Theorem 2 of § 136, this is indeed the case provided all the M_j and all the M_k' are φ-measurable. To ensure the latter condition, it suffices to assume that the finitely-valued place function f be φ-measurable (§ 154) and that we use only such decompositions, in the various representations of f, as consist of somas that are φ-measurable. This assumption, which we shall adhere to from now on, is fundamental to the entire theory of integration.

156. The soma function $\psi(X)$ defined by equation (155.6) or (155.9) is called the *integral, with respect to the measure function $\varphi(X)$, of f over X* and is denoted by

$$\psi(X) = \int_X f\, d\varphi. \qquad (156.1)$$

The suitability of this time-honored notation, which goes back to Leibniz (1646-1716), will be discussed later (§ 175).

By Theorem 3 of § 145, the soma functions $\varphi(M_j X)$ that appear in (155.6) are measure functions cometric to $\varphi(X)$ (§ 143); by Theorem 3 of § 142, the same is then true for the integral $\psi(X)$.

We denote the infimum and supremum of f on the soma X by $\alpha(X)$ and $\beta(X)$, respectively, and remark that

$$\alpha(X) \leqq y_j \leqq \beta(X) \qquad (156.2)$$

for all y_j that appear under the summation sign in (155.5). But the measurability of the M_j implies the equation

$$\sum_j{}' \varphi(M_j X) = \sum_j \varphi(M_j X) = \varphi(X). \qquad (156.3)$$

Thus, by (155.5), we have

$$\alpha(X)\, \varphi(X) \leqq \psi(X) \leqq \beta(X)\, \varphi(X); \qquad (156.4)$$

this is a relation that will be of fundamental significance for what follows.

157. If f and f' are two finitely-valued, bounded, non-negative, and φ-measurable place functions with the same domain of definition M, and if $\varphi(M) < +\infty$, then the integrals

$$\psi(X) = \int_X f\, d\varphi, \quad \psi'(X) = \int_X f'\, d\varphi$$

exist; by the preceding discussion, we have

$$\text{if} \quad f \leqq f' \quad \text{then} \quad \psi(X) \leqq \psi'(X). \qquad (157.1)$$

This simple observation allows us to generalize the notion of the integral. Let f be any bounded, φ-measurable, non-negative place function whose domain of definition M satisfies the condition (155.3). Let $\{h\}$ denote the totality of all finitely-valued, φ-measurable place functions for which $0 \leqq h \leqq f$. Then the integrals

$$\psi_h(X) = \int_X h\, d\varphi \qquad (h \in \{h\}) \qquad (157.2)$$

all exist, and if we introduce, for any two place functions h' and h'' of $\{h\}$, the notation

$$h^* = \max(h', h''), \qquad (157.3)$$

we have the inequality

$$\psi_{h^*}(X) \geqq \max\big(\psi_{h'}(X),\ \psi_{h''}(X)\big). \qquad (157.4)$$

Moreover, every soma U of the ring of measurability $\mathfrak{M}_\varphi$ of $\varphi(X)$ belongs to the ring of measurability of every one of the measure functions $\psi_h(X)$.

Thus, if we define a soma function $\psi(X)$ by means of the equation

$$\psi(X) = \sup\big(\psi_h(X);\ h \in \{h\}\big), \qquad (157.5)$$

then, by Theorem 1 of § 141, this function is a *measure function* that is *cometric to* $\varphi(X)$.

If, in addition, N is a null soma of $\varphi(X)$, the formulas of § 156 show that

$$\psi_h(N) = 0$$

for each of the finitely-valued place functions h, and therefore, by (157.5), we must also have

$$\psi(N) = 0. \qquad (157.6)$$

Thus the measure function $\psi(X)$ is, by § 143, *absolutely continuous* with respect to $\varphi(X)$.

Since, furthermore, f is a bounded place function, § 91 allows us to find, given a positive number ε, a place function h in the set $\{h\}$ for which the inequality

$$\alpha(X) \leqq \alpha_h(X) + \varepsilon$$

holds for every soma $X \subseteqq M$.

Then, by (156.4) and (157.1), we have

$$\big(\alpha(X) - \varepsilon\big)\, \varphi(X) \leqq \alpha_h(X)\, \varphi(X) \leqq \psi_h(X) \leqq \psi(X),$$

and by passage to the limit we obtain $\alpha(X)\varphi(X) \leqq \psi(X)$. On the other hand, for every finitely-valued $h \leqq f$ we have

$$\psi_h(X) \leqq \beta_h(X)\,\varphi(X) \leqq \beta(X)\,\varphi(X),$$

so that we finally obtain the following generalization of (156.4):

$$\alpha(X)\,\varphi(X) \leqq \psi(X) \leqq \beta(X)\,\varphi(X) \qquad (X \subseteqq M). \quad (157.7)$$

158. Before we formulate our final definition of the integral by means of the last result, we shall state and prove a uniqueness theorem that we shall have frequent occasion to make use of.

THEOREM 1: *Let the place functions $f_1, f_2, \ldots, f_m$* be *finite and measurable for a measure function $\varphi(X)$. Let $\varphi(M) < +\infty$ for the common domain of definition M of these f_k. Let the functions*

$$\chi(u_1, u_2, \ldots, u_m),\ \psi(v_1, \ldots, v_m; w_1, \ldots, w_m),\ \Psi(v_1, \ldots, v_m; w_1, \ldots, w_m)$$

have the same significance as in § 111 *and, in addition, be continuous and non-negative. Then there is at most one measure function $\psi(X)$ for which the place functions $f_1, \ldots, f_m$ are ψ-measurable and such that the relations*

$$\psi(\alpha_k(X); \beta_k(X))\,\varphi(X) \leqq \psi(X) \leqq \Psi(\alpha_k(X); \beta_k(X))\,\varphi(X) \qquad (158.1)$$

hold for all $X \subseteqq M$ satisfying $\varphi(X) > 0$.

Proof: We prove the uniqueness of the measure function $\psi(X)$ first under the stronger hypothesis that the place functions $f_1, f_2, \ldots, f_m$ are bounded, by evaluating this function $\psi(X)$ (assuming its existence) on every given soma X with an arbitrarily prescribed degree of accuracy.

To this end, we first choose a positive integer n_0 that is larger than all the $|\alpha_k(M)|$ and $|\beta_k(M)|$. Next, given an arbitrary number $\varepsilon > 0$, we fix a number $\delta > 0$ such that, in the notation of § 113,

$$\varepsilon(\delta, n_0) < \varepsilon.$$

Then, by Theorem 1 of § 79, there is a decomposition

$$M = M_1 + M_2 + \cdots + M_p \qquad (158.2)$$

of the soma M into a finite number of φ-measurable somas M_j such that the oscillation of each place function f_k on each M_j is less than or equal to δ. In this notation, we have the relations

$$\Psi(\alpha_k(M_j); \beta_k(M_j)) \leqq \psi(\alpha_k(M_j); \beta_k(M_j)) + \varepsilon \quad (j = 1, 2, \ldots, p). \quad (158.3)$$

If we had used, say, the lower nests of somas of the functions f_k to determine the M_j, then the somas M_j would also be ψ-measurable by hypothesis. Thus, if X is any non-empty subsoma of M and if we put

$$X_j = XM_j \qquad (j = 1, 2, \ldots, p), \quad (158.4)$$

then we have

$$\varphi(X) = \sum_j{}' \varphi(X_j), \quad \psi(X) = \sum_j{}' \psi(X_j), \qquad (158.5)$$

where the primes on the summation signs indicate that the summation is carried out only with respect to those indices j for which X_j is non-empty. But for these values of j, we always have

$$\alpha_k(M_j) \leqq \alpha_k(X_j), \quad \beta_k(X_j) \leqq \beta_k(M_j),$$

and by (158.3), we can therefore write, as in § 111,

$$\Psi(\alpha_k(X_j); \beta_k(X_j)) \leqq \psi(\alpha_k(X_j); \beta_k(X_j)) + \varepsilon. \qquad (158.6)$$

Hence it follows from (158.1) that for these non-empty somas X_j

$$\psi(\alpha_k(X_j); \beta_k(X_j))\, \varphi(X_j) \leqq \psi(X_j) \leqq \psi(\alpha_k(X_j); \beta_k(X_j))\, \varphi(X_j) + \varepsilon\, \varphi(X_j). \qquad (158.7)$$

If we introduce the abbreviation

$$s = \sum_j{}' \psi(\alpha_k(X_j); \beta_k(X_j))\, \varphi(X_j), \qquad (158.8)$$

then (158.5) and (158.7) yield the relations

$$s \leqq \psi(X) \leqq s + \varepsilon\, \varphi(X) \leqq s + \varepsilon\, \varphi(M). \qquad (158.9)$$

Now $\varphi(M)$ is by assumption a finite number, so that $\varepsilon \cdot \varphi(M)$ can be chosen arbitrarily small. This proves our assertion for bounded place functions.

In the general case, we can obtain a decomposition

$$M = M_1 + M_2 + \cdots + M_j + \cdots$$

such that each M_j is φ-measurable and the inequalities $f_k \leqq j$ hold on M_j $(k = 1, 2, \ldots, m)$. By what we have just proved, there is for each M_j $(j = 1, 2, \ldots)$ at most one measure function $\psi_j(X)$ for which the place functions f, f_2, ..., f_m are ψ_j-measurable and which satisfies (158.1) for all $X \subseteqq M$ for which $\varphi(X) > 0$. A function $\psi(X)$ that satisfies the conditions of our theorem for all $X \subseteqq M$ must therefore be of the form

$$\psi(X) = \psi(M_1 X) + \psi(M_2 X) + \cdots = \psi_1(M_1 X) + \psi_2(M_2 X) + \cdots.$$

159. We shall now define the integral for arbitrary non-negative, φ-measurable place functions whose domain of definition M is a normal soma of the ring of measurability $\mathfrak{M}_\varphi$ (§ 135).

THEOREM 2 (The First Principal Theorem of Integration): *Let $\varphi(X)$ be a measure function and f a φ-measurable, non-negative place function, whose domain of definition M is a normal soma of the ring of measurability $\varphi(X)$.*

Then there is one and only one measure function $\psi(X)$ that is cometric to $\varphi(X)$ and absolutely continuous with respect to $\varphi(X)$, that is defined for all subsomas of M, and that satisfies the relations

$$\alpha(A)\,\varphi(A) \leqq \psi(A) \leqq \beta(A)\,\varphi(A) \tag{159.1}$$

for all those subsomas A of M for which

$$0 < \varphi(A) < +\infty . \tag{159.2}$$

Here $\alpha(A)$ and $\beta(A)$ denote the infimum and the supremum of f on the soma A.

The measure function $\psi(X)$ is called the integral of f on X for the measure function $\varphi(X)$ and is denoted by

$$\psi(X) = \int_X f\,d\varphi . \tag{159.3}$$

Proof: The fact that the validity of (159.1) is required only for those somas A for which (159.2) holds is of course compatible with the fact that (159.1) remains valid also when the products $\alpha(A)\cdot\varphi(A)$ and $\beta(A)\cdot\varphi(A)$ can still be computed but are equal to $+\infty$. We shall see, however, that consideration of the extreme cases $\varphi(A) = 0$ and $\varphi(A) = +\infty$, which would only make the proof more tedious, is unnecessary.

We denote the subsoma of M on which f equals $+\infty$ (cf. § 78) by M_0. Since $M \dotplus M_0$ is a normal soma of the ring of measurability of $\varphi(X)$ on which the place function f is finite, we can obtain a decomposition

$$M = M_0 + M_1 + M_2 + \cdots \tag{159.4}$$

such that every M_j is φ-measurable and such that, furthermore, the numbers $\varphi(M_j)$ and $\beta(M_j)$ are both finite for $j = 1, 2, \ldots$.

It follows from the uniqueness theorem of § 158 that there exists at most *one* measure function $\psi_j(X)$, defined on the subsomas

$$X \subseteqq M_j \qquad (j = 1, 2, \ldots),$$

that is cometric to $\varphi(X)$ and satisfies the relation (159.1). The argument of § 157, however, ensures the existence of such a function $\psi_j(X)$ and, in addition, its absolute continuity with respect to $\varphi(X)$.

For $X \subseteqq M_0$ likewise, there is at most one soma function $\psi_0(X)$ that has the required properties. Indeed, if $\varphi(X) = 0$, the assumption that $\psi(X)$ is absolutely continuous with respect to $\varphi(X)$ implies that $\psi_0(X) = 0$ (§ 143). However, if $\varphi(X) > 0$, there exists at least one soma $A \subseteqq X$ for which (159.2) holds (since M_0 is a normal soma of the ring of measurability of $\varphi(X)$). In this case, however, $\alpha(A) = +\infty$, and consequently (159.1), in view of $\psi_0(X) \geqq \psi_0(A)$, implies

$$\psi_0(X) = +\infty. \tag{159.5}$$

Thus the function $\psi_0(X)$ is defined uniquely; by Theorem 5 of § 133, $\psi_0(X)$ is a measure function that is also cometric to, and absolutely continuous with respect to $\varphi(X)$.

The somas $M_0, M_1, M_2, \ldots$ are φ-measurable. By hypothesis, they must also belong to the ring of measurability of the integral $\psi(X)$, and a function $\psi(X)$ that satisfies the conditions of our theorem must necessarily be of the form

$$\psi(X) = \psi(M_0 X) + \psi(M_1 X) + \cdots = \psi_0(M_0 X) + \psi_1(M_1 X) + \cdots. \tag{159.6}$$

The function $\psi(X)$ computed in this way, however, has all the required properties: it is a measure function that is cometric to, and absolutely continuous with respect to $\varphi(X)$, and the relation (159.1) is a consequence of the properties of the functions $\psi_0(M_0 X), \psi_1(M_1 X), \ldots$ in conjunction with the equation

$$\varphi(X) = \varphi(M_0 X) + \varphi(M_1 X) + \cdots.$$

Thus we have proved the theorem stated above in its entirety, showing in addition that the measure function $\psi(X)$ is independent of the choice of somas M_j in the decomposition (159.4).

160. We introduce the following definition.

DEFINITION: *A φ-measurable place function $f \geqq 0$ is said to be integrable with respect to $\varphi(X)$, or φ-integrable, on M if M is not only a normal soma of the ring of measurability $\mathfrak{M}_\varphi$ of $\varphi(X)$ but also a normal soma of the ring of measurability $\mathfrak{M}_\psi$ of*

$$\psi(X) = \int_X f \, d\varphi.$$

Thus, in the decomposition (159.4) M_0 must also be a normal soma of $\mathfrak{M}_\psi$. That is, M_0 must be representable as the union of an at most countable number of somas X for which $\psi(X)$ is finite. According to § 159, this is the case if and only if M_0 is a null soma of $\psi(X)$, and hence of $\varphi(X)$. Conversely,

M is a normal soma of $\psi(X)$ if $\varphi(M_0) = 0$. We have thus proved the following theorem.

THEOREM 3: *A φ-measurable place function $f \geqq 0$ is integrable on M if and only if the subsoma M_0 of M on which f equals $+\infty$ is a null soma of $\varphi(X)$.*

161. We now derive an important extension of the Principal Theorem of § 159.

Let $f_1, f_2, \ldots, f_m$ be finite, φ-measurable place functions with common domain of definition M and let

$$\chi(u_1, u_2, \ldots, u_m) \geqq 0 \tag{161.1}$$

be a continuous non-negative function that is defined and finite for all finite values of the u_j. Then

$$g = \chi(f_1, f_2, \ldots, f_m) \tag{161.2}$$

is a non-negative, finite, φ-measurable place function (cf. § 154), and the integral

$$\psi(X) = \int_X g \, d\varphi \tag{161.3}$$

exists, provided $X \subseteqq M$ and M is a normal soma of $\mathfrak{M}_\varphi$.

In the notation of § 111, we then have

$$\psi(\alpha_k(X); \beta_k(X)) \leqq \alpha(X) \leqq \beta(X) \leqq \Psi(\alpha_k(X); \beta_k(X));$$

and since under our present assumptions the left-hand side of this relation is non-negative, by (156.4) we have, for $\varphi(X) > 0$,

$$\psi(\alpha_k(X); \beta_k(X)) \, \varphi(X) \leqq \psi(X) \leqq \Psi(\alpha_k(X); \beta_k(X)) \, \varphi(X). \tag{161.4}$$

But by Theorem 1 of §158, there is at most one measure function $\psi(X)$ for which g is measurable and the relations (161.4) are satisfied for all $X \subseteqq M$ with $\varphi(X) > 0$; and we obtain the following theorem.

THEOREM 4: *Let $f_1, f_2, \ldots, f_m$ be finite, φ-measurable place functions whose common domain of definition M is a normal soma of $\mathfrak{M}_\varphi$. Moreover, let*

$$\chi(u_1, u_2, \ldots, u_m) \geqq 0 \tag{161.5}$$

be continuous and finite in the space of the u_j. Then the place function

$$g = \chi(f_1, f_2, \ldots, f_m) \tag{161.6}$$

is φ-integrable on M, and the integral

$$\psi(X) = \int_X g\, d\varphi \tag{161.7}$$

is the only measure function that is cometric to, and absolutely continuous with respect to $\varphi(X)$ *for which the relations*

$$\boldsymbol{\psi}(\alpha_k(X); \beta_k(X))\, \varphi(X) \leqq \psi(X) \leqq \boldsymbol{\Psi}(\alpha_k(X); \beta_k(X))\, \varphi(X) \tag{161.8}$$

always hold under the hypothesis $0 < \varphi(X) < +\infty$.

162. Let

$$\varphi_1(X),\ \varphi_2(X),\ \ldots \tag{162.1}$$

be a countable number of measure functions with a common domain of definition and for which the somas of a complete ring $\mathfrak{M}$ are measurable. Moreover, let f be a non-negative place function of the field whose fundamental ring is $\mathfrak{M}$ (§ 154).

If, recalling Theorem 3 of § 142, we now form the measure function

$$\varphi(X) = \sum a_j\, \varphi_j(X) \quad (a_j > 0;\ j = 1, 2, \ldots), \tag{162.2}$$

then f is measurable for all the $\varphi_j(X)$ and also for $\varphi(X)$. Let the domain of definition M of f satisfy $\varphi(M) < +\infty$; then the integrals

$$\psi_j(X) = \int_X f\, d\varphi_j\ (j = 1, 2, \ldots),\quad \psi(X) = \int_X f\, d\varphi \tag{162.3}$$

all exist.

We consider the expression

$$\psi^*(X) = \sum_j a_j\, \psi_j(X) \tag{162.4}$$

and note that f is also ψ^*-measurable. But now we see that the relations

$$\left.\begin{aligned} \alpha(X)\, \varphi(X) &\leqq \psi(X) \leqq \beta(X)\, \varphi(X), \\ \alpha(X)\, \varphi(X) &\leqq \psi^*(X) \leqq \beta(X)\, \varphi(X) \end{aligned}\right\} \tag{162.5}$$

all hold for every soma $X \subseteqq M$ for which $\varphi(X) > 0$. Therefore, if f is finite, by the uniqueness theorem of § 158, we must have $\psi(X) = \psi^*(X)$; and hence we obtain the formula

$$\int_X f\, d\varphi = \sum_j a_j \int_X f\, d\varphi_j, \tag{162.6}$$

which can easily be extended by the method of § 159 to non-finite f.

This equation is not so trivial as might appear at first glance, since it is not required that the individual $\psi_j(X)$ of the sequence (162.3) be cometric to $\varphi(X)$.

§§ 163-166. Linearity of the Integral and the Integration of Place Functions of Arbitrary Sign

163. We apply Theorem 4 of § 161 to the function

$$\chi(u_1, u_2) = \max\big((a\, u_1 + b\, u_2), 0\big),$$

where a and b are arbitrary positive numbers and where $f_1 \geqq 0$ and $f_2 \geqq 0$; and we obtain the formula

$$\big(a\,\alpha_1(X) + b\,\alpha_2(X)\big)\,\varphi(X) \leqq \int_X (a\,f_1 + b\,f_2)\,d\varphi \leqq$$

$$\leqq \big(a\,\beta_1(X) + b\,\beta_2(X)\big)\,\varphi(X)\,. \quad (163.1)$$

If we now put

$$\psi(X) = a\int_X f_1\,d\varphi + b\int_X f_2\,d\varphi\,, \quad (163.2)$$

then for all $X \subseteqq M$ for which $0 < \varphi(X) < +\infty$, we have

$$\big(a\,\alpha_1(X) + b\,\alpha_2(X)\big)\,\varphi(X) \leqq \psi(X) \leqq \big(a\,\beta_1(X) + b\,\beta_2(X)\big)\,\varphi(X)\,. \quad (163.3)$$

Hence, by the uniqueness theorem of § 158, we have

$$\int_X (a\,f_1 + b\,f_2)\,d\varphi = a\int_X f_1\,d\varphi + b\int_X f_2\,d\varphi\,, \quad (163.4)$$

at least under the assumption that f_1 and f_2 denote finite, non-negative place functions. This result can easily be extended to arbitrary non-negative place functions and yields the following theorem.

THEOREM 1: *If f_1 and f_2 are non-negative, φ-measurable place functions defined on a normal soma M of the ring of measurability of $\varphi(X)$, and if a and b denote positive real numbers, the equation*

$$\int_X (a\,f_1 + b\,f_2)\,d\varphi = a\int_X f_1\,d\varphi + b\int_X f_2\,d\varphi \quad (163.5)$$

holds for all somas $X \subseteqq M$.

164. We shall now compare the two measure functions

$$\psi_1(X) = \int_X f_1\,d\varphi\,, \quad \psi_2(X) = \int_X f_2\,d\varphi\,. \quad (164.1)$$

We first make the assumption that the three numbers $\varphi(M)$, $\psi_1(M)$, and $\psi_2(M)$ are finite for the common domain of definition M of the non-negative place functions f_1 and f_2. If, in addition, we take the place functions f_1 and f_2 to be finite, then the place functions

$$f = f_1 - f_2, \quad p_1 = \max(0, f), \quad p_2 = \max(0, -f) \tag{164.2}$$

are defined and φ-measurable and, by § 100, satisfy the relations

$$p_1 \leqq f_1, \quad p_2 \leqq f_2, \quad f_1 - f_2 = p_1 - p_2. \tag{164.3}$$

Then the place function $r = f_1 - p_1$ also exists and is non-negative; moreover, we have the equalities

$$f_1 = p_1 + r, \quad f_2 = p_2 + r. \tag{164.4}$$

Thus, if we put

$$\pi_1(X) = \int_X p_1\, d\varphi, \quad \pi_2(X) = \int_X p_2\, d\varphi, \quad \varrho(X) = \int_X r\, d\varphi, \tag{164.5}$$

the equations

$$\psi_1(X) = \pi_1(X) + \varrho(X), \quad \psi_2(X) = \pi_2(X) + \varrho(X) \quad (X \subseteqq M) \tag{164.6}$$

are valid, by Theorem 1 above, and also, since

$$\varrho(X) \leqq \psi_1(X) \leqq \psi_1(M) < +\infty,$$

we have

$$\psi_1(X) - \psi_2(X) = \pi_1(X) - \pi_2(X). \tag{164.7}$$

165. Next, let $[S_0(y)]$ be the lower nest of somas of the place function f; then the two somas

$$M' = S_0(0), \quad M'' = M \dotplus M' \tag{165.1}$$

are measurable for $\varphi(X)$ and hence for $\psi_1(X)$ and $\psi_2(X)$ as well. Moreover, p_1 agrees with the constant zero on M' and p_2 agrees with the constant zero on M'', so that we can write

$$\pi_1(M') = 0, \quad \pi_2(M'') = 0. \tag{165.2}$$

By (164.7), for every soma $X \subseteqq M$, we have

$$\psi_2(XM') \geqq \psi_1(XM'), \quad \psi_2(XM'') \leqq \psi_1(XM''). \tag{165.3}$$

Interchanging the rôles of M' and M'', we introduce the following definition.

DEFINITION: *We say that we have a Jordan decomposition*

$$M = M' + M'' \tag{165.4}$$

of a soma M with respect to the pair of measure functions $\psi_1(X)$ *and* $\psi_2(X)$ *whenever the somas* M' *and* M'' *are both measurable for these two measure functions, and the inequalities*

$$\psi_1(XM') \geqq \psi_2(XM'), \quad \psi_1(XM'') \leqq \psi_2(XM'') \tag{165.5}$$

hold for every subsoma X of M.

From our last result, we then easily obtain the following theorem.

THEOREM 2: *If* f_1 *and* f_2 *are non-negative place functions that are integrable on a normal soma M of the ring of measurability of* $\varphi(X)$, *then for the integrals*

$$\psi_1(X) = \int_X f_1\, d\varphi, \quad \psi_2(X) = \int_X f_2\, d\varphi \tag{165.6}$$

there always exists a Jordan decomposition of M with respect to $\psi_1(X)$ *and* $\psi_2(X)$.

Proof: Indeed, if f_1 and f_2 are finite place functions and $\varphi(M)$, $\psi_1(M)$, and $\psi_2(M)$ are finite numbers, the existence of the Jordan decomposition called for by the theorem is assured by the relations (165.3). Now we can find a decomposition

$$M = N + M_1 + M_2 + \cdots \tag{165.7}$$

of M such that on each of the somas M_j both f_1 and f_2 are bounded and $\varphi(M_j)$, $\psi_1(M_j)$, and $\psi_2(M_j)$ are all finite, while N represents that soma of φ-measure zero on which $f_1 + f_2$ is the constant infinity. Then each of the M_j has a Jordan decomposition

$$M_j = M_j' + M_j'', \tag{165.8}$$

and we obtain a Jordan decomposition of M by means of the equations

$$M' = \sum_j M_j', \quad M'' = N + \sum_j M_j''. \tag{165.9}$$

This proves the theorem in its full generality.

The equations (165.1) and (165.2) show, incidentally, that each of the measure functions $\pi_1(X)$ and $\pi_2(X)$ that were considered in § 164 is singular (§ 143) with respect to the other.

166. The formulas of § 164 allow us to define the integral of place functions f of arbitrary sign. For, any place function f can be represented as the difference

$$f = p_1 - p_2 \tag{166.1}$$

of the non-negative place functions $p_1 = \max(0, f)$ and $p_2 = \max(0, -f)$. If f is φ-measurable, i.e., if the somas $S_0(y)$ of the lower nests of somas of f all belong to the ring of measurability of $\varphi(X)$, then p_1 and p_2 are likewise φ-measurable, and the measure functions $\pi_1(X)$ and $\pi_2(X)$ of (164.5) exist. We now write, as our definition,

$$\int_X f\,d\varphi = \int_X p_1\,d\varphi - \int_X p_2\,d\varphi = \pi_1(X) - \pi_2(X), \tag{166.2}$$

provided that the right-hand side of (166.2) is meaningful, i.e., that not both $\pi_1(X)$ and $\pi_2(X)$ are infinite. We say, in this case, that $\int_X f\,d\varphi$ *exists.* Moreover,

$$|f| = p_1 + p_2, \tag{166.3}$$

by § 101, and therefore we can write

$$\int_X |f|\,d\varphi = \pi_1(X) + \pi_2(X). \tag{166.4}$$

Hence, we always have the relation

$$\left|\int_X f\,d\varphi\right| \leq \int_X |f|\,d\varphi. \tag{166.5}$$

We shall say that f is *integrable* on M if $\int_X f\,d\varphi$ exists and $|f|$ is integrable on M (§ 160). For place functions that assume the values $\pm\infty$ only on null somas, not only do all the formulas of the present section remain meaningful and valid but the relation (159.1) also continues to hold.

On the other hand, Theorem 1 of § 163 no longer holds in general for finite integrable place functions of arbitrary sign, as the following example shows:

$$a = b = 1\,; \quad f_1 = \begin{cases} \dfrac{1}{x} \text{ for } x \neq 0 \\ 0 \text{ for } x = 0 \end{cases}; \quad f_2 = -f_1.$$

Here we have

$$\int_0^1 (f_1 + f_2)\,dx = 0, \quad \int_0^1 f_1\,dx = +\infty, \quad \int_0^1 f_2\,dx = -\infty,$$

and the right-hand side of (163.5) becomes meaningless.

§§ 167-172. Comparable Measure Functions and the Lebesgue Decomposition

167. If the two non-negative place functions f_1 and f_2 are φ-integrable on M, and if we write

$$\psi_1(X) = \int_X f_1\, d\varphi, \quad \psi_2(X) = \int_X f_2\, d\varphi, \tag{167.1}$$

then, for every positive number y, the two measure functions

$$y\,\psi_1(X), \quad \psi_2(X) \qquad (y > 0) \tag{167.2}$$

must, by § 165, admit a Jordan decomposition, since yf_1 is also integrable on M.

We introduce the following definition.

DEFINITION: *We say of two measure functions $\psi_1(X)$ and $\psi_2(X)$ whose common domain of definition M is a normal soma of each of their rings of measurability, and only of two such functions, that they are comparable if, for every finite positive y, the two measure functions $y\psi_1(X)$ and $\psi_2(X)$ admit a Jordan decomposition of the soma M.*

Note that the lack of symmetry in $\psi_1(X)$ and $\psi_2(X)$ in this definition is only apparent.

Any two given measure functions need not necessarily be comparable. For example, a Jordan decomposition of $M = A + B + C$ is not possible if we take

$$\left.\begin{aligned} &\psi_1(A) = \psi_1(B) = \psi_1(C) = \psi_1(B + C) = 1, \\ &\psi_1(C + A) = \psi_1(A + B) = \psi_1(A + B + C) = 2, \end{aligned}\right\} \tag{167.3}$$

$$\left.\begin{aligned} &\psi_2(A) = \psi_2(B) = \psi_2(C) = \frac{5}{6}, \\ &\psi_2(B + C) = \psi_2(C + A) = \psi_2(A + B) = \frac{5}{3}, \\ &\psi_2(A + B + C) = \frac{5}{2}. \end{aligned}\right\} \tag{167.4}$$

For in this case, we have

$$\psi_1(X) > \psi_2(X) \quad \text{on} \quad A, B, C, C + A, A + B,$$

$$\psi_2(X) > \psi_1(X) \quad \text{on} \quad B + C, A + B + C.$$

168. Our goal is to show that two comparable measure functions can always be written in the form (167.1).

To this end, we consider two measure functions $\psi_1(X)$ and $\psi_2(X)$ with common domain of definition M, concerning which we make, in the first instance, the following suppositions: First of all,

$$0 < \psi_1(M) < +\infty, \quad 0 < \psi_2(M) < +\infty, \tag{168.1}$$

and second, if $y_1, y_2, \ldots$ denote countably many real numbers that are dense on the positive real axis, the measure functions $y_k\psi_1(X)$ and $\psi_2(X)$ admit a Jordan decomposition. By this supposition, there are decompositions

$$M = M_k' + M_k'' \qquad (k = 1, 2, \ldots) \tag{168.2}$$

of the soma M such that the relations

$$y_k\,\psi_1(XM_k') - \psi_2(XM_k') \geqq 0, \tag{168.3}$$

$$y_k\,\psi_1(XM_k'') - \psi_2(XM_k'') \leqq 0 \tag{168.4}$$

hold for every soma $X \subseteqq M$, and such that the somas M_k' and M_k'' are measurable both for $\psi_1(X)$ and for $\psi_2(X)$.

To each of the numbers $y > 0$ we assign those indices $k = p_j$ $(j = 1, 2, \ldots)$ for which the inequality $y_{p_j} < y$ is satisfied, and we put

$$\left.\begin{aligned} S(y) &= O \qquad && (y \leqq 0), \\ S(y) &= \sum_j \dot{+}\, M_{p_j}' \qquad && (y > 0). \end{aligned}\right\} \tag{168.5}$$

In this way, we obtain the lower nest of somas of a non-negative place function which we shall denote by g_2 and which is measurable both for $\psi_1(X)$ and $\psi_2(X)$. By (168.4), moreover, $y_k\psi_1(M) \leqq \psi_2(M)$ if M_k' is empty; thus if n is a positive integer satisfying

$$n\,\psi_1(M) > \psi_2(M),$$

the soma $S(n)$ cannot be empty. Let A be any non-empty subsoma of $S(n)$. In any event, then, the supremum $\beta(A)$ of g_2 is less than or equal to n, since $A \subseteqq S(n)$. In (168.5), choose $y > \beta(A)$; by Theorem 3 of § 137, the soma A, which is a subsoma of $S(y)$, can be represented as a sum

$$A = A_1 + A_2 + \cdots$$

of somas A_j for which we have

$$\psi_1(A) = \sum_j \psi_1(A_j), \quad \psi_2(A) = \sum_j \psi_2(A_j), \quad A_j \subseteqq M_{p_j}' \quad (j = 1, 2, \ldots). \tag{168.6}$$

From (168.3) we then obtain

$$y_{p_j}\,\varphi_1(A_j M'_{p_j}) - \varphi_2(A_j M'_{p_j}) \geqq 0,$$

whence we conclude, since $y > y_{p_j}$, that

$$y\,\varphi_1(A_j) \geqq \varphi_2(A_j) \qquad (j = 1, 2, \ldots).$$

Then by (168.6) we also have $\varphi_2(A) \leqq y\varphi_1(A)$, and since this relation holds for all $y > \beta(A)$, we have, finally,

$$\varphi_2(A) \leqq \beta(A)\,\varphi_1(A). \tag{168.7}$$

On the other hand, if the infimum $\alpha(A)$ of g_2 is positive and we put

$$y = \alpha(A)$$

in (168.5), the soma A must be disjoint from M'_{p_j} for each p_j; we have then $A \subseteqq M''_{p_j}$ and, by (168.4),

$$y_{p_j}\,\varphi_1(A) \leqq \varphi_2(A);$$

and finally

$$\alpha(A)\,\varphi_1(A) \leqq \varphi_2(A), \tag{168.8}$$

which is a relation that holds even in the excluded case $\alpha(A) = 0$.

169. We now put

$$M_0 = \lim_{n=\infty} S(n), \tag{169.1}$$

and by Theorem 5 of § 138 we find, taking (168.1) into account, that

$$\lim_{n=\infty} \varphi_1\left(M_0 \dotplus S(n)\right) = 0, \quad \lim_{n=\infty} \varphi_2\left(M_0 \dotplus S(n)\right) = 0, \tag{169.2}$$

since the somas $S(n)$ are both φ_1-measurable and φ_2-measurable. Then, if X is any subsoma of M_0 and if we put

$$X_n = X\,S(n), \tag{169.3}$$

it follows that

$$\lim_{n=\infty} \varphi_1(X_n) = \varphi_1(X), \quad \lim_{n=\infty} \varphi_2(X_n) = \varphi_2(X). \tag{169.4}$$

On the other hand, it follows from (168.8) and (168.7) that

$$\alpha(X)\,\varphi_1(X_n) \leqq \alpha(X_n)\,\varphi_1(X_n) \leqq \varphi_2(X_n) \leqq \beta(X_n)\,\varphi_1(X_n) \leqq \beta(X)\,\varphi_1(X_n),$$

so that, by passage to the limit, we obtain

$$\alpha(X)\,\psi_1(X) \leqq \psi_2(X) \leqq \beta(X)\,\psi_1(X) \quad (X \subseteqq M_0). \quad (169.5)$$

By the uniqueness theorem of § 158, there is at most one measure function for which g_2 is measurable and which satisfies the relations (169.5). The integral of g_2 on X with respect to the measure function $\psi_1(X)$, however, is such a measure function, and hence we have the equation

$$\psi_2(X) = \int_X g_2\, d\psi_1 \qquad (X \subseteqq M_0). \quad (169.6)$$

We now examine the soma

$$N_1 = M \dotplus M_0 = \prod_k M_k'' \qquad (169.7)$$

and remark that we must have

$$N_1 \subseteqq M_k'' \qquad (k = 1, 2, \ldots).$$

Hence, by (168.4),

$$\psi_1(N_1) \leqq \frac{\psi_2(N_1)}{y_k} \leqq \frac{\psi_2(M)}{y_k} \qquad (k = 1, 2, \ldots),$$

and from this it follows that

$$\psi_1(N_1) = 0. \qquad (169.8)$$

The equality (169.6) can thus be written

$$\psi_2(X \dotplus N_1 X) = \int_{X \dotplus N_1 X} g_2\, d\psi_1 = \int_X g_2\, d\psi_1 \qquad (X \subseteqq M), \quad (169.9)$$

where X stands for any subsoma of M; and since, by (169.7), N_1 is ψ_2-measurable, it follows from this that

$$\psi_2(X) = \int_X g_2\, d\psi_1 + \psi_2(N_1 X) \qquad (X \subseteqq M). \quad (169.10)$$

This result was proved under the assumption that $\psi_1(M)$ and $\psi_2(M)$ are finite numbers. It can be extended without any difficulty to the case that M is a normal soma of the rings of measurability of $\psi_1(X)$ and $\psi_2(X)$.

170. We introduce the following definition.

Definition: *If $\psi_1(X)$ and $\psi_2(X)$ are measure functions whose common domain of definition M is a normal soma of their rings of measurability, we say that $\psi_2(X)$ admits a Lebesgue decomposition with respect to $\psi_1(X)$ if, for all $X \subseteqq M$ and for a fixed soma N_1, we can write*

$$\psi_2(X) = \omega_2(X) + \psi_2(N_1 X), \quad \omega_2(X) = \int_X g_2\, d\psi_1, \quad \psi_1(N_1) = 0. \quad (170.1)$$

The name "Lebesgue decomposition" is appropriate because Lebesgue was the first to establish a formula of this kind, which he did in the theory of monotone functions of a single variable.[1]

It should be noted that $\omega_2(X)$ is absolutely continuous and $\psi_2(N_1X)$ is singular with respect to $\psi_1(X)$. Now since $\psi_2(X)$ is finite, there is no other representation

$$\psi_2(X) = \Omega(X) + \Psi(X) \tag{170.2}$$

in which $\Omega(X)$ denotes a measure function absolutely continuous with respect to $\psi_1(X)$ and $\Psi(X)$ denotes a non-negative soma function singular with respect to $\psi_1(X)$. Indeed, from these assumptions, we see first

$$0 \leqq \Omega(X) \leqq \psi_2(X), \quad 0 \leqq \Psi(X) \leqq \psi_2(X) \quad (X \subseteqq M). \tag{170.3}$$

We then have

$$\left.\begin{aligned} &\Omega(N_1X) = 0, \quad \Omega(X \dotplus N_1X) \leqq \psi_2(X \dotplus N_1X), \\ &\Omega(X) \leqq \Omega(N_1X) + \Omega(X \dotplus N_1X) \leqq \psi_2(X \dotplus N_1X), \end{aligned}\right\} \tag{170.4}$$

and so, finally,

$$\Omega(X) \leqq \omega_2(X). \tag{170.5}$$

On the other hand, there are always by assumption (§ 143) somas N_X of ψ_1-measure zero for which

$$\Psi(X) = \Psi(N_X X) \leqq \psi_2(N_X X);$$

since we can then write

$$\psi_2(N_X X) = \omega_2(N_X X) + \psi_2(N_1 N_X X) = \psi_2(N_X N_1 X) \leqq \psi_2(N_1 X),$$

we have

$$\Psi(X) \leqq \psi_2(N_1X). \tag{170.6}$$

Finally, by (170.1) through (170.6), we have the equations

$$\Omega(X) = \omega_2(X), \quad \Psi(X) = \psi_2(N_1X), \tag{170.7}$$

which express the uniqueness of the decomposition (170.1).

We can now formulate the result of §§ 168 and 169 in the following way:

Two comparable measure functions each admit a Lebesgue decomposition with respect to the other.

171. It was shown in § 167 that the measure functions (167.1) are comparable. By using the fact that comparable measure functions admit a

[1] Cf. § 284, and in particular, footnote 8 in that section.

Lebesgue decomposition, we can obtain the converse of this result. Indeed, if $\psi_1(X)$ and $\psi_2(X)$ are two measure functions for which the relations (170.1) hold, we define the measure function $\varphi(X)$ by the formula

$$\varphi(X) = \psi_1(X) + \psi_2(N_1 X); \tag{171.1}$$

further, let f_1 and f_2 denote the place functions

$$\left. \begin{array}{ll} f_1 = 0 \text{ on } N_1, & f_1 = 1 \text{ on } M \dotplus N_1, \\ f_2 = 1 \text{ on } N_1, & f_2 = g_2 \text{ on } M \dotplus N_1. \end{array} \right\} \tag{171.2}$$

We then obtain

$$\psi_1(X) = \psi_1(X \dotplus N_1 X) = \varphi(X \dotplus N_1 X) = \int_X f_1 \, d\varphi. \tag{171.3}$$

By (170.1), on the other hand,

$$\psi_2(X \dotplus N_1 X) = \int_{X \dotplus N_1 X} g_2 \, d\psi_1 = \int_{X \dotplus N_1 X} f_2 \, d\varphi, \quad \psi_2(N_1 X) = \varphi(N_1 X) = \int_{N_1 X} f_2 \, d\varphi,$$

so that we can write

$$\psi_2(X) = \int_X f_2 \, d\varphi. \tag{171.4}$$

We can sum up all of this, as follows:

THEOREM 1: *Two measure functions $\psi_1(X)$ and $\psi_2(X)$ are comparable if and only if either*

a) *at least one of these functions admits a Lebesgue decomposition with respect to the other; or*

b) *there exist at least one measure function $\varphi(X)$ and at least one pair of place functions f_1 and f_2 that satisfy the two equations*

$$\psi_1(X) = \int_X f_1 \, d\varphi, \quad \psi_2(X) = \int_X f_2 \, d\varphi \tag{171.5}$$

As a special case of this theorem, we have the following theorem, which characterizes all the measure functions $\psi(X)$ that have representations as integrals.

THEOREM 2 (The Second Principal Theorem of Integration; The Theorem of Nikodym[2]); *A measure function $\psi(X)$ can be written in the form*

$$\psi(X) = \int_X f \, d\varphi$$

[2] O. Nikodym, *Fund. Math.*, Vol. 15 (1930), p. 168.

if and only if $\psi(X)$ is comparable with, and absolutely continuous with respect to $\varphi(X)$.

172. If the two measure functions $\psi_1(X)$ and $\psi_2(X)$ are comparable, then by § 170, we have the equations

$$\psi_2(X) = \omega_2(X) + \psi_2(N_1 X), \quad \omega_2(X) = \int_X g_2 \, d\psi_1, \quad \psi_1(N_1) = 0, \tag{172.1}$$

$$\psi_1(X) = \omega_1(X) + \psi_1(N_2 X), \quad \omega_1(X) = \int_X g_1 \, d\psi_2, \quad \psi_2(N_2) = 0. \tag{172.2}$$

For every soma Y that is disjoint from N_2, we have $\psi_1(N_2 Y) = 0$; and by the first equation of (172.2),

$$\psi_1(Y) = \omega_1(Y), \text{ so that } \psi_1(X \dot{+} N_2 X) = \omega_1(X \dot{+} N_2 X).$$

Therefore, by the second equation of (172.1), we have

$$\omega_2(X \dot{+} N_2 X) = \int_{X \dot{+} N_2 X} g_2 \, d\psi_1 = \int_{X \dot{+} N_2 X} g_2 \, d\omega_1. \tag{172.3}$$

On the other hand,

$$\omega_2(N_2 X) \leqq \psi_2(N_2 X) \leqq \psi_2(N_2) = 0.$$

But we also have $\omega_1(N_2 X) = 0$, since by the second equation of (172.2), $\omega_1(X)$ is absolutely continuous with respect to $\psi_2(X)$.

Consequently, both sides of the equation

$$\omega_2(N_2 X) = \int_{N_2 X} g_2 \, d\omega_1$$

vanish, so that the addition of this equation to (172.3) yields the relation

$$\omega_2(X) = \int_X g_2 \, d\omega_1. \qquad (X \subseteqq M) \tag{172.4}$$

We prove the equation

$$\omega_1(X) = \int_X g_1 \, d\omega_2 \tag{172.5}$$

in the same way.

Thus, each of the measure functions $\omega_1(X)$ and $\omega_2(X)$ is absolutely continuous with respect to the other, and each is cometric to the other.

By way of contrast, neither of the functions $\psi_1(X)$ and $\psi_2(X)$ need be absolutely continuous nor cometric with respect to the other. For obviously, it can happen that $\psi_2(N_1) > 0$ and $\psi_1(N_2) > 0$ and that for some soma Y the soma $N_1 Y$ is not ψ_2-measurable and the soma $N_2 Y$ not ψ_1-measurable.

Furthermore, two measure functions $\psi_2(X)$ and $\psi_3(X)$ need not be comparable even if each of them is comparable with a third function $\psi_1(X)$. For example, it may well happen that the measure functions under consideration are of the form $\psi_2(X) = \psi_2(NX)$ and $\psi_3(X) = \psi_3(NX)$, where N is a soma of ψ_1-measure zero and the functions $\psi_2(X)$ and $\psi_3(X)$ admit no Jordan decomposition.

§§ 173-175. Abstract Differentials

173. On a normal soma M of the ring of measurability of a measure function $\varphi(X)$, consider two φ-measurable, bounded, non-negative place functions f_1 and f_2 and also their comparable integrals

$$\psi_1(X) = \int_X f_1\, d\varphi, \quad \psi_2(X) = \int_X f_2\, d\varphi. \tag{173.1}$$

The relations

$$\alpha_1(X)\, \varphi(X) \leqq \psi_1(X) \leqq \beta_1(X)\, \varphi(X) \quad (\varphi(X) < +\infty), \tag{173.2}$$

which follow from the first equation of (173.1), show, since $\beta_1(X)$ is bounded, that M is also a normal soma of the ring of measurability of $\psi_1(X)$. Thus the integral

$$\psi(X) = \int_X f_2\, d\psi_1 \tag{173.3}$$

exists and satisfies the relations

$$\alpha_2(X)\, \psi_1(X) \leqq \psi(X) \leqq \beta_2(X)\, \psi_1(X) \quad (\psi_1(X) < +\infty). \tag{173.4}$$

A comparison of (173.2) with (173.4) yields the relations

$$\alpha_1(X)\, \alpha_2(X)\, \varphi(X) \leqq \psi(X) \leqq \beta_1(X)\, \beta_2(X)\, \varphi(X) \quad (\varphi(X) < +\infty). \tag{173.5}$$

On the other hand, it follows from Theorem 6 of § 105 and Theorem 4 of § 161 that these last relations imply the equation

$$\psi(X) = \int_X f_1 f_2\, d\varphi, \tag{173.6}$$

and this equation remains valid, as the frequently used decomposition

$$M = M_0 + M_1 + M_2 + \cdots$$

shows, even if we require the place functions f_1 and f_2 no longer to be bounded, but merely to be integrable. We need only extend the definition of the product $f_1 f_2$ to those null somas on which one factor of this product is zero and the other $+\infty$, and we can do this in any way — say, by taking it equal to $+\infty$. We thus obtain the following theorem.

THEOREM 1: *Let the integrals*

$$\psi_1(X) = \int_X f_1\, d\varphi, \quad \psi_2(X) = \int_X f_2\, d\varphi \tag{173.7}$$

be given on a normal soma M of the ring of measurability of a measure function $\varphi(X)$, where the place functions f_1 and f_2 are assumed to be integrable and non-negative. Then we have the equations

$$\int_X f_1 f_2\, d\varphi = \int_X f_2\, d\psi_1 = \int_X f_1\, d\psi_2 \qquad (X \subseteqq M). \tag{173.8}$$

174. Second, under hypotheses similar to those of § 173, we consider a place function f that satisfies

$$0 < f < +\infty. \tag{174.1}$$

Then, if f is a φ-measurable finite place function, so is $1/f$ (cf. § 106).

If we put

$$\psi(X) = \int_X f\, d\varphi \tag{174.2}$$

on every soma X on which f and $1/f$ are bounded and for which in addition $0 < \varphi(X) < +\infty$, we have not only

$$\alpha(X)\, \varphi(X) \leqq \psi(X) \leqq \beta(X)\, \varphi(X), \tag{174.3}$$

but also

$$\frac{1}{\beta(X)}\, \psi(X) \leqq \varphi(X) \leqq \frac{1}{\alpha(X)}\, \psi(X). \tag{174.4}$$

By § 106, however, $1/\beta(X)$ is the infimum and $1/\alpha(X)$ the supremum of $1/f$, so that we can write

$$\varphi(X) = \int_X \frac{1}{f}\, d\psi. \tag{174.5}$$

We have thus proved the following theorem.

THEOREM 2: *Let the φ-measurable place function f be finite and positive. Then each of the equations*

$$\psi(X) = \int_X f\, d\varphi, \quad \varphi(X) = \int_X \frac{1}{f}\, d\psi \tag{174.6}$$

implies the other.

175. The last two theorems enable us to show that the ordinary notation for the integral is quite appropriate even for the generalized integrals which we here consider. For, from the definition of the integral (§ 159), we have the equation

$$\varphi(X) = \int_X d\varphi. \tag{175.1}$$

Consequently, the first equation of (174.6) can be written

$$\int_X d\psi = \int_X f\, d\varphi \qquad (X \subseteqq M), \tag{175.2}$$

or, more briefly,

$$d\psi = f\, d\varphi. \tag{175.3}$$

The last theorems then indicate that we can carry out formal computations upon these *abstract differentials.* For example, the equations $d\psi = f_2 d\psi_1$ and $d\psi_1 = f_1 d\varphi$ imply the equation $d\psi = f_1 f_2 d\varphi$. Similarly, the content of Theorem 2 above is that each of the equations

$$d\psi = f\, d\varphi, \quad d\varphi = \frac{1}{f}\, d\psi \tag{175.4}$$

implies the other, assuming that f and $1/f$ are finite positive place functions.

Using these last two results together, we can obtain most of the formulas that are used in ordinary differential calculus. However, the quotient of two differentials has no meaning here. To carry out a differentiation, i.e., to determine the place function f given the two measure functions $\varphi(X)$ and $\psi(X) = \int_X f\, d\varphi$ we must use the construction explained in §§ 168 ff.

§§ 176-177. The Absolute Continuity of Two Comparable Measure Functions

176. Let $\psi_1(X)$ and $\psi_2(X)$ be two comparable measure functions that are defined for all $X \subseteqq M$ and that satisfy

$$\psi_2(M) < +\infty. \tag{176.1}$$

If $\psi_2(X)$ is absolutely continuous with respect to $\psi_1(X)$, we can write (Theorem 2 of § 171)

$$\psi_2(X) = \int_X g_2\, d\psi_1. \tag{176.2}$$

The lower nest of somas $[S(y)]$ of g_2 then satisfies

$$\lim_{y=\infty} \psi_2(S(y)) = \psi_2(M). \tag{176.3}$$

Given a positive number ε, we can accordingly choose a positive integer n such that

$$\psi_2(M \dotplus S(n)) \leqq \frac{\varepsilon}{2}. \tag{176.4}$$

However, the supremum $\beta(X)$ of g_2 on every subsoma X of $S(n)$ is less than or equal to n, so that we can write

$$\psi_2(X) \leqq n\,\psi_1(X) \qquad (X \subseteqq S(n)). \tag{176.5}$$

We now consider an arbitrary soma X for which

$$\psi_1(X) \leqq \frac{\varepsilon}{2n} = \delta(\varepsilon), \tag{176.6}$$

and we put

$$X = X_1 + X_2, \quad X_1 = S(n)\,X, \quad X_2 = (M \dotplus S(n))\,X. \tag{176.7}$$

We obtain

$$\psi_2(X_1) \leqq n\,\psi_1(X) \leqq \frac{\varepsilon}{2}, \quad \psi_2(X_2) \leqq \psi_2(M \dotplus S(n)) \leqq \frac{\varepsilon}{2}, \tag{176.8}$$

and consequently

$$\psi_2(X) = \psi_2(X_1) + \psi_2(X_2) \leqq \varepsilon. \tag{176.9}$$

Comparable measure functions thus enjoy the following refinement of the property of absolute continuity:

THEOREM 1: *If $\psi_1(X)$ and $\psi_2(X)$ are comparable measure functions, if $\psi_2(M)$ is finite, and if $\psi_2(X)$ is absolutely continuous with respect to $\psi_1(X)$, then we can assign to each positive number ε, a positive number $\delta(\varepsilon)$ such that $\psi_2(X) \leqq \varepsilon$ whenever $\psi_1(X) < \delta(\varepsilon)$.*

177. If we put

$$\varepsilon = \sup(\psi_2(X);\ \psi_1(X) < \delta), \tag{177.1}$$

we obtain a monotonically increasing function $\varepsilon(\delta)$ whose inverse $\delta(\varepsilon)$ satisfies Theorem 1, above. We have, moreover,

$$\lim_{\delta=0} \varepsilon(\delta) = 0, \tag{177.2}$$

from which it follows that the function $\varepsilon(\delta)$ is continuous at the point $\delta = 0$.

It can be proved for certain special measure functions $\psi_1(X)$ that $\varepsilon(\delta)$ is even continuous for $\delta > 0$. We assume that there can be assigned to every soma X that satisfies

$$\psi_1(X) < \delta_1 + \delta_2 \tag{177.3}$$

two somas Y and Z that satisfy the relations

$$X = Y + Z, \quad \psi_1(Y) < \delta_1, \quad \psi_1(Z) < \delta_2. \tag{177.4}$$

This is a property that is enjoyed, in particular, by the ordinary Lebesgue content (§§ 148 ff.). From (177.4) it follows that, for all X that satisfy (177.3),

$$\psi_2(X) \leqq \psi_2(Y) + \psi_2(Z) \leqq \varepsilon(\delta_1) + \varepsilon(\delta_2);$$

and therefore we have also

$$\varepsilon(\delta_1 + \delta_2) \leqq \varepsilon(\delta_1) + \varepsilon(\delta_2) \tag{177.5}$$

Thus, if h is any positive number $< \delta$, we can write

$$\varepsilon(\delta + h) \leqq \varepsilon(\delta) + \varepsilon(h), \quad \varepsilon(\delta) \leqq \varepsilon(\delta - h) + \varepsilon(h), \tag{177.6}$$

and from this relation, in conjunction with $\lim_{h=0} \varepsilon(h) = 0$, it follows that

$$\varepsilon(\delta + 0) \leqq \varepsilon(\delta) \leqq \varepsilon(\delta - 0), \tag{177.7}$$

which is a relation that implies the continuity of $\varepsilon(\delta)$.

§§ 178-180. Transformation of the Integral by Means of Homomorphisms

178. We consider a homomorphism

$$X' = \sigma X \tag{178.1}$$

that carries the complete ring $\mathfrak{A}$ into $\mathfrak{A}'$ and carries the complete $\mathfrak{A}$-hereditary ring $\mathfrak{N}$ into the empty soma O' (cf. §§ 57 and 58).

Let the measure function $\varphi(X)$ be defined on $\mathfrak{A}$, and let the integral

$$\psi(X) = \int_X f \, d\varphi \tag{178.2}$$

be defined for all somas $X \subseteqq M$. We assume first that $M' = \sigma M$ is non-empty, that $\varphi(M) < +\infty$, and that the place function f is bounded and non-negative on M. By §§ 118 ff., the homomorphism transforms the function f into a place function $f' = \sigma f$, and by § 144, the measure functions $\varphi(X)$ and $\psi(X)$ are transformed into $\varphi'(X')$ and $\psi'(X')$, respectively.

By Theorem 1 of § 144, the rings of measurability $\mathfrak{M}_\varphi$, $\mathfrak{M}_\psi$, $\mathfrak{M}'_{\varphi'}$ and $\mathfrak{M}'_{\psi'}$ of these measure functions are connected by the relations

$$\sigma \mathfrak{M}_\varphi \prec \mathfrak{M}'_{\varphi'}, \quad \sigma \mathfrak{M}_\psi \prec \mathfrak{M}'_{\psi'}, \tag{178.3}$$

and we have in addition

$$\mathfrak{M}_\varphi < \mathfrak{M}_\psi, \quad \sigma\mathfrak{M}_\varphi < \sigma\mathfrak{M}_\psi < \mathfrak{M}'_{\psi'}. \tag{178.4}$$

Now if $[S(y)]$ is a nest of somas of f consisting entirely of somas of $\mathfrak{M}_\varphi$, every soma of the nest of somas must belong both to $\mathfrak{M}'_{\varphi'}$ and to $\mathfrak{M}'_{\psi'}$. The place function $f' = \sigma f$ is thus measurable both for $\varphi'(X')$ and $\psi'(X')$.

If next we take any positive number ε and any non-empty soma

$$X' \subseteqq M' = \sigma M,$$

we can determine (cf. § 144) two somas X_1 and X_2 of $\mathfrak{A}$ for which we have

$$\sigma X_1 = \sigma X_2 = X', \tag{178.5}$$

$$\varphi'(X') \leqq \varphi(X_1) \leqq \varphi'(X') + \varepsilon, \tag{178.6}$$

$$\psi'(X') \leqq \psi(X_2) \leqq \psi'(X') + \varepsilon. \tag{178.7}$$

Moreover, by Theorem 2 of § 120, there exists a soma X_3 for which

$$\sigma X_3 = X', \quad \alpha'(X') = \alpha(X_3), \quad \beta'(X') = \beta(X_3) \tag{178.8}$$

holds. Hence, if we put

$$Y = X_1 X_2 X_3, \tag{178.9}$$

then $\sigma Y = X'$, so that Y is not the empty soma; moreover, taking into account the fact that Y is a subsoma of each of the somas X_1, X_2, and X_3, we see that (178.5) through (178.8), together with (120.11), imply the relations

$$\left.\begin{aligned} &\varphi'(X') \leqq \varphi(Y) \leqq \varphi'(X') + \varepsilon, \quad && \psi'(X') \leqq \psi(Y) \leqq \psi'(X') + \varepsilon, \\ &\alpha'(X') = \alpha(Y), && \beta'(X') = \beta(Y). \end{aligned}\right\} \tag{178.10}$$

On the other hand, it follows from (178.2), inasmuch as $Y \subseteqq M$, that

$$\alpha(Y)\,\varphi(Y) \leqq \psi(Y) \leqq \beta(Y)\,\varphi(Y), \tag{178.11}$$

and therefore we also have

$$\alpha'(X')\,\varphi'(X') \leqq \psi'(X') + \varepsilon \leqq \beta'(X')\big(\varphi'(X') + \varepsilon\big) + \varepsilon. \tag{178.12}$$

By assumption, all the numbers occurring in this relation are finite; hence, if we let ε tend to zero, we obtain the relation

$$\alpha'(X')\,\varphi'(X') \leqq \psi'(X') \leqq \beta'(X')\,\varphi'(X') \tag{178.13}$$

Since, as we have already seen, the place function f' is measurable both for $\varphi'(X')$ and $\psi'(X')$, it follows from Theorem 2 of § 159 that we can write

$$\psi'(X') = \int_{X'} f'\, d\varphi' \qquad (X' \subseteqq M'). \quad (178.14)$$

179. This result can readily be generalized, as follows:

THEOREM 1: *We consider a homomorphism*

$$X' = \sigma X \quad (179.1)$$

that transforms the measure function $\varphi(X)$ into the measure function $\varphi'(X')$. This homomorphism then transforms each integral

$$\psi(X) = \int_X f\, d\varphi \qquad (X \subseteqq M) \quad (179.2)$$

into the integral

$$\psi'(X') = \int_{X'} f'\, d\varphi' \qquad (X' \subseteqq M'). \quad (179.3)$$

Here M denotes a normal soma of the ring of measurability $\mathfrak{M}_\varphi$ of $\psi(X)$, the place function f is assumed to be integrable on M, and f' designates the homomorphic image of f.

Proof: In the wording of this theorem, we have no longer assumed that $\varphi(M)$ is finite or that f is bounded and non-negative. However, we can obviously decompose M into a null soma M_0 and an at most countable number of additional subsomas M_j such that on each of the latter somas either the function f or the function $-f$ has the stated properties. The function $\psi(X)$ is the difference of two measure functions each of which is singular with respect to the other (§§ 165 and 166). Each of these measure functions is transformed by the homomorphism into a measure function (§ 144); the difference of these last measure functions is taken to be $\psi'(X')$, and the function computed in this way satisfies equation (179.3).

If the homomorphism is measure-preserving, that is, if

$$\varphi'(X') = \varphi(X), \quad (179.4)$$

then we also have

$$\psi'(X') = \psi(X), \quad (179.5)$$

since by (120.11) we always have

$$\alpha(X) \leqq \alpha'(X') \leqq \beta'(X') \leqq \beta(X)$$

and there is only one measure function $\psi(X)$ for which

$$\alpha(X)\, \varphi(X) \leqq \psi(X) \leqq \beta(X)\, \varphi(X).$$

In this case, we can replace equation (179.3) by the following:

$$\int_{\sigma X} \sigma f \, d(\sigma \varphi) = \int_{X} f \, d\varphi. \tag{179.6}$$

180. It is very remarkable that in the derivation of the above theorem it was unnecessary to assume that the somas making up the ring $\mathfrak{N}$ that is carried into O' are measurable for $\varphi(X)$. The most important case, of course, is that in which $\mathfrak{N}$ coincides with the null ring $\mathfrak{N}_\varphi$ of the measure function $\varphi(X)$. Then the homomorphism is *measure-preserving* for each of the measure functions $\varphi(X)$ and $\psi(X)$, and the homomorphic image $\varphi'(X')$ of $\varphi(X)$ is a *reduced* measure function (cf. §§ 146 and 147).

According to the last theorem, we have

$$\int_X f_1 \, d\varphi = \int_X f_2 \, d\varphi \qquad (X \subseteqq M) \tag{180.1}$$

for every two non-negative measurable place functions f_1 and f_2 that are equivalent (§ 119) with respect to this homomorphism, i.e., for which $\sigma f_1 = \sigma f_2$.

If, on the contrary, the two functions f_1 and f_2 are not equivalent, then the two inequalities

$$f_1' \leqq f_2', \quad f_2' \leqq f_1' \qquad (f_1' = \sigma f_1, f_2' = \sigma f_2)$$

cannot both hold. Thus, by Theorem 1 of § 89, there exists a non-empty subsoma A' of M', for which, say,

$$\beta_2'(A') < \alpha_1'(A').$$

Then for every non-empty subsoma of A', the same inequality holds, and it therefore entails no loss of generality to assume that $\varphi'(A')$ is finite. Since, in addition, $\varphi'(X')$ is a reduced measure function and A' is non-empty, we must have $\varphi'(A') > 0$. Consequently,

$$\int_{A'} f_2' \, d\varphi' \leqq \beta_2'(A') \, \varphi'(A') < \alpha_1'(A') \, \varphi'(A') \leqq \int_{A'} f_1' \, d\varphi'. \tag{180.2}$$

Thus, if A denotes a subsoma of M for which $\sigma A = A'$, we have

$$\int_A f_2 \, d\varphi = \int_{A'} f_2' \, d\varphi' < \int_{A'} f_1' \, d\varphi' = \int_A f_1 \, d\varphi. \tag{180.3}$$

This result can be extended immediately to functions f_1 and f_2 of arbitrary sign, and we have the following theorem.

THEOREM 2: *Let the place functions $\mathfrak{f}_1$ and $\mathfrak{f}_2$ be φ-measurable and φ-integrable on their common domain of definition M. Under this hypothesis, the equation*

$$\int_{\dot{X}} f_1 \, d\varphi = \int_{\dot{X}} f_2 \, d\varphi \tag{180.4}$$

holds for all subsomas X of M if and only if $\mathfrak{f}_1$ and $\mathfrak{f}_2$ are equivalent with respect to the homomorphism that transforms the null ring $\mathfrak{N}_\varphi$ of $\varphi(X)$ into the empty soma.

CHAPTER SEVEN

APPLICATION OF THE THEORY OF INTEGRATION TO LIMIT PROCESSES

§§ 181-183. The Theorem of Egoroff

181. We shall now consider the integral

$$\psi(X) = \int_X f\, d\varphi$$

on a fixed soma X as a functional depending upon the place function f that is being integrated. Aside from the linearity of this functional, which we discussed in § 163, what we must emphasize first and foremost is its "continuity." This continuity, however, is the consequence of a theorem on convergent sequences of place functions, which we are yet to obtain.

Let $\varphi(X)$ be an arbitrary measure function, and let M be a soma of the ring of measurability of $\varphi(X)$ for which

$$0 < \varphi(M) < +\infty. \tag{181.1}$$

We consider a convergent sequence $\{f_k\}$ of finite, φ-measurable place functions and assume that the limit function

$$f = \lim_{k=\infty} f_k \tag{181.2}$$

is likewise a finite place function. We shall suppose that the common domain of definition of all these place functions is the soma M.

If we now put

$$g_k = f_k - f \qquad (k = 1, 2, \ldots), \tag{181.3}$$

then the functions g_k are all finite and φ-measurable, and in addition, by Theorem 3 of § 103, we have

$$\lim_{k=\infty} g_k = 0. \tag{181.4}$$

By assumption, we can assign a nest of somas $[S_k(y)]$ consisting entirely of φ-measurable somas to each of the functions g_k. According to § 92, (181.4) implies that the equations

$$\underline{S}(y) = \underline{\lim}_{k=\infty} S_k(y), \quad \bar{S}(y) = \overline{\lim}_{k=\infty} S_k(y) \tag{181.5}$$

yield two nests of somas of the place function that vanishes identically on its domain of definition M.

Now, if δ is any positive number, we must have

$$\overline{\lim}_{k=\infty} S_k(-\delta) = O, \quad \underline{\lim}_{k=\infty} S_k(\delta) = M. \tag{181.6}$$

Next, we put

$$U_k = \prod_{j=0}^{\infty} S_{k+j}(\delta), \tag{181.7}$$

$$V_k = \sum_{j=0}^{\infty} \dot{+}\, S_{k+j}(-\delta), \tag{181.8}$$

so that we have

$$U_1 \subseteqq U_2 \subseteqq \ldots, \quad V_1 \supseteqq V_2 \supseteqq \ldots. \tag{181.9}$$

Employing the notation

$$A_k = U_k \dot{+} U_k V_k, \quad B_k = M \dot{+} A_k, \tag{181.10}$$

we therefore also have

$$A_1 \subseteqq A_2 \subseteqq \ldots, \quad B_1 \supseteqq B_2 \supseteqq \ldots. \tag{181.11}$$

Now we have by § 25, taking (181.6) into consideration,

$$\lim_{k=\infty} U_k = \underline{\lim}_{k=\infty} S_k(\delta) = M, \quad \lim_{k=\infty} V_k = \overline{\lim}_{k=\infty} S_k(-\delta) = O, \tag{181.12}$$

from which we deduce, using Theorem 7 of § 31, that

$$\lim_{k=\infty} A_k = \lim_{k=\infty} (U_k \dot{+} U_k V_k) = M \dot{+} MO = M, \tag{181.13}$$

$$\lim_{k=\infty} B_k = \lim_{k=\infty} (M \dot{+} A_k) = M \dot{+} M = O. \tag{181.14}$$

The somas $S_k(\delta)$ and $S_k(-\delta)$ are all measurable for $\varphi(X)$; the same is true also of the somas U_k, V_k, A_k, and B_k. Moreover,

$$\varphi(B_1) \leqq \varphi(M) < +\infty.$$

Thus, by Theorems 4 and 5 of § 138, we have

$$\lim_{k=\infty} \varphi(A_k) = \varphi(M), \quad \lim_{k=\infty} \varphi(B_k) = 0. \tag{181.15}$$

182. We choose a positive number ε for which

$$0 < \varepsilon < \varphi(M). \tag{182.1}$$

Then, by (181.15), there is at least one positive integer n for which

$$\varphi(B_n) < \varepsilon. \tag{182.2}$$

However, since

$$\varphi(M) = \varphi(A_n) + \varphi(B_n),$$

we also have

$$\varphi(A_n) > 0, \tag{182.3}$$

from which it follows that the soma A_n is *non-empty*. Now, from (181.10) and (181.8), it follows that

$$A_n \circ V_n, \quad V_n \supseteqq S_{n+p}(-\delta) \qquad (p = 1, 2, \ldots),$$

and we therefore also have

$$A_n \circ S_{n+p}(-\delta) \qquad (p = 1, 2, \ldots). \tag{182.4}$$

On the other hand, we deduce from (181.10) and (181.7) that

$$A_n \subseteqq U_n \subseteqq S_{n+p}(\delta) \qquad (p = 1, 2, \ldots). \tag{182.5}$$

Thus, if we denote the infimum and supremum of the place function g_k on the soma X by $\alpha_k(X)$ and $\beta_k(X)$, then according to (80.1) and (80.2), the inequalities

$$-\delta \leqq \alpha_{n+p}(A_n), \quad \beta_{n+p}(A_n) \leqq \delta \quad (p = 1, 2, \ldots) \tag{182.6}$$

follow from (182.4) and (182.5).

Thus, the relations

$$-\delta \leqq g_{n+p} \leqq \delta, \tag{182.7}$$

which, in view of (181.3), can also be written as

$$f - \delta \leqq f_{n+p} \leqq f + \delta \qquad (p = 1, 2, \ldots), \tag{182.8}$$

are valid on A_n.

From these considerations we deduce the following theorem.

THEOREM 1: *Let $\varphi(X)$ be a measure function whose ring of measurability contains a soma M for which*

$$0 < \varphi(M) < +\infty. \tag{182.9}$$

Moreover, let $\{f_k\}$ be a sequence of finite, φ-measurable place functions that converges on M to a finite limit function f.

Then, given any two positive numbers δ and ε, we can find a measurable, non-empty subsoma A of M and a positive integer n such that the relation

$$\varphi(M \dotplus A) < \varepsilon \tag{182.10}$$

on the one hand, and the inequalities

$$f - \delta \leqq f_{n+p} \leqq f + \delta \qquad (p = 1, 2, \ldots) \tag{182.11}$$

on the other, are all valid on A.

183. By repeated application of the last theorem, we finally obtain a result that is linked with the name of Egoroff,[1] although it was already implicit in the works of Lebesgue.

We choose a positive integer k and a positive number ε. Under the assumptions of the last theorem we can find a non-empty, measurable subsoma A_k of M and a positive integer n_k such that, in the first place, the relation

$$\varphi(M \dotplus A_k) < \frac{\varepsilon}{2^k} \tag{183.1}$$

holds and, in the second place, the inequalities

$$f - \frac{1}{k} \leqq f_{n_k+p} \leqq f + \frac{1}{k} \qquad (p = 1, 2, \ldots) \tag{183.2}$$

are valid on A_k.

We determine the somas A_k and the numbers n_k successively for $k = 1, 2, \ldots$, and we put

$$A = \prod_k A_k. \tag{183.3}$$

Then, by (24.15), we have

$$M \dotplus A = \sum_k \dotplus (M \dotplus A_k), \tag{183.4}$$

and consequently

$$\varphi(M \dotplus A) < \frac{\varepsilon}{2} + \frac{\varepsilon}{2^2} + \cdots = \varepsilon. \tag{183.5}$$

The soma A is φ-measurable, and

$$\varphi(A) = \varphi(M) - \varphi(M \dotplus A). \tag{183.6}$$

Hence, for $\varepsilon < \varphi(M)$ we have $\varphi(A) > 0$, so that the soma A cannot be empty.

If now η is any positive number and if we choose

$$k > \frac{2}{\eta}, \tag{183.7}$$

[1] D. T. Egoroff, *C. R. Acad. Sci. Paris*, Vol. 152 (1911), pp. 244-246.

then the relations

$$f - \frac{1}{k} \leqq f_j \leqq f + \frac{1}{k}, \quad f - \frac{1}{k} \leqq f_m \leqq f + \frac{1}{k} \tag{183.8}$$

hold on A_k for every pair of positive integers $j > n_k$ and $m > n_k$; and hence, on the subsoma A of A_k,

$$|f_m - f_j| < \eta. \tag{183.9}$$

The sequence of the f_k is therefore uniformly convergent on A, and we have the following theorem, known as Egoroff's Theorem.

THEOREM 2: *Under the assumptions of the preceding theorem, for each positive number ε there can be found a non-empty, measurable subsoma A of M on which the given sequence of place functions converges uniformly, and for which*

$$\varphi(M \dotplus A) < \varepsilon. \tag{183.10}$$

The assumption that $\varphi(M) < +\infty$ is essential for the validity of Egoroff's Theorem; it does not even suffice to assume that M is a normal soma of the ring of measurability $\mathfrak{M}_\varphi$ of $\varphi(X)$. For, if $M_1, M_2, \ldots$ are pairwise disjoint somas of $\mathfrak{M}_\varphi$, that satisfy

$$\varphi(M_n) = n \qquad (n = 1, 2, \ldots), \tag{183.11}$$

let us put

$$M = M_1 + M_2 + M_3 + \cdots, \tag{183.12}$$

and let the place function that agrees with the constant one on M_n and with the constant zero on $M \dotplus M_n$ be denoted by f_n. Then the sequence of place functions $f_1, f_2, \ldots$ converges to zero. But there is no subsoma A of M in $\mathfrak{M}_\varphi$, for which

$$\varphi(M \dotplus A) < +\infty$$

and on which the sequence of f_n converges uniformly.

If, in this example, we replace the assumption (183.11) by

$$\varphi(M_n) = \frac{1}{2^n},$$

we see that, under the hypotheses of the Theorem of Egoroff, there need not be any soma A for which

$$\varphi(M \dotplus A) = 0$$

and on which the sequence of the f_n converges uniformly.

§§ 184-189. Continuity of the Integral as a Functional

184. We now consider a convergent sequence of non-negative place functions $f_1, f_2, \ldots$ all of which are φ-measurable. The limit function

$$f = \lim_{k=\infty} f_k, \tag{184.1}$$

which, by § 154, is also φ -measurable, need not be finite, but the functions f_k will be assumed to admit a common, φ-measurable *majorant* s, so that we can write

$$0 \leqq f_k \leqq s \quad (k = 1, 2, \ldots); \quad 0 \leqq f \leqq s. \tag{184.2}$$

Let the common domain of definition M of the functions f_k, f, and s be a normal soma of the ring of measurability $\mathfrak{M}_\varphi$ of $\varphi(X)$ for which the relation

$$0 < \int_M s\, d\varphi < +\infty \tag{184.3}$$

holds.

We introduce the integrals

$$\sigma(X) = \int_X s\, d\varphi, \quad \psi_k(X) = \int_X f_k\, d\varphi, \quad \psi(X) = \int_X f\, d\varphi, \tag{184.4}$$

as well as a decomposition

$$M = M_0 + M_1 + M_2 + \cdots \tag{184.5}$$

of M that has the following property: It consists of an infinite number of subsomas of M, some of which may, however, coincide with the empty soma O. All the somas M_j are φ-measurable and all the numbers $\varphi(M_j)$ are finite; if M_0 is non-empty, then the place function s agrees with the constant $+\infty$ on M_0 and is bounded on each of the remaining somas $M_1, M_2, \ldots$ (insofar as they are non-empty). It follows from (184.3), in any case, that

$$\varphi(M_0) = 0,$$

and then, by (184.4), we also have

$$\sigma(M_0) = 0. \tag{184.6}$$

Thus, if we put

$$B_n = M_1 + M_2 + \cdots + M_n, \quad C_n = M \dotplus B_n, \tag{184.7}$$

we have, since the M_j are measurable,

$$\lim_{n=\infty} \sigma(B_n) = \sigma(M) - \sigma(M_0) = \sigma(M), \quad \lim_{n=\infty} \sigma(C_n) = 0. \tag{184.8}$$

We choose any number ε satisfying the condition

$$0 < \varepsilon < \sigma(M). \tag{184.9}$$

By the second equation of (184.8), there is then a positive integer n_0 for which we can write

$$\sigma(C_{n_0}) < \varepsilon, \quad \sigma(B_{n_0}) > \sigma(M) - \varepsilon > 0. \tag{184.10}$$

By (184.4), then, in any case we also have

$$\varphi(B_{n_0}) > 0. \tag{184.11}$$

The majorant s is bounded on the soma B_{n_0}, and hence is smaller than some constant positive number, which we shall denote by λ.

We can now apply Theorem 1 of § 182 to the sequence of place functions f_k, provided we restrict this sequence to the soma B_{n_0}. We thus obtain a decomposition

$$B_{n_0} = D + E \qquad (D, E \in \mathfrak{M}_\varphi) \tag{184.12}$$

of B_{n_0} and a positive integer k_0 such that, first,

$$\varphi(D) < \frac{\varepsilon}{\lambda}, \tag{184.13}$$

and second,

$$f - \frac{\varepsilon}{\varphi(B_{n_0})} < f_{k_0+p} < f + \frac{\varepsilon}{\varphi(B_{n_0})} \qquad (p = 1, 2, \ldots) \tag{184.14}$$

on E. Now $s \leqq \lambda$ on D; thus, by (184.13), we have

$$\sigma(D) = \int_D s \, d\varphi \leqq \lambda \, \varphi(D) < \varepsilon. \tag{184.15}$$

185. Let X denote an arbitrary (not necessarily measurable) subsoma of M, and put

$$X' = X C_{n_0}, \quad X'' = XD, \quad X''' = XE. \tag{185.1}$$

From the fact that the somas C_{n_0}, D, and E are measurable and pairwise disjoint, we obtain the equations

$$\left.\begin{aligned} X &= X' + X'' + X''', \\ \psi_k(X) &= \psi_k(X') + \psi_k(X'') + \psi_k(X''') \quad (k = 1, 2, \ldots), \\ \psi(X) &= \psi(X') + \psi(X'') + \psi(X'''), \end{aligned}\right\} \tag{185.2}$$

by Theorem 2 of § 136. Now, by (184.10) and (184.15), we have

$$\left.\begin{array}{l} \psi_k(X') \leqq \sigma(X') \leqq \sigma(C_{n_0}) < \varepsilon \\ \psi_k(X'') \leqq \sigma(X'') \leqq \sigma(D) \quad < \varepsilon \end{array} \quad (k = 1, 2, \ldots), \right\} \tag{185.3}$$

and in the same way we see that

$$\psi(X') < \varepsilon, \quad \psi(X'') < \varepsilon. \tag{185.4}$$

Moreover, the equations

$$\int_{X'''} \left(f \pm \frac{\varepsilon}{\varphi(B_{n_0})}\right) d\varphi = \psi(X''') \pm \frac{\varepsilon\, \varphi(X''')}{\varphi(B_{n_0})},$$

in conjunction with (184.14) and with

$$\varphi(X''') \leqq \varphi(E) \leqq \varphi(B_{n_0}),$$

yield the relations

$$\psi(X''') - \varepsilon \leqq \psi_{k_0+p}(X''') \leqq \psi(X''') + \varepsilon \quad (p = 1, 2, \ldots). \tag{185.5}$$

Since $\psi_k(X)$ $(k = 1, 2, \ldots)$ and $\psi(X)$ are non-negative soma functions, however, we can also write, by virtue of (185.3) and (185.4),

$$\psi(X') - \varepsilon < \psi_{k_0+p}(X') < \psi(X') + \varepsilon,$$

$$\psi(X'') - \varepsilon < \psi_{k_0+p}(X'') < \psi(X'') + \varepsilon.$$

Term-by-term addition of the last three relations yields finally

$$\psi(X) - 3\,\varepsilon < \psi_{k_0+p}(X) < \psi(X) + 3\,\varepsilon \quad (p = 1, 2, \ldots),$$

and hence also

$$\psi(X) - 3\,\varepsilon \leqq \varliminf_{k=\infty} \psi_k(X) \leqq \varlimsup_{k=\infty} \psi_k(X) \leqq \psi(X) + 3\,\varepsilon. \tag{185.6}$$

If we now let ε tend to zero, we obtain as our final result the equation

$$\lim_{k=\infty} \psi_k(X) = \psi(X). \tag{185.7}$$

We thus have the following theorem, first obtained by Lebesgue for the case in which the $\psi(X)$ are ordinary integrals.[2]

[2] H. Lebesgue, *Bull. Soc. Math. France,* Vol. 36 (1908), p. 12.

THEOREM 1: *Let the non-negative place functions* $f_1, f_2, \ldots$ *all be* φ*-measurable and defined on a normal soma* M *of the ring of measurability of* $\varphi(X)$. *Let them converge on* M *to a function* f *and admit on* M *a* φ*-measurable majorant* s *for which*

$$\int_M s\,d\varphi < +\infty. \tag{185.8}$$

Then, if we put

$$\psi_k(X) = \int_X f_k\,d\varphi \quad (k = 1, 2, \ldots), \quad \psi(X) = \int_X f\,d\varphi, \tag{185.9}$$

the integrals $\psi_k(X)$ *converge to* $\psi(X)$ *for all* $X \subseteqq M$, *i.e., we have the equation*

$$\psi(X) = \lim_{k=\infty} \psi_k(X). \tag{185.10}$$

The relation $\sigma(M) > 0$ used in the proof of this theorem can of course be omited, since equation (185.10) is automatically satisfied for $\sigma(M) = 0$.

186. The relation (185.8), i.e., $\sigma(M) < +\infty$, cannot be dispensed with, however, if the Lebesgue Theorem is to remain valid without other restriction. It is not even enough to assume that the soma M is a normal soma of the ring of measurability of $\sigma(X)$. To show this, we consider an infinite number of φ-measurable somas $A_1, A_2, \ldots$ that are pairwise disjoint and for which the numbers $\varphi(A_j)$ are all finite and distinct from zero. We put

$$M = A_1 + A_2 + A_3 + \cdots$$

and take f_k equal to the constant zero on $M \dot{+} A_k$ and equal to the constant $1/\varphi(A_k)$ on A_k itself. The majorant

$$s = \sup(f_1, f_2, \ldots)$$

is finite on M, and M is a normal soma of $\sigma(X)$. But now we have

$$\lim_{k=\infty} f_k = f = 0, \quad \int_M f_k\,d\varphi = 1 \quad (k = 1, 2, \ldots);$$

hence the equation (185.10) cannot hold here.

If more specialized assumptions are made with regard to the place functions f_k, however, the condition $\sigma(M) < +\infty$ can be dropped. This is the case, in particular, if the sequence of functions f_k is monotonically increasing, so that we can write

$$0 \leqq f_1 \leqq f_2 \leqq f_3 \leqq \cdots, \tag{186.1}$$

and if, in addition, M is a normal soma of $\mathfrak{M}_\varphi$. The limit function

$$f = \lim_{k=\infty} f_k \tag{186.2}$$

always exists in this case and can be viewed as the majorant s of the functions f_k. Thus, if X is a subsoma of the domain of definition M of the f_k for which

$$\psi(X) = \int_X f\, d\varphi < +\infty, \tag{186.3}$$

we may apply Theorem 1 of § 185 and obtain $\psi(X) = \lim_{k=\infty} \psi_k(X)$.

Thus, it remains only to show that if $\psi(X) = +\infty$ then $\lim_{k=\infty} \psi_k(X) = +\infty$ or, what amounts to the same thing, the relation

$$\psi_k(X) \geqq p \tag{186.4}$$

holds for any positive number p for k sufficiently large.

Let X_0 denote the subsoma of X on which the limit function f is equal to the constant $+\infty$, and consider first the case that $\varphi(X_0) = \varphi(X_0 M) > 0$. There is then certainly a subsoma X_0' of X_0 for which

$$0 < \varphi(X_0') < +\infty. \tag{186.5}$$

Let n_0 denote the smallest positive integer for which

$$n_0 \geqq \frac{p+1}{\varphi(X_0')}, \tag{186.6}$$

and consider on X_0' the sequence of place functions

$$f_k' = \min(n_0, f_k) \qquad (k = 1, 2, \ldots). \tag{186.7}$$

The sequence of these bounded functions f_1', f_2', ... is monotonically increasing and, by Theorem 4 of § 104, converges to the function

$$f' = \min(n_0, f) = n_0; \tag{186.8}$$

and using the notation

$$\psi_k'(X_0') = \int_{X_0'} f_k'\, d\varphi, \tag{186.9}$$

we obtain the relations

$$\lim_{k=\infty} \psi_k'(X_0') = \int_{X_0'} f'\, d\varphi = n_0\, \varphi(X_0') \geqq p + 1. \tag{186.10}$$

Thus, for sufficiently large values of k, we have $\psi_k'(X_0) \geqq p$ and, for these same values of k, we have

$$\psi_k(X) \geqq \psi_k(X_0') \geqq \psi_k'(X_0') \geqq p. \tag{186.11}$$

For our second case, we have $\varphi(X_0) = 0$, which of course implies $\psi(X_0) = 0$. Then there exists a decomposition of X into pairwise disjoint somas

$$X = X_0 + X_1 + X_2 + \cdots \tag{186.12}$$

for which we have

$$\left.\begin{aligned} &\psi(X_j) < +\infty \quad (j = 1, 2, \ldots), \\ &\psi(X) = \psi(X_1) + \psi(X_2) + \cdots. \end{aligned}\right\} \tag{186.13}$$

Since our supposition, however, is that $\psi(X) = +\infty$, we can choose a positive integer m so large that, writing

$$A_k = X_1 + X_2 + \cdots + X_k, \tag{186.14}$$

we have the relation

$$p + 1 \leqq \psi(A_m) = \psi(X_1) + \cdots + \psi(X_m) < +\infty. \tag{186.15}$$

But here again, by Theorem 1 of § 185, we obtain

$$\lim_{k=\infty} \psi_k(A_m) = \psi(A_m) \geqq p + 1, \tag{186.16}$$

and for sufficiently large values of k,

$$\psi_k(X) \geqq \psi_k(A_m) \geqq p. \tag{186.17}$$

This completes the proof of the following theorem.

THEOREM 2: *Given a monotonically increasing sequence*

$$f_1 \leqq f_2 \leqq \cdots \tag{186.18}$$

of non-negative φ-measurable place functions defined on a normal soma M of the ring of measurability $\mathfrak{M}_\varphi$, if we write

$$f = \lim_{k=\infty} f_k, \tag{186.19}$$

$$\psi_k(X) = \int_X f_k \, d\varphi, \quad \psi(X) = \int_X f \, d\varphi \tag{186.20}$$

then the equation

$$\psi(X) = \lim_{k=\infty} \psi_k(X) \tag{186.21}$$

holds for all somas $X \subseteqq M$.

187. Let $f_1, f_2, \ldots$ now denote φ-measurable place functions of arbitrary sign whose absolute values $|f_k|$ admit a common finite measurable majorant s; and let

$$\int_M s\, d\varphi < +\infty \tag{187.1}$$

for the soma M.

Then the functions

$$f'_k = f_k + s \qquad (k = 1, 2, \ldots) \tag{187.2}$$

are non-negative and measurable, and admit the common majorant $2s$. As in § 92, we put

$$g'_k = \sup(f'_k, f'_{k+1}, \ldots), \tag{187.3}$$

and, if we write

$$\psi_k(X) = \int_X f_k\, d\varphi, \quad \sigma(X) = \int_X s\, d\varphi \qquad (X \subseteqq M), \tag{187.4}$$

we obtain the relations

$$\psi_{k+p}(X) + \sigma(X) = \int_X f'_{k+p}\, d\varphi \leqq \int_X g'_k\, d\varphi \qquad (p = 0, 1, 2, \ldots). \tag{187.5}$$

From this it follows that

$$\overline{\lim_{n=\infty}}\, \psi_n(X) + \sigma(X) \leqq \int_X g'_k\, d\varphi. \tag{187.6}$$

On the other hand, the monotonically decreasing sequence

$$g'_1 \geqq g'_2 \geqq \ldots$$

converges, in accordance with Theorem 3 of § 103, to the place function

$$\overline{\lim_{k=\infty}}\, f'_k = \overline{\lim_{k=\infty}}\, f_k + s, \tag{187.7}$$

and Theorem 1 of § 185, all of whose hypotheses are satisfied here, yields the equation

$$\lim_{k=\infty} \int_X g'_k\, d\varphi = \int_X \overline{\lim_{n=\infty}}\, f_n\, d\varphi + \sigma(X). \tag{187.8}$$

A comparison of (187.6) with (187.8) gives the relation

$$\lim_{n=\infty} \psi_n(X) \leqq \int_X \overline{\lim_{n=\infty}} f_n \, d\varphi. \tag{187.9}$$

The corresponding inequality for the lower limit can be obtained in an entirely similar way; these relations also hold in the case that s agrees with $+\infty$ on a soma of measure zero, and we obtain the following theorem, which was first enunciated for Lebesgue integrals by P. Fatou (1878-1929).[3]

THEOREM 3: *Let the place functions $f_1, f_2, \ldots$ of a given sequence, as well as a further place function s, be φ-measurable, and on the common domain of definition M of all these functions let them satisfy the relations*

$$|f_k| \leqq s \quad (k = 1, 2, \ldots), \qquad \int_M s \, d\varphi < +\infty. \tag{187.10}$$

Then the inequalities

$$\int_X \underline{\lim_{n=\infty}} f_n \, d\varphi \leqq \underline{\lim_{n=\infty}} \int_X f_n \, d\varphi \leqq \overline{\lim_{n=\infty}} \int_X f_n \, d\varphi \leqq \int_X \overline{\lim_{n=\infty}} f_n \, d\varphi \tag{187.11}$$

hold for all the subsomas X of M.

188. Entirely similar techniques enable us to extend Theorem 2 of § 186 to place functions of arbitrary sign. Let a monotone sequence of finite place functions $f_1, f_2, \ldots$ be given; moreover, let the soma M satisfy

$$\int_M |f_1| \, d\varphi < +\infty. \tag{188.1}$$

If, first, $f_1 \leqq f_2 \leqq \ldots$, we apply Theorem 2 of § 186 to the sequence of non-negative functions

$$f'_k = f_k - f_1 \qquad (k = 1, 2, \ldots); \tag{188.2}$$

second, if $f_1 \geqq f_2 \geqq \ldots$, we apply the same theorem to the sequence of functions

$$f''_k = f_1 - f_k \qquad (k = 1, 2, \ldots). \tag{188.3}$$

In this way, we obtain the following result.

THEOREM 4: *Let $f_1, f_2, \ldots$ denote the elements of a monotone sequence of finite, φ-measurable place functions. Then if M is a soma for which*

$$\int_M |f_1| \, d\varphi < +\infty, \tag{188.4}$$

the equation

[3] P. Fatou, *Acta Math.*, Vol. 30 (1906), pp. 375-376.

$$\lim_{n=\infty} \int_X f_n \, d\varphi = \int_X \lim_{n=\infty} f_n \, d\varphi \tag{188.5}$$

holds for every subsoma X of M.

189. Let $f_1, f_2, \ldots$ be finite, φ-measurable place functions that satisfy

$$|f_k| \leqq s \quad (k = 1, 2, \ldots), \quad \lim_{k=\infty} f_k = f; \tag{189.1}$$

moreover, let the common domain of definition M of all these place functions satisfy

$$\int_M s \, d\varphi < +\infty. \tag{189.2}$$

We can write

$$\lim_{k=\infty} (f_k - f) = 0 \tag{189.3}$$

in place of the second relation of (189.1), and by Theorem 5 of § 104, we then have also

$$\lim_{k=\infty} |f_k - f| = 0. \tag{189.4}$$

But we have here

$$|f_k - f| \leqq 2s \qquad (k = 1, 2, \ldots), \tag{189.5}$$

and by Theorem 1 of § 185, the equation

$$\lim_{k=\infty} \int_X |f_k - f| \, d\varphi = 0 \qquad (X \subseteqq M) \tag{189.6}$$

holds. We have thus proved the following theorem.

Theorem 5: *Let the absolute values of the finite, φ-measurable place functions $f_1, f_2, \ldots$ of a convergent sequence have a φ-measurable majorant s; let*

$$\int_M s \, d\varphi < +\infty \tag{189.7}$$

for the common domain of definition M of these functions and their limit function. Then it follows from the equation

$$f = \lim_{k=\infty} f_k \tag{189.8}$$

that the relation

$$\lim_{k=\infty} \int_X |f_k - f| \, d\varphi = 0 \qquad (X \subseteqq M) \tag{189.9}$$

holds.

§§ 190-197. Convergence in the Mean

190. By Theorem 5 above, if

$$\lim_{n=\infty} f_n = 0, \quad |f_n| \leqq s, \quad \int_M s \, d\varphi < +\infty, \tag{190.1}$$

then we have the relation

$$\lim_{n=\infty} \int_M |f_n| \, d\varphi = 0. \tag{190.2}$$

The subsistence of equation (190.2), however, is not confined to the conditions (190.1). For example, if $f_n(x)$ denote periodic functions of one variable, with period unity, that agree with the constant $\sqrt{n}$ on an interval δ_n of length $1/n$ in each of its periods and vanish elsewhere, then (190.2) holds, where M is taken to be any bounded interval $a < x < b$. If, however, $\delta_1, \delta_2, \ldots$ are so chosen that the left-hand end-point of each of the intervals δ_{n+1} coincides with the center of δ_n, then there exists no finite majorant s, and there is no value of x for which the sequence of function values $f_n(x)$ converges. In those cases in which the relation (190.2) is satisfied, even though the conditions (190.1) may possibly not hold, we say that the functions $f_n(x)$ converge to zero *in the mean* on $a < x < b$.

In general, we shall say that a sequence $\{f_n\}$ of place functions *converges in the mean to the function* g on the common domain of definition of these functions, the soma M, if the equation

$$\lim_{n=\infty} \int_M |f_n - g| \, d\varphi = 0 \quad (0 < \varphi(M) < +\infty) \tag{190.3}$$

holds. It is assumed here, as before, that the functions f_n and g are φ-measurable, and by (190.3), M must be a normal soma of the ring of measurability $\mathfrak{M}_\varphi$. Whereas the functions under consideration have thus far been assumed to be finite, we shall now allow them to be infinite on a soma of measure zero. If the difference of two functions should then be meaningless on a null soma, we shall replace it on that soma by zero.

In (190.3), we may obviously replace g by an equivalent place function g^* (Theorem 2 of § 180). Conversely, if g and g^* are two place functions to which $\{f_n\}$ converges in the mean on M, they must be equivalent, as can be seen from the relations

$$\int_M |g^* - g| \, d\varphi \leqq \int_M |f_n - g| \, d\varphi + \int_M |f_n - g^*| \, d\varphi \tag{190.4}$$

by passing to the limit.

We shall now give a theorem that corresponds to the Cauchy criterion for ordinary sequences of numbers.

THEOREM 1: *Let $\{f_n\}$ be a sequence of φ-measurable place functions. Under the assumption that all the relations*

$$0 < \varphi(M) < +\infty, \quad \int_M |f_n| \, d\varphi < +\infty \quad (n = 1, 2, \ldots), \tag{190.5}$$

$$\int_M |f_{n+m} - f_n| \, d\varphi \leqq \varepsilon_n \quad (n, m = 1, 2, \ldots), \tag{190.6}$$

$$\lim_{n=\infty} \varepsilon_n = 0 \tag{190.7}$$

hold, the sequence $\{f_n\}$ converges in the mean on M to a place function g.

191. Indeed, as remarked by Hermann Weyl,[4] the functions f_n themselves converge to a limit function g on a soma $M - N$, where $\varphi(N) = 0$, whenever the ε_n converge to zero rapidly enough. We demonstrate this as follows: Always under the assumption that

$$0 < \varphi(M) < +\infty, \tag{191.1}$$

we consider a sequence of φ-measurable place functions $g_1, g_2, \ldots$, that satisfy the conditions

$$\int_M |g_n| \, d\varphi < +\infty, \quad \int_M |g_{n+m} - g_n| \, d\varphi \leqq \frac{1}{4^n} \quad (n, m = 1, 2, \ldots). \tag{191.2}$$

Meaningless differences are again to be replaced by zero. Let $[T_n(y)]$ denote a nest of somas of $|g_{n+1} - g_n|$ and introduce the notation

$$U_n = M - T_n\left(\frac{1}{2^n}\right), \quad M - V_k = U_k \dotplus U_{k+1} \dotplus \cdots, \tag{191.3}$$

so that, by Theorem 1 of § 23, we must have

$$V_k = \prod_{p=0}^{\infty} T_{k+p}\left(\frac{1}{2^{k+p}}\right). \tag{191.4}$$

Thus, $|g_{n+1} - g_n| \geqq 1/2^n$ on the soma U_n and, by Theorem 2 of § 159, in conjunction with (191.2), we must have

$$\frac{1}{2^n} \varphi(U_n) \leqq \int_{U_n} |g_{n+1} - g_n| \, d\varphi \leqq \frac{1}{4^n}.$$

---

[4] H. Weyl, "Uber die Konvergenz von Reihen, die nach Orthogonalfunktionen fortschreiten," *Math. Ann.*, Vol. 67 (1909), pp. 225-245, especially p. 243.

Thus we obtain

$$\varphi(U_n) \leqq \frac{1}{2^n} \tag{191.5}$$

and, by (191.3),

$$\varphi(M - V_k) \leqq \varphi(U_k) + \varphi(U_{k+1}) + \cdots \leqq \frac{1}{2^{k-1}}. \tag{191.6}$$

In particular, with the notation

$$V = \sum_{k=1}^{\infty} \dot{+} V_k, \tag{191.7}$$

we obtain

$$\varphi(M - V) = 0. \tag{191.8}$$

From this it follows by (191.1) that not all the somas V_k are null somas of $\varphi(X)$.

192. Since, according to (191.4), V_k is a subsoma of each of the somas $T_{k+m}(1/2^{k+m})$ $(m = 0, 1, 2, \ldots)$, the inequalities

$$|g_{k+m+1} - g_{k+m}| \leqq \frac{1}{2^{k+m}} \qquad (m = 0, 1, \ldots) \tag{192.1}$$

must hold on each of the somas V_k, insofar as it is non-empty. Consequently, it follows from the relations

$$|g_{k+p} - g_k| \leqq |g_{k+1} - g_k| + |g_{k+2} - g_{k+1}| + \cdots \quad (p = 1, 2, \ldots)$$

that, for every value of p,

$$|g_{k+p} - g_k| \leqq \frac{1}{2^{k-1}}. \tag{192.2}$$

Next, we write this last relation in the form

$$g_k - \frac{1}{2^{k-1}} \leqq g_{k+p} \leqq g_k + \frac{1}{2^{k-1}} \quad (p = 1, 2, \ldots), \tag{192.3}$$

from which we obtain the relations

$$g_k - \frac{1}{2^{k-1}} \leqq \underline{g} \leqq \bar{g} \leqq g_k + \frac{1}{2^{k-1}}, \tag{192.4}$$

where $\underline{g}$ and $\bar{g}$ denote the lower and upper limits of the sequence of functions g_n.

Let N_k be the null soma on which at least one of the place functions $|g_{k+p}|$ $(p = 0, 1, 2, \ldots)$ takes the value $+\infty$. By (192.4), we then have, on the soma $V_k - V_k N_k$,

$$0 \leqq \bar{g} - \underline{g} \leqq \frac{1}{2^{k-2}}. \tag{192.5}$$

Since, by (191.4), the relation $V_k \subseteqq V_{k+p+2}$ holds for every value of p, not only is the condition (192.5) satisfied on the soma $V_k - V_k N_k$, but also the stronger condition

$$0 \leqq \bar{g} - \underline{g} \leqq \frac{1}{2^{k+p}} \qquad (p = 1, 2, \ldots);$$

thus on this soma the sequence of g_n converges. If we now put

$$N = (M - V) \dotplus N_1 \dotplus N_2 \dotplus \cdots, \tag{192.6}$$

the soma N is a null soma; and a place function

$$g = \lim_{n=\infty} g_n \tag{192.7}$$

is defined on the soma $M - N$ and is finite on that soma. We define g on the whole soma M by stipulating, say, that g is to vanish on the null soma N.

193. We now let

$$s_k = |g_1| + |g_2| + \cdots + |g_k| + \frac{1}{2^{k-1}} \tag{193.1}$$

and observe that, for each k, the place function s_k is a majorant of the functions $|g_1|$, $|g_2|$, ... on the soma V_k; for, by (192.3), we always have

$$|g_{k+p}| \leqq |g_k| + \frac{1}{2^{k-1}} \qquad (p = 1, 2, \ldots).$$

On the other hand, s_k is integrable on V_k and $\int_{V_k} s_k d\varphi$ is finite. Thus, we can apply Theorem 5 of § 189, obtaining

$$\lim_{n=\infty} \int_{V_k} |g - g_n| \, d\varphi = 0. \tag{193.2}$$

Hence, for every choice of the indices k, m, and n, we have

$$\int_{V_k} |g - g_n| \, d\varphi \leqq \int_{V_k} |g - g_{n+m}| \, d\varphi + \int_{V_k} |g_{n+m} - g_n| \, d\varphi. \tag{193.3}$$

The second of the integrals on the right-hand side of the above relation is, by (191.2), less than or equal to $1/4^n$; the first of the integrals on the right-hand side converges to zero, by (193.2), as m tends to ∞; and consequently

$$\int_{V_k} |g - g_n| \, d\varphi \leqq \frac{1}{4^n} \qquad (k = 1, 2, \ldots). \tag{193.4}$$

From this we deduce further that

$$\int_{M} |g - g_n| \, d\varphi = \lim_{k=\infty} \int_{V_k} |g - g_n| \, d\varphi \leqq \frac{1}{4^n} \tag{193.5}$$

and obtain the relation

$$\lim_{n=\infty} \int_M |g - g_n| \, d\varphi = 0, \tag{193.6}$$

which is what we were to prove.

194. It is now quite easy to prove Theorem 1 of § 190. We choose an increasing sequence of positive integers

$$n_1 < n_2 < \dots \tag{194.1}$$

that satisfy

$$\varepsilon_{n_k} \leqq \frac{1}{4k} \tag{194.2}$$

and put

$$f_{n_k} = g_k. \tag{194.3}$$

By the preceding sections, there is a place function g for which (193.6) holds for the above sequence of g_k. But if n is any positive integer and if we choose from (194.1) a number $n_k > n$, then we obtain

$$\int_M |g - f_n| \, d\varphi \leqq \int_M |g - g_k| \, d\varphi + \int_M |f_{n_k} - f_n| \, d\varphi.$$

From this we conclude, using (193.6) and (190.6), that we can also write

$$\int_M |g - f_n| \, d\varphi \leqq \varepsilon_n; \tag{194.4}$$

then by (190.7), the sequence of functions f_n converges in the mean, as was to be shown, to the place function g.

195. The fact that from formulas (190.6) and (190.7) we can prove the existence of a class of equivalent place functions g for which (194.4) holds is in itself extremely remarkable and deservedly created a great sensation upon its first appearance (1907) in the mathematical literature. The oldest theorem of this sort was not, however, the theorem of § 190, but the *Riesz-Fischer Theorem*,[5] which deals with *"mean-square convergence."*

We say that a place function f is *square integrable on M* if

$$\int_M f^2 \, d\varphi < +\infty. \tag{195.1}$$

If two functions f and g are square integrable on M, then so is every linear combination $uf + vg$ of these functions. This is an immediate con-

[5] E. Fischer, *C. R. Acad. Sci. Paris,* Vol. 144 (1907), pp. 1022-1024. —— F. Riesz, *C. R. Acad. Sci. Paris,* Vol. 144 (1907), pp. 615-619; Vol. 148 (1909), pp. 1303-1305.

sequence of the well-known Schwarz Inequality: if, for the moment, the place functions f and g are bounded, the identity

$$\int_M (u f + v g)^2 \, d\varphi = u^2 \int_M f^2 \, d\varphi + 2 u v \int_M f g \, d\varphi + v^2 \int_M g^2 \, d\varphi, \quad (195.2)$$

whose right-hand side can be looked upon as a positive definite (or semi-definite) quadratic form in u and v, implies the inequality

$$\left(\int_M f g \, d\varphi\right)^2 \leqq \int_M f^2 \, d\varphi \int_M g^2 \, d\varphi, \quad (195.3)$$

and this inequality holds in general for arbitrary square-integrable place functions, since they can be represented as limits of bounded functions. The left-hand side of (195.3) in that case, just like the right-hand side, takes on a finite value.

196. THEOREM 2 (The Riesz-Fischer Theorem): *Let $f_1, f_2, \ldots$ denote a sequence of φ-measurable place functions that satisfy the conditions*

$$0 < \varphi(M) < +\infty, \quad \int_M f_n^2 \, d\varphi = \alpha_n^2 < +\infty \qquad (n = 1, 2, \ldots), \quad (196.1)$$

$$\int_M (f_{n+m} - f_n)^2 \, d\varphi \leqq \delta_n^2 \quad (n, m = 1, 2, \ldots), \quad (196.2)$$

$$\lim_{n=\infty} \delta_n = 0. \quad (196.3)$$

Then there exists a square-integrable place function g for which we have

$$\lim_{n=\infty} \int_M (f_n - g)^2 \, d\varphi = 0, \quad (196.4)$$

i.e., the sequence of functions $f_1, f_2, \ldots$ converges in the mean square to g.

Proof: In all generality, we can assume that $\alpha_n \geqq 0$ and $\delta_n \geqq 0$. By the Schwarz Inequality, the relations (196.1) imply

$$\int_M |f_{n+m} f_n| \, d\varphi \leqq \alpha_{n+m} \alpha_n; \quad (196.5)$$

from this, after expanding the left-hand side of (196.2), we obtain

$$(\alpha_{n+m} - \alpha_n)^2 \leqq \delta_n^2,$$

and consequently, we have also

$$\alpha_{n+m} \leqq \alpha_n + \delta_n \qquad (n, m = 1, 2, \ldots). \quad (196.6)$$

Thus $\alpha_1 + \delta_1$ is an upper bound for the set of numbers α_n and hence the least upper bound α of this set of numbers is finite.

Letting $[S_n(y)]$ denote a nest of somas of $|f_n|$, we have in any case that

$$\int_M |f_n|\, d\varphi \leqq \int_{S_n(1)} d\varphi + \int_{M-S_n(1)} f_n^2\, d\varphi \leqq \varphi(M) + \alpha^2 < +\infty. \qquad (196.7)$$

Consequently, the place functions $|f_{n+m} - f_n|$ are integrable on M, and a further application of the Schwarz Inequality yields the relation

$$\int_M |f_{n+m} - f_n|\, d\varphi \leqq \left(\int_M (f_{n+m} - f_n)^2\, d\varphi \int_M d\varphi\right)^{1/2}.$$

Hence, if we put

$$\varepsilon_n^2 = \delta_n^2\, \varphi(M), \quad \varepsilon_n = \delta_n \sqrt{\varphi(M)},$$

the hypotheses of Theorem 1 of § 190 are satisfied, and there exists a place function g that satisfies the relation

$$\lim_{n=\infty} \int_M |f_n - g|\, d\varphi = 0. \qquad (196.8)$$

This place function g is square integrable. For, if $[S_g(y)]$ denotes a nest of somas of g, we have

$$\int_M g^2\, d\varphi = \lim_{y=\infty} \int_{S_g(y)} g^2\, d\varphi. \qquad (196.9)$$

But now

$$0 \leqq (f_n - g)^2 = f_n^2 + 2\,g\,(g - f_n) - g^2,$$

whence it follows that

$$\int_{S_g(y)} g^2\, d\varphi \leqq \int_{S_g(y)} f_n^2\, d\varphi + 2 \int_{S_g(y)} |g| \cdot |f_n - g|\, d\varphi \leqq \alpha^2 + 2\,y \int_{S_g(y)} |f_n - g|\, d\varphi.$$

Using (196.8) and (196.9), we find first

$$\int_{S_g(y)} g^2\, d\varphi \leqq \alpha^2 \qquad \text{and then} \qquad \int_M g^2\, d\varphi \leqq \alpha^2. \qquad (196.10)$$

197. By the last result, the place functions

$$h_n = f_n - g \qquad (197.1)$$

as well are square integrable. We let $[T_n(y)]$ denote one of the nests of somas of h_n and estimate the integral

$$\int_M h_n^2\, d\varphi = \lim_{y=\infty} \int_{T_n(y)} h_n^2\, d\varphi. \qquad (197.2)$$

By (196.2), from the relation

$$(h_{n+m} - h_n)^2 = (f_{n+m} - f_n)^2$$

there follows the relation

$$\int_M (h_{n+m} - h_n)^2 \, d\varphi \leqq \delta_n^2. \tag{197.3}$$

On the other hand,

$$\int_{T_n(y)} (h_{n+m} - h_n)^2 \, d\varphi = \int_{T_n(y)} h_{n+m}^2 \, d\varphi + \int_{T_n(y)} h_n^2 \, d\varphi - 2 \int_{T_n(y)} h_n \, h_{n+m} \, d\varphi,$$

and consequently we have the relation

$$\int_{T_n(y)} h_n^2 \, d\varphi \leqq \delta_n^2 + 2\, y \int_{T_n(y)} |h_{n+m}| \, d\varphi. \tag{197.4}$$

But now, in accordance with (196.8),

$$\lim_{m=\infty} \int_M |h_{n+m}| \, d\varphi = 0;$$

thus, it follows from (197.4) that

$$\int_{T_n(y)} h_n^2 \, d\varphi \leqq \delta_n^2,$$

and, using (197.1) and (197.2), we finally obtain

$$\int_M (f_n - g)^2 \, d\varphi \leqq \delta_n^2. \tag{197.5}$$

A last passage to the limit yields the relation

$$\lim_{n=\infty} \int_M (f_n - g)^2 \, d\varphi = 0, \tag{197.6}$$

which is (196.4).

§§ 198-205. Ergodic Theory

198. Ergodic theory stems from the problem in statistical mechanics of determining, from the statistical behavior of a family of trajectories, the asymptotic behavior of the individual trajectories. It has become more and more evident, however, that the theorems which were set up for this purpose are of fundamental significance for the entire integral calculus.

We consider a measure function $\varphi(X)$, defined for all somas $X \subseteqq M$ belonging to a complete ring, for which

$$0 < \varphi(M) < +\infty, \tag{198.1}$$

as well as a measure-preserving homomorphism that transforms the ring of measurability $\mathfrak{M}_\varphi$ of $\varphi(X)$ onto itself or part of itself. That is, the images

$$X' = \tau X \qquad (X \in \mathfrak{M}_\varphi) \tag{198.2}$$

of the X under this homomorphism are assumed to belong, just like the X themselves, to $\mathfrak{M}_\varphi$ and the relation

$$\varphi(\tau X) = \varphi(X) \tag{198.3}$$

is assumed to hold throughout. We assume moreover that $M \in \mathfrak{M}_\varphi$ and $M' = \tau M = M$.

It is not assumed, however, that every soma of $\mathfrak{M}_\varphi$ can be represented as the image $X' = \tau X$ of some soma X in $\mathfrak{M}_\varphi$. A very simple example of a measure-preserving homomorphism for the Lebesgue content on the real line, for which no inverse mapping $\tau^{-1}X$ exists is the following: We consider a continuous and continuously differentiable function $f(x)$ defined on the interval

$$J: 0 \leqq x \leqq 1 \tag{198.4}$$

for which

$$f(0) = 0, \quad 0 < f'(x) < 1 \qquad (0 \leqq x \leqq 1) \tag{198.5}$$

and put

$$g(x) = f(1) + x - f(x). \tag{198.6}$$

Next, to each point x of the half-open interval $0 \leqq x < 1$ we assign the pair of points

$$x_1' = f(x), \quad x_2' = g(x), \tag{198.7}$$

while to the point $x = 1$ we assign the single point $x' = 1$.

This definition assigns to each sub-interval δ of (198.4) two sub-intervals δ_1' and δ_2', and the sum of the lengths of δ_1' and δ_2' is equal to the length of δ. In the same way, each subset X of J is mapped on a point set $X' = \tau X$ that has the same outer Lebesgue content as X. But not every subset of J can be looked upon as the image $X' = \tau X$ of a point set X. For example, no point set lying in the interval $0 < x < f(1)$ is such an image set.

199. We now consider the field F of φ-measurable place functions f for which the integral

$$\int_X f\, d\varphi \tag{199.1}$$

exists and especially those that are integrable on M and for which

$$\int_M |f|\, d\varphi = \alpha < +\infty. \tag{199.2}$$

The homomorphism considered in § 198 assigns to each of these functions f a place function τf (cf. § 118), which likewise belongs to the field F, so that the operation τf is iterable, and to each place function f there can be assigned the sequence of place functions

$$\tau f,\ \tau^2 f,\ \ldots,\ \tau^k f,\ \ldots. \tag{199.3}$$

We are also in a position, in addition, to consider the sequence of mean values

$$\sigma_1 f = f, \quad \sigma_2 f = \frac{f + \tau f}{2}, \quad \ldots, \quad \sigma_k f = \frac{f + \tau f + \cdots + \tau^{k-1} f}{k}, \quad \ldots, \tag{199.4}$$

which will play an important role in our theory. Indeed, while the sequence of place functions (199.3) is convergent only in isolated exceptional cases, the Principal Ergodic Theorem, proved in 1931 by George D. Birkhoff[6] states that the sequence of place functions (199.4) is convergent everywhere on M, except perhaps on a null soma of $\varphi(X)$, and is also convergent in the mean.

In earlier proofs of this theorem, it was necessary to assume that the homomorphism $X' = \tau X$ is an isomorphism and that the inverse transformation $\tau^{-1}X$ exists; however, a trick due to H. R. Pitt,[7] which can be simplified somewhat further, makes possible a proof of the theorem under the more general conditions stated above.

The measure-preserving homomorphism $X' = \tau X$ is not used directly in the proof, but only the properties of the mapping τf of place functions, which, by §§ 123 ff., is equivalent to it.

Thus, as in § 123, we shall assume that the mapping τf is linear and continuous and satisfies the equation

$$\tau |f| = |\tau f|. \tag{199.5}$$

From this it follows not only that the relation $f \geqq 0$ implies $\tau f \geqq 0$, but also that the equation

$$\tau \max(f_1, f_2, \ldots, f_p) = \max(\tau f_1, \tau f_2, \ldots, \tau f_p) \tag{199.6}$$

---

[6] G. D. Birkhoff, *Proc. Nat. Acad. Sci.*, Vol. 17 (1931), pp. 650-660=*Collected Mathematical Papers*, Vol. II (Amer. Math. Soc., 1950), pp. 398-408.

[7] H. R. Pitt, "Some Generalizations of the Ergodic Theorem," *Proc. Cambridge Philos. Soc.*, Vol. 38 (1943), pp. 325-342.

holds, from which, by iteration, we obtain

$$\tau^k \max(f_1, f_2, \ldots, f_p) = \max(\tau^k f_1, \tau^k f_2, \ldots, \tau^k f_p). \tag{199.7}$$

The fact that our homomorphism is measure-preserving now yields, by § 179, the equation

$$\int_{\tau X} \tau f \, d\varphi = \int_X f \, d\varphi; \tag{199.8}$$

then, since $\tau M = M$, we also have

$$\int_M f \, d\varphi = \int_M \tau f \, d\varphi = \cdots = \int_M \tau^k f \, d\varphi. \tag{199.9}$$

Moreover, taking (199.5) into consideration, we obtain

$$\int_M |\tau^k f| \, d\varphi = \int_M \tau^k |f| \, d\varphi = \int_M |f| \, d\varphi = \alpha. \tag{199.10}$$

Finally, if we apply equations (199.9) and (199.10) to the relations (199.4), we obtain first

$$\int_M \sigma_k f \, d\varphi = \int_M f \, d\varphi, \tag{199.11}$$

and then

$$\int_M |\sigma_k f| \, d\varphi \leqq \alpha. \tag{199.12}$$

200. We now establish a lemma the ideas for which are due to Pitt. We consider an infinite sequence of place functions

$$h_1, h_2, h_3, \ldots, \tag{200.1}$$

all of which have the same domain of definition M, and we introduce the notation

$$s_{pq} = h_{p+1} + h_{p+2} + \cdots + h_{p+q} \quad (p = 0, 1, 2, \ldots; q = 1, 2, \ldots). \tag{200.2}$$

Next, let n be a positive integer that will be held fixed throughout this discussion; we put

$$s_p^* = \max(s_{p1}, s_{p2}, \ldots, s_{pn}) \qquad (p = 0, 1, \ldots), \tag{200.3}$$

$$t_p^* = \max(s_{0(p+1)}, s_{0(p+2)}, \ldots, s_{0(p+n)}) \tag{200.4}$$

and shall prove, to begin with, that under the assumption

$$s_p^* \geqq 0 \quad \text{for} \quad p = 0, 1, \ldots, \tag{200.5}$$

all the t_p^* are $\geqq 0$.

We remark that, by (200.3) and (200.4),

$$s_0^* = t_0^*, \tag{200.6}$$

so that we need only show that $t_p^* \geqq 0$ if $t_{p-1}^* \geqq 0$.

But if indeed

$$t_{p-1}^* = \max(s_{0p}, s_{0(p+1)}, \ldots, s_{0(p+n-1)}) \geqq 0, \tag{200.7}$$

M admits a decomposition

$$M = M' + M'' \tag{200.8}$$

such that the relation $s_{0p} \geqq 0$ holds on M' while

$$\max(s_{0(p+1)}, \ldots, s_{0(p+n-1)}) \geqq 0$$

holds on M''. Hence $t_p^* \geqq 0$ on M'' also, and it suffices to verify this relation on M'. But on M' we have, on the one hand,

$$s_{0p} = h_1 + h_2 + \cdots + h_p \geqq 0, \tag{200.9}$$

and on the other, by hypothessis, we have $s_p^* \geqq 0$. This last inequality indicates that M' admits at least one decomposition

$$M' = M_1' + M_2' + \cdots + M_n'$$

such that the inequality

$$s_{pj} = h_{p+1} + \cdots + h_{p+j} \geqq 0 \quad (j = 1, 2, \ldots, n) \tag{200.10}$$

holds on every M_j'. By termwise addition of the inequalities (200.9) and (200.10), then, we find

$$h_1 + h_2 + \cdots + h_{p+j} = s_{0(p+j)} \geqq 0.$$

This shows that on each of the somas $M_1', \ldots, M_n'$ the place function t_p^* is $\geqq 0$, which proves that, for every p, t_p^* is greater than or equal to zero everywhere on M.

Thus, by (200.4), for every positive integer p there is a decomposition

$$M = M_1^{(p)} + M_2^{(p)} + \cdots + M_n^{(p)}$$

such that the relation

$$h_1 + h_2 + \cdots + h_{p+j} \geqq 0$$

holds on every non-empty $M_j^{(p)}$. Then, a fortiori, the relation

$$h_1 + h_2 + \cdots + h_p + |h_{p+1}| + \cdots + |h_{p+n}| \geqq 0$$

must hold for every $p = 1, 2, \ldots$ everywhere on M. We can thus state the following theorem.

Theorem 1: *We consider a sequence*

$$h_1, h_2, h_3, \ldots \tag{200.11}$$

of place functions defined on a soma M and introduce the abbreviations

$$s_{pq} = h_{p+1} + h_{p+2} + \cdots + h_{p+q} \quad (p = 0, 1, 2, \ldots; q = 1, 2, \ldots), \tag{200.12}$$

$$s_p^* = \max(s_{p1}, s_{p2}, \ldots, s_{pn}), \tag{200.13}$$

where n denotes a fixed positive integer. Under the assumption that

$$s_p^* \geqq 0 \quad \text{for} \quad p = 0, 1, 2, \ldots, \tag{200.14}$$

it follows that for every positive integer p the relation

$$h_1 + h_2 + \cdots + h_p + |h_{p+1}| + |h_{p+2}| + \cdots + |h_{p+n}| \geqq 0 \tag{200.15}$$

holds on the entire domain of definition M.

201. We apply Theorem 1 to sequences of place functions of the form

$$h_1 = f, \quad h_2 = \tau f, \quad \ldots, \quad h_k = \tau^{k-1} f, \quad \ldots, \tag{201.1}$$

where the operator τ is assumed to satisfy the conditions of § 199. In place of (200.12) and (200.13) we can now write

$$\left.\begin{aligned} s_{pq} &= \tau^p f + \tau^{p+1} f + \cdots + \tau^{p+q-1} f \\ &= \tau^p (f + \tau f + \cdots + \tau^{q-1} f) \\ &= \tau^p s_{0q}, \end{aligned}\right\} \tag{201.2}$$

$$s_p^* = \tau^p \max(s_{01}, s_{02}, \ldots, s_{0n}). \tag{201.3}$$

Accordingly, by the positivity of the operator τ, all the s_p^* are $\geqq 0$ as soon as $s_0^* \geqq 0$, and thus Theorem 1 can be applied, under the assumption $s_0^* \geqq 0$.

By (199.4), however, we have

$$s_{0k} = f + \tau f + \cdots + \tau^{k-1} f = k\, \sigma_k f,$$

and hence

$$s_0^* = \max(\sigma_1 f, 2\,\sigma_2 f, \ldots, n\,\sigma_n f). \tag{201.4}$$

Thus, if we put

$$f_n^* = \max(\sigma_1 f, \sigma_2 f, \ldots, \sigma_n f), \tag{201.5}$$

f_n^* is a non-negative place function if and only if $s_0^* \geqq 0$ everywhere on M. By (200.15), then, we have

$$f + \tau f + \cdots + \tau^{p-1} f + |\tau^p f| + |\tau^{p+1} f| + \cdots + |\tau^{p+n-1} f| \geqq 0,$$

under the assumption that $f_n^* \geqq 0$. By making use now of equations (199.9) and (199.10), we find

$$p \int_M f \, d\varphi + n\alpha \geqq 0 \qquad (p = 1, 2, \ldots),$$

from which it follows immediately that

$$\int_M f \, d\varphi \geqq 0. \tag{201.6}$$

Consequently, we have the following theorem.

THEOREM 2: *Let f be a place function of* F, *integrable on M, for which*

$$\int_M |f| \, d\varphi < +\infty.$$

Using the functions of the sequence f, τf, $\tau^2 f$, ..., we form the functions

$$\sigma_1 f = f, \quad \sigma_2 f = \frac{f + \tau f}{2}, \quad \ldots, \quad \sigma_k f = \frac{f + \tau f + \cdots + \tau^{k-1} f}{k}, \quad \ldots \tag{201.7}$$

and put

$$f_n^* = \max(\sigma_1 f, \sigma_2 f, \ldots, \sigma_n f) \quad (n = 1, 2, \ldots). \tag{201.8}$$

Then, if there is a value of n for which

$$f_n^* \geqq 0, \tag{201.9}$$

we have

$$\int_M f \, d\varphi \geqq 0. \tag{201.10}$$

202. We now let $[S_n^*(y)]$ denote a nest of somas of f_n^* and choose a value of y that will be held fixed throughout the discussion. Furthermore, we define a place function g by means of the equations

$$\left.\begin{aligned} g &= 0 \quad \text{on} \quad S_n^*(y) \\ g &= f - y \quad \text{on} \quad M \dotplus S_n^*(y) \end{aligned}\right\} \tag{202.1}$$

and remark that, in view of (198.1), the place function g, like f, is integrable on M.

Now $f \leqq f_n^*$ on M, and $f_n^* \leqq y$ on $S_n^*(y)$; thus $f - y \leqq 0$ on $S_n^*(y)$; by (202.1), then, we have

$$g \geqq f - y \tag{202.2}$$

everywhere on M. From this, it follows further that

$$\tau^k g \geqq \tau^k (f - y) = \tau^k f - y, \quad \sigma_k g \geqq \sigma_k f - y,$$

and finally that

$$g_n^* \geqq f_n^* - y, \tag{202.3}$$

where we put

$$g_n^* = \max(\sigma_1 g, \sigma_2 g, \ldots, \sigma_n g). \tag{202.4}$$

Furthermore, it follows from (203.3) and $g_n^* \geqq \sigma_1 g = g$ that

$$g_n^* \geqq \max(g, f_n^* - y);$$

now $g = 0$ on $S_n^*(y)$, and $f_n^* - y \geqq 0$ on $M \dotplus S_n^*(y)$, so that

$$g_n^* \geqq 0$$

everywhere on M. Then, by Theorem 2,

$$\int_M g \, d\varphi \geqq 0,$$

which, by (202.1), can be written as

$$\int_{M \dotplus S_n(y)} (f - y) \, d\varphi \geqq 0. \tag{202.5}$$

Now, according to (201.5), we have

$$f_1^* \leqq f_2^* \leqq \ldots.$$

Thus if we put

$$f^* = \lim_{n=\infty} f_n^* = \sup(\sigma_1 f, \sigma_2 f, \ldots), \tag{202.6}$$

a nest of somas $[S^*(y)]$ of f^* is given by the equation

$$S^*(y) = \lim_{n=\infty} S_n^*(y). \tag{202.7}$$

Finally, carrying out in the relation (202.5) the passage to the limit indicated in (202.7), we obtain the following theorem.

THEOREM 3: *If* $[S^*(y)]$ *denotes a nest of somas of*

$$f^* = \sup(\sigma_1 f, \sigma_2 f, \ldots), \tag{202.8}$$

then, for every real number y, the inequality

$$\int_{M-S^*(y)} (f - y)\, d\varphi \geqq 0 \tag{202.9}$$

holds.

We call (202.9) the *principal ergodic inequality.*

Making use of this theorem, we can replace the condition $f_n^* \geqq 0$ of Theorem 2 of § 201 by the more general condition $f^* \geqq 0$. Indeed, if $f^* \geqq 0$, then $S^*(y) = O$ for $y < 0$, and (202.9) yields

$$\int_M (f - y)\, d\varphi \geqq 0 \quad \text{for} \quad y < 0, \tag{202.10}$$

from which (201.10) follows immediately.

203. It is now easy to prove the Birkhoff Theorem for the case of bounded functions that satisfy

$$|f| \leqq \beta < +\infty. \tag{203.1}$$

For by (120.11) we have

$$|\tau^m f| \leqq \beta, \quad |\sigma_n f| \leqq \beta, \quad |\sigma_n \tau^m f| \leqq \beta \tag{203.2}$$

for all positive integers n and m; and similar relations hold for the upper and lower limits

$$\bar{g} = \overline{\lim_{n=\infty}}\, \sigma_n f, \quad \underline{g} = \underline{\lim_{n=\infty}}\, \sigma_n f. \tag{203.3}$$

Using the identity

$$\tau\, \sigma_n f = \sigma_n f + \frac{1}{n}(\tau^n f - f), \tag{203.4}$$

in conjunction with equation (121.4), in which we must replace σ by τ, we obtain the relations

$$\tau\, \bar{g} = \bar{g}, \quad \sigma_n \bar{g} = \bar{g}. \tag{203.5}$$

Then, if we put

$$h = f - \bar{g}, \tag{203.6}$$

we obtain

$$\sigma_n h = \sigma_n f - \bar{g}$$

and

$$\overline{\lim_{n=\infty}}\, \sigma_n h = \bar{g} - \bar{g} = 0.$$

Thus if we denote the least upper bound of the set of $\sigma_n h$ by h^*, we have

$$h^* \geqq 0.$$

Hence, by the remark at the end of § 202, we also have

$$\int_M (f - \bar{g})\, d\varphi \geqq 0. \tag{203.7}$$

Similarly, the equation

$$\overline{\lim_{n=\infty}} \sigma_n(-f) = -\underline{g}$$

implies

$$\int_M (\underline{g} - f)\, d\varphi \geqq 0. \tag{203.8}$$

By adding the relations (203.7) and (203.8) and taking into account the fact that $\underline{g} \leqq \bar{g}$, we obtain

$$\int_M (\underline{g} - \bar{g})\, d\varphi = 0. \tag{203.9}$$

Thus, there is a—possibly empty—null soma N such that the limit

$$\lim_{n=\infty} \sigma_n f = g \tag{203.10}$$

exists on the soma $M \dotplus N$. If we also put $g = 0$ on N, then, in the first place, in accordance with (199.11), the equation

$$\int_M g\, d\varphi = \int_M f\, d\varphi \tag{203.11}$$

is meaningful and, in the second place, the sequence of functions $\sigma_n f$, being uniformly bounded, converges in the mean on M, by Theorem 5 of § 189; that is, we have the equation

$$\lim_{n=\infty} \int_M |\sigma_n f - g|\, d\varphi = 0. \tag{203.12}$$

204. We extend these results to non-negative functions f that are integrable on M and for which $\int_M f\, d\varphi < +\infty$. Such place functions can be approximated by monotonically increasing sequences of bounded functions

$$f_1 \leqq f_2 \leqq \dots \leqq f_p \leqq \dots \tag{204.1}$$

that can be so chosen as to satisfy all the conditions

$$\lim_{p=\infty} f_p = f, \tag{204.2}$$

$$k_p = f - f_p, \quad \int_M k_p\, d\varphi \leqq \frac{1}{4^p}. \tag{204.3}$$

To each k_p we assign the place function

$$k_p^* = \sup(\sigma_1 k_p, \sigma_2 k_p, \dots) \tag{204.4}$$

and we let $[T_p^*(y)]$ denote a nest of somas of k_p^*.

We now apply Theorem 3 of § 202 to k_p and observe that

$$y\,\varphi(M \dotplus T_p^*(y)) \leqq \int\limits_{M \dotplus T_p^*(y)} k_p\,d\varphi \leqq \int\limits_M k_p\,d\varphi \leqq \frac{1}{4^p}$$

follows from (202.9) in conjunction with $k_p \geqq 0$ and (204.3). If we now put $y = 1/2^p$, we obtain

$$\varphi\left(M \dotplus T_p^*\left(\frac{1}{2^p}\right)\right) \leqq \frac{1}{2^p}\,. \tag{204.5}$$

Next, as in § 191, we introduce the notation

$$U_p = M \dotplus T_p^*\left(\frac{1}{2^p}\right),\quad M \dotplus V_p = U_p \dotplus U_{p+1} \dotplus \cdots,$$
$$V = V_1 \dotplus V_2 \dotplus \cdots \tag{204.6}$$

and we prove, just as before, that

$$\varphi(M \dotplus V) = 0. \tag{204.7}$$

By the results of § 203, we can assign a null soma N_p to each of the uniformly bounded sequences of functions $(\sigma_1 f_p, \sigma_2 f_p, \ldots)$ such that the limit

$$g_p = \lim_{n=\infty} \sigma_n f_p \tag{204.8}$$

exists on the soma $M \dotplus N_p$.

We put

$$N = (M \dotplus V) \dotplus \sum_{p=1}^{\infty} \dotplus N_p \tag{204.9}$$

and observe that $\varphi(N) = 0$. However, we have

$$V_p \subseteqq T_p^*\left(\frac{1}{2^p}\right),\quad 0 \leqq \sigma_n k_p \leqq k_p^*,\quad \sigma_n f = \sigma_n f_p + \sigma_n k_p.$$

Thus, we have

$$\sigma_n f_p \leqq \sigma_n f \leqq \sigma_n f_p + \frac{1}{2^p}$$

on the soma $(M \dotplus N)V_p$ and, making use of the notation of (203.3), we obtain

$$g_p \leqq \underline{g} \leqq \bar{g} \leqq g_p + \frac{1}{2^p}\,. \tag{204.10}$$

Thus, we also have

$$0 \leqq \bar{g} - \underline{g} \leqq \frac{1}{2^p} \tag{204.11}$$

on $(M \dotplus N)V_p$; therefore the sequence of place functions $\sigma_n f$ must converge to a function

$$g = \lim_{p=\infty} g_p \tag{204.12}$$

on each of the somas $(M \dotplus N)V_p$, and hence, since $V_p \subseteqq V_{p+q}$, on the soma $M \dotplus N$ itself.

205. We must now show that the sequence of place functions $\sigma_n f$ also converges in the mean to g on M.

The equations

$$\left.\begin{aligned} \sigma_{n+m} f &= \sigma_{n+m} f_p + \sigma_{n+m} k_p \\ \sigma_n f &= \sigma_n f_p + \sigma_n k_p \end{aligned}\right\} \tag{205.1}$$

imply the relation

$$|\sigma_{n+m} f - \sigma_n f| \leqq |\sigma_{n+m} f_p - \sigma_n f_p| + \sigma_{n+m} k_p + \sigma_n k_p. \tag{205.2}$$

But now, by (199.11) and (204.3), we have

$$\int_M \sigma_{n+m} k_p \, d\varphi = \int_M \sigma_n k_p \, d\varphi = \int_M k_p \, d\varphi \leqq \frac{1}{4^p},$$

whence we obtain

$$\int_M |\sigma_{n+m} f - \sigma_n f| \, d\varphi \leqq \int_M |\sigma_{n+m} f_p - \sigma_n f_p| \, d\varphi + \frac{2}{4^p}. \tag{205.3}$$

By (204.8), the sequence of uniformly bounded functions $\sigma_n f_p$ $(n = 1, 2, \ldots)$ is convergent on a soma $M \dotplus N_p$, where $\varphi(N_p) = 0$; for this reason, it also converges in the mean. Therefore, to every positive integer p we can assign a positive integer n_p such that

$$\int_M |\sigma_{n+m} f - \sigma_n f| \, d\varphi \leqq \frac{1}{4^{p-1}} \tag{205.4}$$

for every $n \geqq n_p$ and every m. Thus, by Theorem 1 of § 190 and in view of (199.12), the sequence of the $\sigma_n f$ also converges in the mean, and there is a function g' for which we have

$$\lim_{n=\infty} \int_M |\sigma_n f - g'| \, d\varphi = 0. \tag{205.5}$$

Moreover, there is a null soma N' for which

$$\lim_{p=\infty} \sigma_{n_p} f = g' \tag{205.6}$$

on $M \dotplus N'$. Then g' must agree on $M - (N \dotplus N')$ with the place function g that we determined in § 204; and we have, finally,

$$\lim_{n=\infty} \int_M |\sigma_n f - g| \, d\varphi = 0. \tag{205.7}$$

In conclusion, we remark that we have

$$\int_M g \, d\varphi = \lim_{p=\infty} \int_M g_p \, d\varphi = \lim_{p=\infty} \int_M f_p \, d\varphi = \int_M f \, d\varphi < +\infty.$$

Since every place function can be represented as a difference of non-negative place functions, all the results of the preceding sections can be carried over to functions of arbitrary sign, and we obtain the following theorem.

THEOREM 4 (The Principal Ergodic Theorem): *If f is a place function of* F *for which*

$$\int_M |f| \, d\varphi < +\infty, \tag{205.8}$$

then there is a soma N (which may be the empty soma) such that

$$\varphi(N) = 0 \tag{205.9}$$

and such that the limit of the functions (199.4)

$$\lim_{n=\infty} \sigma_n f = g \tag{205.10}$$

exists on $M \dotplus N$.

The sequence of the $\sigma_n f$ also converges to g in the mean:

$$\lim_{n=\infty} \int_M |\sigma_n f - g| \, d\varphi = 0. \tag{205.11}$$

Moreover, the equations

$$\tau g = g, \quad \sigma_n g = g \tag{205.12}$$

hold on $M \dotplus N$, and we also have

$$\int_M g \, d\varphi = \int_M f \, d\varphi, \quad \int_M |g| \, d\varphi = \int_M |f| \, d\varphi. \tag{205.13}$$

CHAPTER EIGHT

THE COMPUTATION OF MEASURE FUNCTIONS

§§ 206-210. Maximal Measure Functions

206. We consider an arbitrary subset $\mathfrak{B}$, containing the empty soma O, of a complete ring of somas $\mathfrak{A}$. To each soma U of $\mathfrak{B}$ we assign a finite non-negative number $p(U)$ and, in particular, we assign the number zero to the empty soma O. In this way, there is defined a soma function with domain of definition $\mathfrak{B}$; we shall call this function a *weight function.*

Using the weight function $p(U)$, we compute a soma function $\psi(X)$ with domain of definition $\mathfrak{A}$ in the following way. Let $\mathfrak{B}^*$ be the $\mathfrak{B}$-coverable part of $\mathfrak{A}$ (cf. § 55). To each soma A of the set of somas $\mathfrak{A} - \mathfrak{B}^*$, we assign the number $\psi(A) = +\infty$. To each soma A of the set of somas $\mathfrak{B}^*$ there corresponds, by assumption, an at most countable sequence $\{U_j\}$ of somas of $\mathfrak{B}$ whose union

$$V(U_j) = \sum_j \dot{+}\, U_j \tag{206.1}$$

covers A. Every sequence of somas $\{U_j\}$ of this type is called a *covering sequence* of A. To each possible covering sequence of A we associate the non-negative, finite or infinite number

$$\sum_j p(U_j) \tag{206.2}$$

and we let $\psi(A)$ be the greatest lower bound, which may be $+\infty$, of all these numbers. That is, the following formula is to hold:

$$\psi(A) = \inf\Bigl(\sum_j p(U_j)\,;\ U_j \in \mathfrak{B}\,,\ V(U_j) \supseteq A\Bigr). \tag{206.3}$$

As we shall now show, the soma function $\psi(X)$ given by this formula is a measure function. Since $\psi(O) = 0$, all we need show, according to § 131, is that whenever

$$B \subseteq A_1 \dot{+} A_2 \dot{+} \cdots \qquad (B \in \mathfrak{A},\ A_k \in \mathfrak{A}) \tag{206.4}$$

we have

$$\psi(B) \leqq \psi(A_1) + \psi(A_2) + \cdots. \tag{206.5}$$

We can assume in addition, with no loss of generality, that the series on the right-hand side of (206.5) has a finite sum. This is possible, however, only if each of the somas $A_1, A_2, \ldots$ belongs to $\mathfrak{B}^*$.

We fix an arbitrary positive number ε; for every soma A_k there is at least one covering sequence $U_{k1}, U_{k2}, \ldots$ of A_k for which we have both the relations

$$A_k \subseteqq U_{k1} \dotplus U_{k2} \dotplus \cdots, \qquad \sum_j p(U_{kj}) \leqq \psi(A_k) + \frac{\varepsilon}{2^k}. \tag{206.6}$$

The soma B is then covered by the at most countable number of somas U_{kj}, and hence we have

$$\psi(B) \leqq \sum_{k,j} p(U_{kj}) \leqq \sum_k \psi(A_k) + \varepsilon. \tag{206.7}$$

By passage to the limit, we obtain the relation (206.5), which was to be proved.

207. It should be observed that the normal somas of $\psi(X)$ (cf. § 135) are precisely the somas of $\mathfrak{B}^*$. Moreover, since each soma U of $\mathfrak{B}$ covers itself, (206.3) yields

$$\psi(U) \leqq p(U) \qquad (U \in \mathfrak{B}). \tag{207.1}$$

Now let $\varphi(X)$ be any measure function having the same domain of definition $\mathfrak{A}$ as $\psi(X)$ and which likewise satisfies

$$\varphi(U) \leqq p(U) \qquad (U \in \mathfrak{B}). \tag{207.2}$$

Since $\varphi(X)$ is cover-bounded, for every covering sequence $\{U_j\}$ of a soma A of $\mathfrak{B}^*$, we have

$$\varphi(A) \leqq \sum_j \varphi(U_j) \leqq \sum_j p(U_j), \tag{207.3}$$

from which we deduce

$$\varphi(A) \leqq \psi(A). \tag{207.4}$$

The relation (207.4) also holds, of course, for every soma A of $\mathfrak{A} - \mathfrak{B}^*$, since $\psi(A) = +\infty$ for such somas.

Thus, of all the measure functions $\varphi(X)$ that satisfy $\varphi(U) \leqq p(U)$ for all U in $\mathfrak{B}$, $\psi(X)$ is the largest: the measure function $\psi(X)$ is therefore called the *maximal measure function subordinate to* $p(U)$. The domain of definition $\mathfrak{B}$ of the weight function $p(U)$ is called a *base* of $\psi(X)$.

Summing up, we have the following theorem.

THEOREM 1: *Given a non-negative, finite weight function $p(U)$ that is defined on a subset $\mathfrak{B}$ of a complete ring of somas $\mathfrak{A}$ and that need satisfy no condition other than $p(O) = 0$, there exists on $\mathfrak{A}$ a uniquely defined* *maximal measure function* $\psi(X)$ *that satisfies the condition* $\psi(U) \leqq p(U)$ *for every soma* U *in* $\mathfrak{B}$.

208. The maximal measure function $\psi(X)$ is already cover-bounded if we restrict ourselves exclusively to somas of the base $\mathfrak{B}$. Thus, the equation

$$\psi(U) = p(U) \tag{208.1}$$

can hold for every soma U of $\mathfrak{B}$ only if $p(U)$ is also cover-bounded on $\mathfrak{B}$.

If, conversely, the weight function $p(U)$ is cover-bounded on its domain of definition $\mathfrak{B}$, then for *every* covering sequence $\{U_j\}$ of the soma U, we have

$$p(U) \leqq \sum_j p(U_j). \tag{208.2}$$

Then by (206.3), we have $p(U) \leqq \psi(U)$, and by (207.1), we conclude that (208.1) must hold. We thus have the following theorem.

THEOREM 2: *The maximal measure function* $\psi(X)$ *subordinate to a weight function* $p(U)$ *satisfies the equation*

$$\psi(U) = p(U) \tag{208.3}$$

for every soma U *of the base* $\mathfrak{B}$ *of* $\psi(X)$ *if and only if* $p(U)$ *is cover-bounded.*

Thus, if a weight function $p(U)$ is not cover-bounded on $\mathfrak{B}$, there is at least one soma U_0 in $\mathfrak{B}$ for which we have

$$\psi(U_0) < p(U_0). \tag{208.4}$$

Then there are an infinite number of different functions $p_1(U)$ that satisfy the conditions

$$\psi(U) \leqq p_1(U) \leqq p(U) \tag{208.5}$$

for all somas U in $\mathfrak{B}$. Let $\psi_1(X)$ be the maximal measure function with domain of definition $\mathfrak{A}$ subordinate to $p_1(U)$. Since $p_1(U) \leqq p(U)$, $\psi_1(X)$ cannot be larger than the maximal measure function $\psi(X)$ subordinate to $p(U)$; since $\psi(U) \leqq p_1(U)$, $\psi(X)$ cannot be larger than the maximal measure function $\psi_1(X)$ subordinate to $p_1(U)$. Thus $\psi_1(X) = \psi(X)$, and we have the following theorem.

THEOREM 3: *If the weight function* $p(U)$ *generates the maximal measure function* $\psi(X)$ *with base* $\mathfrak{B}$, *then* $\psi(X)$ *is also generated by any other weight function* $P_1(U)$ *defined on* $\mathfrak{B}$ *for which*

$$\psi(U) \leqq p_1(U) \leqq p(U) \qquad (U \in \mathfrak{B}). \tag{208.6}$$

209. The base $\mathfrak{B}$ of the maximal measure function $\psi(X)$ subordinate to $p(U)$ is now assumed to be a *subtractive* set of somas (§ 33); moreover, let the weight function $p(U)$ be *superadditive* (§ 126).

We consider a soma U of $\mathfrak{B}$ and an arbitrary soma A of $\mathfrak{A}$ for which $\psi(A) < +\infty$. Given any positive number ε, we choose a covering sequence $\{U_j\}$ of A from $\mathfrak{B}$, for which we can write

$$A \subseteqq \sum_j \dot{+} U_j, \quad \sum_j p(U_j) \leqq \psi(A) + \varepsilon. \tag{209.1}$$

If, next, we put

$$V = \sum_j \dot{+} U_j, \tag{209.2}$$

then it follows from $AV = A$ that

$$AU \subseteqq VU, \quad A \dot{+} AU = A(V \dot{+} VU) \subseteqq V \dot{+} VU; \tag{209.3}$$

thus, recalling Theorem 5 of § 15 and equation (24.15), we can write

$$AU \subseteqq \sum_j \dot{+} U_j U, \quad A \dot{+} AU \subseteqq \sum_j \dot{+} (U_j \dot{+} U_j U). \tag{209.4}$$

From this, there follow the inequalities

$$\psi(AU) \leqq \sum_j p(U_j U), \quad \psi(A \dot{+} AU) \leqq \sum_j p(U_j \dot{+} U_j U), \tag{209.5}$$

which are obtained by using the fact that $\mathfrak{B}$ is a subtractive set of somas, so that it contains both the somas $U_j \dot{+} U_j U$ and, by Theorem 1 of § 34, the somas $U_j U$.

On the other hand, the fact that $p(U)$ is superadditive is expressed by the relations

$$p(U_j) \geqq p(U_j U) + p(U_j \dot{+} U_j U) \quad (j = 1, 2, \ldots). \tag{209.6}$$

Comparing (209.5) and (209.6) with the second part of condition (209.1), we obtain

$$\psi(AU) + \psi(A \dot{+} AU) \leqq \psi(A) + \varepsilon; \tag{209.7}$$

if we let ε tend to zero and make use of the fact that $\psi(X)$ is union-bounded, we see that

$$\psi(A) = \psi(AU) + \psi(A \dot{+} AU). \tag{209.8}$$

Thus, the soma U must be ψ-measurable, and we have the following theorem.

THEOREM 4: *Let the base* $\mathfrak{B}$ *of a maximal measure function* $\psi(X)$ *be a subtractive set of somas and let the weight function* $p(U)$ *be superadditive on* $\mathfrak{B}$. *Then the set of somas* $\mathfrak{B}$ *is a subset of the ring of measurability* $\mathfrak{M}_\psi$ *of* $\psi(X)$.

210. If the base $\mathfrak{B}$ of a maximal measure function $\psi(X)$ is contained in the ring of measurability of this function and if $p(U) = \psi(U)$ for every soma U of $\mathfrak{B}$, then the weight function $p(U)$ must be completely additive on $\mathfrak{B}$ (Theorem 1 of § 136). Conversely, if $p(U)$ is completely additive on $\mathfrak{B}$ and if, moreover, $\mathfrak{B}$ is a subtractive set of somas, then, by the last theorem, the set $\mathfrak{B}$ must be contained in the ring of measurability of the maximal measure function $\psi(X)$ subordinate to $p(U)$.

The non-negative and completely additive weight function $p(U)$ is, of course, monotonically increasing on $\mathfrak{B}$. By Theorem 2 of § 127, this function is also union-bounded. Thus, by Theorem 3 of § 128 and Theorem 1 of § 34, it is also cover-bounded; and by Theorem 2 of § 208, we must have $p(U) = \psi(U)$. Thus, we have the following theorem.

THEOREM 5: *If the base* $\mathfrak{B}$ *of a maximal measure function is a subtractive set of somas, then a necessary and sufficient condition for the complete additivity of the weight function* $p(U)$ *is that* $\mathfrak{B}$ *be a subset of the ring of measurability of* $\psi(X)$ *and that, in addition, the equation* $\psi(U) = p(U)$ *hold for all somas* U *of* $\mathfrak{B}$.

§§ 211-215. The Bases of an Arbitrary Measure Function

211. Let $\varphi(X)$ be any measure function with domain of definition $\mathfrak{A}$, and let $\mathfrak{B}$ be a subset, containing the empty soma O, of $\mathfrak{E}_\varphi$, where, as in § 135, $\mathfrak{E}_\varphi$ denotes the totality of somas X of $\mathfrak{A}$ for which $\varphi(X)$ is finite. Then there is a maximal measure function $\psi(X)$ on $\mathfrak{A}$ with base $\mathfrak{B}$ that is calculated by using the weight function

$$p(U) = \varphi(U) \qquad (U \in \mathfrak{B}). \quad (211.1)$$

Then, for all the somas X in $\mathfrak{A}$, we have

$$\varphi(X) \leqq \psi(X) \qquad (X \in \mathfrak{A}). \quad (211.2)$$

But since the weight function (211.1) is cover-bounded, it follows from Theorem 2 of § 208 that we must have

$$\varphi(U) = \psi(U) \qquad (U \in \mathfrak{B}). \quad (211.3)$$

Next, if the equation $\varphi(X) = \psi(X)$ is satisfied not only on $\mathfrak{B}$, but everywhere on $\mathfrak{A}$, then $\mathfrak{B}$ is called a *base of the measure function* $\varphi(X)$. At the same time, $\varphi(X)$ is the maximal measure function subordinate to $\varphi(U)$ with base $\mathfrak{B}$, in the earlier sense (§ 207).

$\mathfrak{C}_\varphi$ is of course a base of $\varphi(X)$, since $\varphi(X) = +\infty$ for every soma X that does not belong to $\mathfrak{C}_\varphi$, and then $\varphi(X) = \psi(X)$ by (211.2).

Aside from $\mathfrak{C}_\varphi$, however, there are other sets of somas $\mathfrak{B} \prec \mathfrak{C}_\varphi$ that are bases of $\varphi(X)$. This is the case, for example, if $\varphi(X)$ was to begin with computed as a maximal measure function using such a base.

If $\mathfrak{B}$ is a base of $\varphi(X)$, then every set of somas $\mathfrak{B}_1$ that satisfies

$$\mathfrak{B} \prec \mathfrak{B}_1 \prec \mathfrak{C}_\varphi \tag{211.4}$$

is itself a base of $\varphi(X)$.

We again denote the $\mathfrak{B}$-coverable part of $\mathfrak{A}$ by $\mathfrak{B}^*$ (Theorem 1 of § 55), and we observe that every normal soma of $\varphi(X)$, i.e., every soma that belongs to $\mathfrak{C}_\varphi$ (§ 135), must also be a soma of $\mathfrak{B}^*$. Then, since $\mathfrak{B} \prec \mathfrak{C}_\varphi$, we have

$$\mathfrak{B}^* = \mathfrak{C}_\varphi^* . \tag{211.5}$$

212. Let $\mathfrak{B}$ be a base of a measure function $\varphi(X)$, which we transform into the measure function $\varphi'(X')$ by means of a homomorphism $X' = \sigma X$ (Theorem 1 of § 144). If ε is a positive number and if X' is a soma for which $\varphi'(X') < +\infty$, then, by § 144, there is at least one soma X that satisfies

$$X' = \sigma X, \quad \varphi(X) < \varphi'(X') + \varepsilon . \tag{212.1}$$

Moreover, there is a covering sequence $\{U_j\}$ made up of somas of $\mathfrak{B}$ for which

$$X \subseteqq \sum_j \dot{+}\, U_j, \quad \sum_j \varphi(U_j) < \varphi(X) + \varepsilon . \tag{212.2}$$

If we now consider the somas $U_j' = \sigma U_j$, all of which belong to the set of somas $\mathfrak{B}' = \sigma\mathfrak{B}$, we have

$$X' \subseteqq \sum_j \dot{+}\, U_j', \quad \varphi'(U_j') \leqq \varphi(U_j),$$

and thus, by the foregoing,

$$\varphi'(X') \leqq \sum_j \varphi'(U_j') < \varphi'(X') + 2\,\varepsilon .$$

But this just means that $\varphi'(X')$ is the maximal measure function subordinate to the weight function $\varphi'(U')$ with base $\mathfrak{B}'$, or in other words, that the set of somas

$$\mathfrak{B}' = \sigma\, \mathfrak{B} \tag{212.3}$$

is a base of $\varphi'(X')$.

213. If $\mathfrak{B}$ is a base of the measure function $\varphi(X)$ and A is a soma of $\mathfrak{C}_\varphi$, then, for each positive integer k, there is a sequence

$$U_{k1}, U_{k2}, \dots \tag{213.1}$$

of somas of $\mathfrak{B}$, for which we have

$$A \subseteqq \sum_j \dot{+} U_{kj}, \quad \sum_j \varphi(U_{kj}) \leqq \varphi(A) + \frac{1}{k}. \tag{213.2}$$

Then if we put

$$V_k = \sum_j \dot{+} U_{kj}, \quad \bar{A} = \prod_k V_k, \tag{213.3}$$

the relations

$$A \subseteqq \bar{A}, \quad \varphi(A) \leqq \varphi(\bar{A}) \leqq \varphi(V_k) \leqq \varphi(A) + \frac{1}{k} \tag{213.4}$$

hold, and therefore we also have

$$\varphi(\bar{A}) = \varphi(A). \tag{213.5}$$

Since the somas U_{kj} belong to $\mathfrak{B}$, the somas V_k belong to the countably additive closure $\mathfrak{B}_\sigma$ of $\mathfrak{B}$ (§ 42), and the soma $\bar{A}$ belongs to the countably multiplicative closure $\mathfrak{B}_{\sigma\delta}$ of $\mathfrak{B}_\sigma$. A soma $\bar{A}$ that enjoys the given properties exists even in the case that $\varphi(A) = +\infty$, if A is a normal soma of $\varphi(X)$. Thus, we have proved the following theorem.

THEOREM 1: *If $\mathfrak{B}$ is a base of the measure function $\varphi(X)$, then to each normal soma A of $\varphi(X)$ there can be assigned a soma A of the set of somas $\mathfrak{B}_{\sigma\delta}$ such that the relations*

$$A \subseteqq \bar{A}, \quad \varphi(\bar{A}) = \varphi(A) \tag{213.6}$$

both hold.

214. If a base of the measure function $\varphi(X)$ is known, the criterion (§ 129) for the measurability of a soma can be weakened. Indeed, we have:

THEOREM 2: *A given soma W of the domain of definition $\mathfrak{A}$ of a measure function $\varphi(X)$ is φ-measurable if only the equation*

$$\varphi(U) = \varphi(UW) + \varphi(U \dot{+} UW) \tag{214.1}$$

holds for every soma U of a base $\mathfrak{B}$ of $\varphi(X)$.

Proof: To prove the measurability of W, we must show, according to (132.3), that the relation

$$\varphi(A) \geqq \varphi(AW) + \varphi(A \dot{+} AW) \tag{214.2}$$

holds for every soma A in $\mathfrak{C}_\varphi$.

Now, an arbitrary number $\varepsilon > 0$ having been chosen, there are covering sequences $\{U_j\}$ of A whose elements belong to the base $\mathfrak{B}$ and satisfy the relations

$$A \subseteqq \sum_j \dot{+}\, U_j, \quad \varphi(A) + \varepsilon \geqq \sum_j \varphi(U_j). \tag{214.3}$$

Under the assumption that (214.1) holds for all the somas of $\mathfrak{B}$, however, we must have

$$\varphi(U_j) = \varphi(U_j W) + \varphi(U_j \dot{+} U_j W) \quad (j = 1, 2, \ldots). \tag{214.4}$$

On the other hand, it follows from the first of the relations (214.3), just as in § 209, that

$$AW \subseteqq \sum_j \dot{+}\, U_j W, \quad A \dot{+} AW \subseteqq \sum_j \dot{+}\, (U_j \dot{+} U_j W), \tag{214.5}$$

and since $\varphi(X)$ is cover-bounded, we obtain

$$\varphi(AW) \leqq \sum_j \varphi(U_j W), \quad \varphi(A \dot{+} AW) \leqq \sum_j \varphi(U_j \dot{+} U_j W). \tag{214.6}$$

From all these relations we conclude that

$$\varphi(A) + \varepsilon \geqq \varphi(AW) + \varphi(A \dot{+} AW), \tag{214.7}$$

from which the desired relation (214.2) follows by passage to the limit.

215. The simplest way to obtain a measure function is, of course, to compute it from a base $\mathfrak{B}$ and a weight function $p(U)$. In many important applications, however (cf. §§ 285 ff.), we must use a complicated procedure and consider measure functions that are defined as limits of maximal measure functions.

We take a monotonically decreasing sequence

$$\mathfrak{B}_1 \succ \mathfrak{B}_2 \succ \cdots \tag{215.1}$$

of subsets of a complete ring of somas $\mathfrak{A}$, each containing the empty soma O, and also a finite, non-negative weight function $p(U)$ that is defined on $\mathfrak{B}_1$, and hence on all the other $\mathfrak{B}_k$. We let $\varphi_k(X)$ be the maximal measure function subordinate to $p(U)$ with base $\mathfrak{B}_k$, and we observe that we always have

$$\varphi_k(X) \leqq \varphi_{k+1}(X). \tag{215.2}$$

For in fact, every covering sequence $\{U_j\}$ of X that is formed by using somas of $\mathfrak{B}_{k+1}$ is also a covering sequence with somas from $\mathfrak{B}_k$.

Thus, the limit function

$$\varphi(X) = \lim_{k=\infty} \varphi_k(X) \tag{215.3}$$

exists and, by Theorem 1 of § 141, is a measure function.

Now the interest in this construction lies in the fact that the limit function $\varphi(X)$ need not be identically equal to $+\infty$, not even if the intersection $\prod_j \mathfrak{B}_j$ of all the successive bases $\mathfrak{B}_j$ consists of the empty soma alone (cf. § 221).

To be able to examine the rings of measurability of the limit functions that arise from this procedure, we must now bring in, along with the notion of the ordinary measurability of a soma, a still more general notion.

§§ 216-221. Relative Measurability

216. If the soma U is measurable for the measure function $\varphi(X)$, then the equation

$$\varphi(X) = \varphi(XU) + \varphi(X \dotplus XU) \tag{216.1}$$

must hold for every soma X of the domain of definition $\mathfrak{A}$ of $\varphi(X)$. With the notation

$$L = X \dotplus XU, \quad M = XU, \tag{216.2}$$

we then have

$$L \circ U, \quad M \subseteqq U, \tag{216.3}$$

and the equation (216.1) can be written as follows:

$$\varphi(L + M) = \varphi(L) + \varphi(M). \tag{216.4}$$

If, conversely, (216.4) is always a consequence of condition (216.3), then (216.1) must also hold for every X in $\mathfrak{A}$, and U is φ-measurable. With these preliminaries, we make the following definition.

Definition: *Let V and $W \subseteqq V$ be two somas in the domain of definition $\mathfrak{A}$ of a measure function $\varphi(X)$. We say that W is φ-measurable relative to V if*

$$L \circ V, \quad M \subseteqq W \qquad (L, M \in \mathfrak{A}) \tag{216.5}$$

implies the relation

$$\varphi(L + M) = \varphi(L) + \varphi(M). \tag{216.6}$$

Thus, according to this definition, the soma U is measurable in the ordinary sense if and only if it is measurable relative to itself.

217. We consider a monotonically increasing sequence

$$U_1 \subseteqq U_2 \subseteqq \cdots \tag{217.1}$$

of an infinite number of somas that converges to the soma

$$U = \lim_{k=\infty} U_k. \tag{217.2}$$

We assume, moreover, that for some given measure function $\varphi(X)$, every soma U_k is φ-measurable relative to U_{k+1}. We shall show that the limit U of the somas U_k is measurable in the ordinary sense.

Let A be a soma for which $\varphi(A)$ is finite. We put

$$B_k = A U_k \qquad (k = 1, 2, \ldots) \tag{217.3}$$

and observe that we obtain

$$B_{k+1} = B_k + (B_{k+1} - B_k) \supseteqq B_{k-1} + (B_{k+1} - B_k) \quad (k = 2, 3, \ldots). \tag{217.4}$$

Now, we have

$$(B_{k+1} - B_k) \circ U_k, \quad B_{k-1} \subseteqq U_{k-1}, \tag{217.5}$$

and hence, from (217.4) and from the assumption that U_{k-1} is φ-measurable relative to U_k, it follows that

$$\varphi(B_{k+1}) \geqq \varphi(B_{k-1}) + \varphi(B_{k+1} - B_k),$$

i.e.,

$$\varphi(B_{k+1} - B_k) \leqq \varphi(B_{k+1}) - \varphi(B_{k-1}) \quad (k = 2, 3, \ldots). \tag{217.6}$$

Similarly, we see that

$$(A - AU) \circ U_{k+1}, \quad B_k \subseteqq U_k$$

and that

$$A \supseteqq B_k + (A - AU).$$

Hence it follows that

$$\varphi(A) \geqq \varphi(B_k) + \varphi(A - AU) \quad (k = 1, 2, \ldots). \tag{217.7}$$

Thus, if we put

$$\lambda = \lim_{k=\infty} \varphi(B_k), \tag{217.8}$$

we obtain

$$\varphi(A) \geqq \lambda + \varphi(A - AU). \tag{217.9}$$

Next, observe that the equation

$$AU = B_{m+1} + (B_{m+2} - B_{m+1}) + (B_{m+3} - B_{m+2}) + \cdots \tag{217.10}$$

holds for every positive integer m. From this, it follows, to begin with, that

$$\varphi(AU) \leqq \varphi(B_{m+1}) + \varphi(B_{m+2} - B_{m+1}) + \cdots,$$

or, according to (217.6),

$$\varphi(AU) \leqq \varphi(B_{m+1}) + \big(\varphi(B_{m+2}) - \varphi(B_m)\big) + \cdots. \tag{217.11}$$

This last relation can be written as

$$\varphi(AU) \leqq \lim_{k=\infty} (\varphi(B_{m+k+1}) + \varphi(B_{m+k}) - \varphi(B_m)),$$

or, by (217.8),

$$\varphi(AU) \leqq 2\lambda - \varphi(B_m).$$

Thus we also have

$$\varphi(AU) \leqq \lim_{m=\infty} (2\lambda - \varphi(B_m)) = \lambda,$$

and taking (217.9) into consideration,

$$\varphi(A) \geqq \varphi(AU) + \varphi(A - AU). \tag{217.12}$$

This relation, which is valid for all somas A, shows that the soma U is φ-measurable in the ordinary sense.

A similar result can be obtained for monotonically decreasing sequences of somas, and we have the following theorem.

THEOREM 1: *The soma U to which a monotonically increasing (monotonically decreasing) sequence of somas converges is φ-measurable if every U_j is φ-measurable relative to U_{j+1} (every U_{j+1} is φ-measurable relative to U_j).*

218. The fact that, of two somas V and $W \subseteqq V$, the second is measurable relative to the first, can be deduced, for some measure functions, from the structure of their base $\mathfrak{B}$ alone. Indeed, we have the following theorem.

THEOREM 2: *Let a pair of somas V and $W \subseteqq V$ have the property that the two relations*

$$U \dotplus UV \neq O \quad \textit{and} \quad UW \neq O \tag{218.1}$$

can never both hold for any soma U of a given set of somas $\mathfrak{B}$. Then for every measure function that has $\mathfrak{B}$ as base, the soma W is measurable relative to V.

Proof: We must show that for any measure function $\varphi(X)$ that has the base $\mathfrak{B}$, any two somas L and M for which the conditions

$$L \circ V, \quad M \subseteqq W \tag{218.2}$$

hold, satisfy the relation

$$\varphi(L + M) \geqq \varphi(L) + \varphi(M). \tag{218.3}$$

With no loss of generality, we can assume that $\varphi(L + M) < +\infty$.

Given an arbitrary positive number ε, we determine a sequence $U_1, U_2, \ldots$ of somas of $\mathfrak{B}$ that satisfy the two relations

$$L + M \subseteqq \sum_j \dot{+}\, U_j, \quad \sum_j \varphi(U_j) \leqq \varphi(L+M) + \varepsilon. \tag{218.4}$$

We let U_k' denote those of the somas $U_1, U_2, \ldots$ for which

$$U_k' L \neq O \qquad (k = 1, 2, \ldots) \tag{218.5}$$

and let U_m'' denote those of the somas $U_1, U_2, \ldots$ for which

$$U_m'' M \neq O \qquad (m = 1, 2, \ldots) \tag{218.6}$$

(see Fig. 10). Now, comparing (218.2) with the last two relations, we obtain

$$U_k' \dot{+} U_k' V \neq O, \quad U_m'' W \neq O. \tag{218.7}$$

According to the assumptions of the theorem, then, there can be no soma

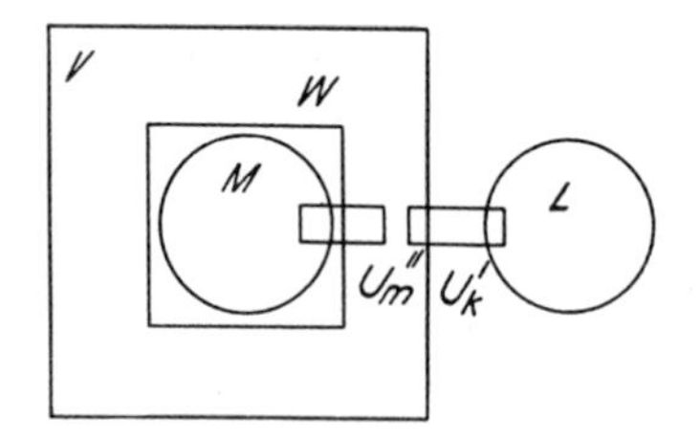

Fig. 10

U_j that belongs to both the sequences $\{U_k'\}$ and $\{U_m''\}$, and hence we see that

$$\sum_j \varphi(U_j) \geqq \sum_k \varphi(U_k') + \sum_m \varphi(U_m''). \tag{218.8}$$

On the other hand, however, we have, by construction,

$$L \subseteqq \sum_k \dot{+}\, U_k', \quad M \subseteqq \sum_m \dot{+}\, U_m'', \tag{218.9}$$

and hence also

$$\varphi(L) \leqq \sum_k \varphi(U_k'), \quad \varphi(M) \leqq \sum_m \varphi(U_m''). \tag{218.10}$$

If we compare (218.8) and (218.10) with the second of the relations (218.4) and then let ε tend to zero, we obtain the desired relation (218.3), from which our theorem follows.

219. The above results open up the possibility of establishing the φ-measurability of certain somas V also in the case that the measure function $\varphi(X)$ is calculated by means of the limit process of § 215.

We consider a monotonically decreasing sequence

$$\mathfrak{B}_1 \succ \mathfrak{B}_2 \succ \mathfrak{B}_3 \succ \dots \tag{219.1}$$

of sets of somas and a monotonically increasing sequence

$$V_1 \subseteqq V_2 \subseteqq V_3 \subseteqq \dots \tag{219.2}$$

of somas.

We suppose that to each positive integer k there can be assigned a positive integer p_k such that the set of somas $\mathfrak{B}_{p_k}$ in the sequence (219.1) contains no soma U that satisfies the pair of conditions

$$U \dotplus UV_{k+1} \neq O, \quad UV_k \neq O. \tag{219.3}$$

If we take a weight function on $\mathfrak{B}_1$ and let the maximal measure function subordinate to this weight function with base $\mathfrak{B}_m$ be denoted, as in § 215, by $\varphi_m(X)$, then Theorem 2 of § 218 tells us that the soma V_k is φ_m-measurable relative to V_{k+1} whenever $m \geqq p_k$. Consider the measure function

$$\varphi(X) = \lim_{m=\infty} \varphi_m(X); \tag{219.4}$$

the soma V_k is then φ-measurable relative to V_{k+1} for every value of k. Then, by Theorem 1 of § 217, the soma

$$V = \lim_{k=\infty} V_k \tag{219.5}$$

is φ-measurable in the ordinary sense.

220. An excellent illustration of the application of the above idea is obtained by choosing the totality of subsets of euclidean n-dimensional space as our complete ring $\mathfrak{A}$. To begin with, we shall prove a theorem about measure functions $\varphi(X)$ defined on $\mathfrak{A}$ whose rings of measurability contain all the Borel sets (§ 151). If this is the case, and if A and B are point sets whose distance

$$\boldsymbol{E}(A, B) = \delta \tag{220.1}$$

from each other is distinct from zero, let A_β, denote the (topological) closure of A. The point set A is a subset of A_β, and the point set B is a subset of the complement, which is open, of A_β; since the point set A_β and its complement are both measurable and mutually disjoint, it follows from Theorem 2 of § 136 that

$$\varphi(A+B) = \varphi(A) + \varphi(B). \tag{220.2}$$

If, conversely, this equation is always valid under the assumption that the distance (220.1) between the two point sets A and B is distinct from zero then, given two point sets W and $V \supseteqq W$, the first, by the definition given in § 216, is measurable relative to the second if the distance $\boldsymbol{E}(W, V')$ between W and the complement V' of V is not zero.

Now any interval I can be looked upon as the limit of a monotonically increasing sequence of concentric intervals

$$I_1 \subset I_2 \subset I_3 \subset \cdots \tag{220.3}$$

for which

$$\boldsymbol{E}(I_k, I'_{k+1}) > 0 \qquad (k = 1, 2, \ldots). \tag{220.4}$$

Then, by Theorem 1 of § 217, the interval I is φ-measurable, and likewise every Borel set is φ-measurable. We thus have the following theorem.

THEOREM 3: *The Borel sets of a euclidean space belong to the ring of measurability of a measure function $\varphi(X)$ that is defined on every subset of the space if and only if the equation*

$$\varphi(A+B) = \varphi(A) + \varphi(B) \tag{220.5}$$

holds for any two point sets A and B with non-zero distance $\boldsymbol{E}(A, B) > 0$.

221. Let a monotonically decreasing sequence of sets of point sets be denoted by

$$\mathfrak{B}_1 \succ \mathfrak{B}_2 \succ \mathfrak{B}_3 \succ \cdots \tag{221.1}$$

and let the least upper bounds of the diameters of the point sets belonging to the individual $\mathfrak{B}_k$ be denoted by

$$\delta_1 \geqq \delta_2 \geqq \delta_3 \geqq \cdots. \tag{221.2}$$

Let us assume, moreover, that

$$\lim_{m=\infty} \delta_m = 0. \tag{221.3}$$

Given a weight function defined on $\mathfrak{B}_1$, let us calculate, as in § 215, the maximal measure functions $\varphi_m(X)$ subordinate to this weight function with the base $\mathfrak{B}_m$, where we take $m = 1, 2, \ldots$.

Then if A and B are two point sets with non-zero distance

$$\boldsymbol{E}(A, B) = \delta > 0, \tag{221.4}$$

let us choose a positive integer m_0 such that

$$\delta > \delta_{m_0}. \tag{221.5}$$

Then, using the reasoning of § 218 and taking $W = A$ and V equal to the complement of B, we have

$$\varphi_m(A + B) = \varphi_m(A) + \varphi_m(B) \tag{221.6}$$

whenever $m \geqq m_0$; and therefore we see that, in the limit,

$$\varphi(A + B) = \varphi(A) + \varphi(B). \tag{221.7}$$

Then by Theorem 3 of § 220, all the Borel sets must be φ-measurable. Hence we have the following theorem.

THEOREM 4: *We consider a monotonically decreasing sequence of sets*

$$\mathfrak{B}_1 \succ \mathfrak{B}_2 \succ \cdots \tag{221.8}$$

whose elements are subsets of a euclidean n-dimensional space. Let the least upper bounds δ_m *of the diameters of all the point sets belonging to* $\mathfrak{B}_m$ *satisfy the condition*

$$\lim_{m=\infty} \delta_m = 0. \tag{221.9}$$

Then all the Borel sets are measurable for every measure function $\varphi(X)$ *that is computed by the procedure given in* § 215, *using the bases* $\mathfrak{B}_m$.

CHAPTER NINE

REGULAR MEASURE FUNCTIONS

§§ 222-224. The Definition and Principal Properties of Regular Measure Functions

222. The *Borel-Lebesgue* content, which was examined in §§ 148 ff., as well as other measure functions used in such applications of our theory as Analysis, Geometry, and Probability, all enjoy the property we are about to study. We start with the following definition.

DEFINITION: *A measure function μ^*X is called a regular measure function, or an outer measure, if it admits at least one base $\mathfrak{B}$ consisting entirely of μ^*-measurable somas.*

For regular measure functions μ^*X, we shall on principle make use only of bases $\mathfrak{B}$ whose elements are all μ^*-measurable.

The completely additive soma function obtained by considering an outer measure μ^*X on its ring of measurability $\mathfrak{M}_\mu$ is called a *measure* and is denoted, with omission of the asterisk, by μX. This notation is very convenient, since in what follows, we shall also define an *inner measure* $\mu_* X$ that coincides with μ^*X on $\mathfrak{M}_\mu$.

According to Theorem 4 of § 209, we obtain a regular measure function by considering a superadditive weight function $p(U)$ on a *subtractive* set of somas $\mathfrak{B}$ and constructing the maximal measure function subordinate to $p(U)$ with base $\mathfrak{B}$. All regular measure functions can of course be obtained in this way, since the subtractive closure $\mathfrak{B}^-$ of a base $\mathfrak{B}$ of any given outer measure μ^*X is itself a base of μ^*X contained in the ring of measurability $\mathfrak{M}_\mu$ of this measure function. On this base $\mathfrak{B}^-$ we choose the weight function $p(U) = \mu U$, which is in fact completely additive, so that we are assured of the applicability of the above-mentioned theorem.

Examples of non-regular measure functions can be found by use of Theorem 2 of § 240.

223. We now consider a (not necessarily regular) measure function $\varphi(X)$ and a (not necessarily subtractive) subset $\mathfrak{B}$ of the ring of measurability $\mathfrak{M}_\varphi$ of $\varphi(X)$ on whose somas U the function $\varphi(X)$ is finite. We assume, moreover, that all the somas of $\mathfrak{B}$ are measurable for the maximal measure function μ^*X subordinate to the weight function $p(U) = \varphi(U)$ with base $\mathfrak{B}$ and that μ^*X is therefore an outer measure. Let $\overline{\mathfrak{B}}$ denote the complete ring generated by $\mathfrak{B}$ (§ 53), and let $\mathfrak{B}^0$ denote the subset of $\overline{\mathfrak{B}}$ on which $\varphi(X) = \mu X$. By Theorem 2 of § 208, every soma of $\mathfrak{B}$ belongs to $\mathfrak{B}^0$.

Now if A and B are two somas of $\mathfrak{B}^0$, we have

$$\left.\begin{aligned} &\varphi(A) = \mu A, \quad \varphi(AB) \leqq \mu AB, \quad \varphi(A \dot{+} AB) \leqq \mu(A \dot{+} AB), \\ &\varphi(A) = \varphi(AB) + \varphi(A \dot{+} AB), \quad \mu A = \mu AB + \mu(A \dot{+} AB). \end{aligned}\right\} \tag{223.1}$$

Under the assumption that $\varphi(A) < +\infty$, these various relations are compatible with each other if and only if

$$\varphi(AB) = \mu AB, \quad \varphi(A \dot{+} AB) = \mu(A \dot{+} AB), \tag{223.2}$$

i.e., the somas AB and $A \dot{+} AB$ must belong to $\mathfrak{B}^0$. From this it follows, in particular, that the subtractive closure $\mathfrak{B}^-$ of $\mathfrak{B}$ is contained in the set of somas $\mathfrak{B}^0$.

Next, let

$$V = A_1 \dot{+} A_2 \dot{+} \cdots \tag{223.3}$$

be the union of an at most countable number of somas of $\mathfrak{B}^0$. Since each soma A_j, being a soma of $\overline{\mathfrak{B}}$, can be covered by the union of an at most countable number of somas of $\mathfrak{B}$ (Theorem 2 of § 55), our last result indicates that there is no loss of generality in assuming that all the $\varphi(A_j)$ are $< +\infty$; for we can replace each soma A_j in (223.3) for which this is not the case by the union of an at most countable number of somas A_jU_k ($k = 1, 2, \ldots$), where U_k belongs to $\mathfrak{B}$, so that, by (223.2), $A_jU_k \in \mathfrak{B}^0$. In view of (223.2), therefore, we can also represent the soma V as a sum

$$V = B_1 + B_2 + \cdots \tag{223.4}$$

of pairwise disjoint somas belonging to $\mathfrak{B}^0$. But since both $\varphi(X)$ and μ^*X are completely additive on $\overline{\mathfrak{B}}$, we have

$$\varphi(V) = \sum_j \varphi(B_j), \quad \mu V = \sum_j \mu B_j. \tag{223.5}$$

Finally, for every j ($j = 1, 2, \ldots$), we have

$$\varphi(B_j) = \mu B_j, \tag{223.6}$$

and consequently $\varphi(V) = \mu V$. This shows that V belongs to $\mathfrak{B}^0$, and that $\mathfrak{B}^0$ is therefore a countably additive set of somas. But $\mathfrak{B}^0$ is also subtractive.

For, as we saw above, we can assign a sequence of pairwise disjoint somas $U_1, U_2, \ldots$ belonging to $\mathfrak{B}^-$ to every pair of somas A and B belonging to $\mathfrak{B}^0$ in such a way that

$$A = \sum_j A U_j, \quad B = \sum_j B U_j; \tag{223.7}$$

and then we have, on the one hand,

$$A \dotplus AB = \sum_j (A \dotplus AB)\, U_j,$$

and on the other hand,

$$(A \dotplus AB)\, U_j = A U_j \dotplus (A U_j)\, B,$$

so that $(A \dotplus AB)U_j \in \mathfrak{B}^0$. The set of somas $\mathfrak{B}^0$ is consequently a complete ring, and so is identical with $\overline{\mathfrak{B}}$. This result yields the following theorem.

THEOREM 1: *If the base $\mathfrak{B}$ of a regular measure function μ^*X is contained in the ring of measurability $\mathfrak{M}_\varphi$ of an arbitrary measure function $\varphi(X)$, and if the equation*

$$\varphi(U) = \mu U \tag{223.8}$$

holds for every soma U in $\mathfrak{B}$, then it also holds for all the somas of the complete ring $\overline{\mathfrak{B}}$ generated by $\mathfrak{B}$.

In addition to this, our discussion, taken together with Theorem 4 of § 209, yields the following theorem.

THEOREM 2: *If $\mathfrak{B}$ denotes a subtractive subset of the ring of measurability $\mathfrak{M}_\varphi$ of an arbitrary measure function $\varphi(X)$ and if $\varphi(U) < +\infty$ for every $U \in \mathfrak{B}$, then the maximal measure function subordinate to $\varphi(U)$ with base $\mathfrak{B}$ is an outer measure for which the theorem above holds.*

224. To each soma A for which the outer measure μ^*X with base $\mathfrak{B}$ has a finite value, there can be assigned, according to Theorem 1 of § 213, a soma $\overline{A} \supseteqq A$ belonging to $\mathfrak{B}_{\sigma\delta}$ and satisfying $\mu\overline{A} = \mu^*A$. The soma $\overline{A}$ is obviously μ^*-measurable; it will be shown that this property serves to characterize the regular measure functions. To begin with, we prove the following theorem.

THEOREM 3: *Let $\mathfrak{E}_\varphi$ denote the set of somas on which the measure function $\varphi(X)$ is finite, and let $\mathfrak{M}_\varphi$ be the ring of measurability of $\varphi(X)$. Moreover, let $\mathfrak{B}$ be a subtractive subset of $\mathfrak{E}_\varphi \mathfrak{M}_\varphi$, and let $\overline{\mathfrak{B}}$ be the complete ring generated by $\mathfrak{B}$. Then $\varphi(X)$ is a regular measure function with base $\mathfrak{B}$ if* *to each soma A in $\mathfrak{E}_\varphi$ there can be assigned at least one soma A^0 in $\overline{\mathfrak{B}}$ that satisfies the two relations*

$$A \subseteqq A^0, \quad \varphi(A) = \varphi(A^0). \tag{224.1}$$

Proof: By Theorem 2 above, the maximal measure function subordinate to $\varphi(U)$ with base $\mathfrak{B}$ is an outer measure μ^*X which agrees with $\varphi(X)$ on all the somas of $\overline{\mathfrak{B}}$.

Now if A is a soma of $\mathfrak{E}_\varphi$ and A^0 is a soma of $\overline{\mathfrak{B}}$ that satisfy relations (224.1), we have

$$\mu A^0 = \varphi(A^0) = \varphi(A) < +\infty, \tag{224.2}$$

and consequently $\mu^* A < +\infty$. According to the discussion at the beginning of the present section, there is then a soma $\overline{A} \supseteqq A$ in $\mathfrak{B}_{\sigma\delta}$ for which $\mu\overline{A} = \mu^* A$. Then the soma $A^0\overline{A}$ belongs to $\overline{\mathfrak{B}}$, and consequently,

$$\varphi(A^0\bar{A}) = \mu A^0 \bar{A}.$$

On the other hand, we have $A \subseteqq A^0\overline{A}$, and this yields the relations

$$\begin{aligned} \varphi(A) &\leqq \varphi(A^0\bar{A}) \leqq \varphi(A^0) = \varphi(A), \\ \mu^* A &\leqq \mu A^0 \bar{A} \quad \leqq \mu \bar{A} \quad = \mu^* A, \end{aligned}$$

from which, finally, we deduce the equation

$$\mu^* A = \varphi(A) \qquad (A \in \mathfrak{E}_\varphi). \tag{224.3}$$

But this equation holds also if the soma A does not belong to $\mathfrak{E}_\varphi$, for in this case we have $\varphi(A) = +\infty$, and $\varphi(A) \leqq \mu^* A$. This proves the theorem.

This theorem contains an especially convenient criterion for determining whether a set of somas $\mathfrak{B}$ is a base of a given regular measure function. Also, as a consequence of Theorem 1 of § 213, the soma A^0 that occurs in (224.1) can always be chosen from the set of somas $\mathfrak{B}_{\sigma\delta}$.

We have concomitantly derived the following theorem as well.

THEOREM 4: *A necessary and sufficient condition for a measure function $\varphi(X)$ to be an outer measure is that to each soma A in $\mathfrak{E}_\varphi$ there be assignable a φ-measurable soma $U \supseteqq A$ for which $\varphi(U) < +\infty$, and that, moreover, $\varphi(A)$ be equal to the greatest lower bound of all such $\varphi(U)$.*

Proof: In view of Theorem 5 of § 138, and because of the fact that the ring of measurability of any measure function is always complete, the existence of a measurable soma A^0 for which (224.1) holds is a consequence of the necessary and sufficient condition in the wording of our theorem. By Theorem 3, the subtractive set of somas $\mathfrak{B} = \mathfrak{E}_\varphi \mathfrak{M}_\varphi$ is a base of $\varphi(X)$, and consequently, by the same theorem, $\varphi(X)$ is an outer measure.

§§ 225-229. Inner Measure

225. We consider *monotonically increasing* soma functions $F(X)$ defined on a complete ring of somas $\mathfrak{A}$ which, like measure functions, satisfy the equation $F(O) = 0$. Theorem 1 of § 129 is applicable to such functions; it shows that the F-measurable somas U form a ring $\mathfrak{M}_F$, which need not, however, be a complete ring. We now assume that to each soma X for which $F(X) < +\infty$ there can be associated at least one soma $U \supseteqq X$ in $\mathfrak{M}_F$ for which, also, $F(U) < +\infty$. By Theorem 4 above, the class $\mathfrak{C}$ of functions $F(X)$ singled out in this way contains all the outer measures; however, as we shall see shortly, it also contains other soma functions that are not outer measures.

Just as the projective plane can be mapped involutively onto itself by means of the polar reciprocation with respect to a conic, so we can deal with the class $\mathfrak{C}$.

For a soma X in $\mathfrak{A}$ let $F(X) < +\infty$; moreover, let U_1 and U_2 be two somas of $\mathfrak{M}_F$ for which

$$U_1 \supseteqq X, \quad U_2 \supseteqq X, \quad F(U_1) < +\infty, \quad F(U_2) < +\infty. \tag{225.1}$$

Since $\mathfrak{M}_F$ is a ring, both the somas $U_1 U_2$ and $U_1 \dot{+} U_1 U_2$ are F-measurable, and by the theorems of § 130, we can deduce from the equation

$$(U_1 - X) = (U_1 \dot{+} U_1 U_2) + (U_1 U_2 - X) \tag{225.2}$$

the relations

$$F(U_1 - X) = F(U_1 \dot{+} U_1 U_2) + F(U_1 U_2 - X) \tag{225.3}$$

and

$$F(U_1) = F(U_1 U_2) + F(U_1 \dot{+} U_1 U_2), \tag{225.4}$$

from which we obtain, by subtraction,

$$F(U_1) - F(U_1 - X) = F(U_1 U_2) - F(U_1 U_2 - X).$$

In the same way, we find

$$F(U_2) - F(U_2 - X) = F(U_1 U_2) - F(U_1 U_2 - X),$$

and consequently we have

$$F(U_1) - F(U_1 - X) = F(U_2) - F(U_2 - X). \tag{225.5}$$

Thus, the expression $F(U) - F(U - X)$ has the same value for all measurable somas $U \supseteqq X$ that satisfy $F(U) < +\infty$. If we put

$$\left. \begin{aligned} F'(X) &= F(U) - F(U - X) \quad \{U \in \mathfrak{M}_F,\, U \supseteqq X,\, F(U) < +\infty\}, \\ F'(X) &= F(X) \quad \{F(X) = +\infty\}, \end{aligned} \right\} \tag{225.6}$$

a soma function $F'(X)$ is defined *uniquely* for all X in $\mathfrak{A}$; we call this soma function $F'(X)$, following the terminology of J. Ridder,[1] the soma function *adjoint* to $F(X)$.

226. The function $F'(X)$ adjoint to $F(X)$ is, by virtue of its definition, finite if and only if $F(X)$ itself is finite. Furthermore, $F'(X)$ is a monotonically increasing soma function. Indeed, if $Y \subseteqq X$ and $F'(X) < +\infty$, then there is an F-measurable soma $U \supseteqq X$ for which we can write

$$F'(X) - F'(Y) = F(U - Y) - F(U - X) \geqq 0. \tag{226.1}$$

Let U be a soma of $\mathfrak{M}_F$ and X another soma for which $F'(X) < +\infty$. Then there exists at least one soma $V \supseteqq X$ in $\mathfrak{M}_F$ for which $F(V) < +\infty$. Now, from $X \subseteqq V$, it follows that

$$XU \subseteqq VU, \quad X \dotplus XU \subseteqq V \dotplus VU, \tag{226.2}$$

and since the somas VU and $V \dotplus VU$, like V and U, are F-measurable, we can write

$$\left. \begin{aligned} F'(X) &= F(V) - F(V \dotplus X), \\ F'(XU) &= F(VU) - F(VU \dotplus XU), \\ F'(X \dotplus XU) &= F(V \dotplus VU) - F(V \dotplus VU \dotplus X \dotplus XU). \end{aligned} \right\} \tag{226.3}$$

Now, the soma U belongs to $\mathfrak{M}_F$, and the equations

$$\left. \begin{aligned} F(V) &= F(VU) + F(V \dotplus VU), \\ F(V \dotplus X) &= F(VU \dotplus XU) + F(V \dotplus X \dotplus VU \dotplus XU) \end{aligned} \right\} \tag{226.4}$$

hold; finally, a comparison of the relations (226.3) and (226.4) yields

$$F'(X) = F'(XU) + F'(X \dotplus XU), \tag{226.5}$$

and this relation, which holds whenever $F'(X) < +\infty$, asserts that the soma U is also F'-measurable (§ 129). Thus, if $\mathfrak{M}_{F'}$ denotes the ring of measurability of the adjoint function $F'(X)$, we have the relation

[1] J. Ridder, "Mass- und Integrationstheorie in Strukturen," *Acta Math.*, Vol. 73 (1941), pp. 131-173.

$$\mathfrak{M}_F \prec \mathfrak{M}_{F'}. \tag{226.6}$$

Now if the soma X itself belongs to $\mathfrak{M}_F$, and if $F(X) < +\infty$, we can put $U = X$ in (225.6); in this way, we obtain

$$F'(X) = F(X) \quad \text{for} \quad X \in \mathfrak{M}_F, \tag{226.7}$$

and this equation always holds, since it holds by definition for the case $F(X) = +\infty$. Thus, in particular, we have

$$F'(O) = F(O) = 0. \tag{226.8}$$

A comparison of all these results shows that the adjoint soma function $F'(X)$ also belongs to the class of function $\mathfrak{C}$. We form the adjoint $F''(X)$ to $F'(X)$: if $F'(X) = +\infty$, we have $F''(X) = F'(X) = F(X)$; if $F'(X) < +\infty$, on the other hand, we can find a soma $U \supseteqq X$ in $\mathfrak{M}_F$ for which we have, by (226.7),

$$F'(U) = F(U) < +\infty,$$

and we can write

$$F''(X) = F'(U) - F'(U \dotplus X).$$

Making use of

$$F'(U \dotplus X) = F(U) - F(U \dotplus (U \dotplus X)) = F(U) - F(X),$$

we then find that in this case as well we have

$$F''(X) = F(X). \tag{226.9}$$

In the same way as (226.6), the relation

$$\mathfrak{M}_{F'} \prec \mathfrak{M}_{F''} = \mathfrak{M}_F \tag{226.10}$$

holds, and a comparison of (226.6) and (226.10) shows that the ring of measurability of a function and that of its adjoint consist of the same somas. We gather all these results into the following theorem.

THEOREM 1: *Every soma function $F(X)$ that belongs to the class $\mathfrak{C}$ admits an adjoint function $F'(X)$ which, by* (225.6), *belongs to the same class. This relation is an involution; that is, the adjoint of $F'(X)$ is $F(X)$ itself. The ring of measurability of a soma function and that of its adjoint are identical, and $F(U) = F'(U)$ for every soma U of this ring of measurability.*

The adjoint of an *outer measure* μ^*X is called an *inner measure* and is denoted μ_*X. The adjoint of any inner measure is then always an outer measure.

227. We now prove the following theorem.

THEOREM 2: *Outer measures $\mu^* X$ are functions of the class $\mathfrak{C}$ that can be characterized by the following two properties:*

α) for every soma A in $\mathfrak{C}_\mu$, $\mu^* A$ is equal to the greatest lower bound of the set of numbers μU, obtained as U runs through the μ^*-measurable somas $\supseteqq A$;

β) for every monotonically increasing sequence $U_1 \subseteqq U_2 \subseteqq \ldots$ of measurable somas, the equation $\mu^* B = \lim_{n=\infty} \mu U_n$ holds, where $B = \lim_{n=\infty} U_n$.

Proof: Regular measure functions satisfy the conditions of the theorem: this is a consequence of Theorem 4 of § 224 and Theorem 4 of § 138.

To establish, conversely, that a soma function that satisfies these conditions is an outer measure, it suffices to show that such a function is union-bounded. For, being monotonic, it is a measure function (Theorem 1 of § 131), which, by virtue of assumption α), must be regular (Theorem 4 of § 224).

Thus, we must show that, under the assumption

$$V = \sum_j \dot{+} A_j \tag{227.1}$$

we obtain the relation

$$\mu^* V \leqq \sum_j \mu^* A_j, \tag{227.2}$$

and it suffices to consider the case that the sum on the right-hand side of (227.2) is finite.

If, then, ε is any positive number, by assumption α) there are somas $U_j \supseteqq A_j$ in $\mathfrak{M}_\mu$ for which we have

$$\mu U_j \leqq \mu^* A_j + \frac{\varepsilon}{2^j} \qquad (j = 1, 2, \ldots). \tag{227.3}$$

If we then put

$$V_k = U_1 \dot{+} U_2 \dot{+} \cdots \dot{+} U_k \qquad (k = 1, 2, \ldots) \tag{227.4}$$

and take into account the fact that the monotonically increasing and non-negative soma function $\mu^* X$ is additive on its ring of measurability $\mathfrak{M}_\mu$ (Theorem 3 of § 130), we find that

$$\mu V_k \leqq \sum_{j=1}^{k} \mu U_j \leqq \sum_j \mu^* A_j + \varepsilon. \tag{227.5}$$

If, on the other hand, we apply assumption β) to the monotone sequence $V_1 \subseteqq V_2 \subseteqq \ldots$ and put

$$B = \lim_{k=\infty} V_k, \tag{227.6}$$

then, observing that $V \subseteqq B$, we obtain

$$\mu^* V \leqq \mu^* B = \lim_{k=\infty} \mu V_k \leqq \sum_j \mu^* A_j + \varepsilon. \tag{227.7}$$

Passing to the limit, we obtain the relation (227.2), which was to be proved.

228. We now examine the inner measure $\mu_* X$ adjoint to $\mu^* X$. If X is a soma for which $\mu^* X < +\infty$, then, by the definition of the inner measure, there is a μ^*-measurable soma $V \supseteqq X$ which, by Theorem 1 of § 226, is also μ_*-measurable and for which $\mu V < +\infty$ and also

$$\mu_* X = \mu V - \mu^* (V - X). \tag{228.1}$$

By property α) of Theorem 2 above, there is, for each prescribed number $\varepsilon > 0$, at least one measurable soma $W \supseteqq V - X$ such that

$$\mu W \leqq \mu^* (V - X) + \varepsilon. \tag{228.2}$$

A comparison of the last two relations yields

$$\mu_* X \leqq \mu V - \mu W + \varepsilon. \tag{228.3}$$

Next, if we put $U = V \dotplus VW$, we have

$$\mu V - \mu W \leqq \mu V - \mu VW = \mu U, \tag{228.4}$$

and from this it follows that

$$\mu_* X \leqq \mu U + \varepsilon. \tag{228.5}$$

On the other hand, $V \dotplus X = VW \dotplus WX$, and therefore

$$U = V \dotplus VW = X \dotplus WX \subseteqq X. \tag{228.6}$$

Thus $\mu_* X$, if finite, is equal to the least upper bound of the set of numbers μU obtained for $U \subseteqq X$ and $U \in \mathfrak{M}_\mu$.[2]

Next, we consider a monotonically decreasing sequence $V_1 \supseteqq V_2 \supseteqq \ldots$ of measurable somas and their intersection $C = \lim_{n=\infty} V_n$. If we put $U_n = V_1 - V_n$ and $B = \lim_{n=\infty} U_n$, then, by property β) of the last theorem, we obtain

[2] This result can be arrived at by a somewhat shorter path if, making use of the remark at the beginning of § 224, we choose the soma W in such a way as to ensure the validity of the equation $\mu W = \mu^* (V - X)$. This allows us to dispense with the introduction of the number ε. The proof in the text is nonetheless preferable, because it runs parallel to the proof of Theorem 3 below.

$$\mu^* B = \lim_{n=\infty} \mu U_n. \tag{228.7}$$

But now, by (24.15), we also have $B = V_1 - C$; hence if $\mu V_1 < +\infty$, we have

$$\mu_* C = \mu V_1 - \mu^* B = \lim_{n=\infty} (\mu V_1 - \mu U_n) = \lim_{n=\infty} \mu V_n. \tag{228.8}$$

Finally, let $U_1 \subseteqq U_2 \subseteqq \ldots$ again be a monotonically increasing sequence of measurable somas, and let $B = \lim_{n=\infty} U_n$. If $\mu_* B = +\infty$, we have $\mu_* B = \mu^* B$, and hence, by property β) of the last theorem, $\lim_{n=\infty} \mu U_n = +\infty$.

It is now easy to prove the following theorem.

THEOREM 3: *Inner measures $\mu_* X$ are functions of the class $\mathfrak{C}$ that are characterized by the following three properties:*

α') for each soma A in $\mathfrak{C}_\mu$, $\mu_* A$ is equal to the least upper bound of the set of numbers μU obtained by letting U run through the μ_*-measurable somas $\subseteqq A$;

β') for every monotonically decreasing sequence $V_1 \supseteqq V_2 \supseteqq \ldots$ of measurable somas, the equation $\mu_* C = \lim_{n=\infty} \mu V_n$, where $C = \lim_{n=\infty} V_n$, is valid, provided its right-hand side is finite;

β'') for every monotonically increasing sequence $U_1 \subseteqq U_2 \subseteqq \ldots$ of measurable somas, the relation $\lim_{n=\infty} \mu U_n = +\infty$ follows from $\mu_* B = +\infty$, where $B = \lim_{n=\infty} U_n$.

Proof: The above discussion shows that every inner measure satisfies the conditions of the theorem. Conversely, if $\mu_* X$ is a function of the class $\mathfrak{C}$ that, to begin with, satisfies conditions α') and β'), then it can be shown in an entirely similar way that the function $\mu^* X$ adjoint to $\mu_* X$ enjoys property α) of Theorem 2 of § 227 and, if $\mu_* B < +\infty$, also enjoys property β). Now if $\mu_* X$ also satisfies β''), then $\mu^* X$ enjoys property β) also in the case that $\mu_* B = +\infty$. Thus, by Theorem 2, $\mu^* X$ is an outer measure; and consequently $\mu_* X$, the soma function adjoint to $\mu^* X$, must be an inner measure.

229. Theorems 2 and 3 characterize outer and inner measures, independently of each other, by means of "intrinsic" properties. It is highly remarkable that in the passage from $\mu^* X$ to the adjoint soma function $\mu_* X$ the condition β) splits into, and is replaced by two conditions β') and β'') that are radically different from each other. The following example shows that the condition β'') cannot be dispensed with.

We let M denote a set of a countable number of elements $e_1, e_2, \ldots$, and we consider the complete ring $\mathfrak{A}$ of somas X each of which is a subset of M. To each element e_k we assign the positive number $\alpha_k = 1/2^k$. Now if X is a *proper* subset of M, let $F(X)$ be equal to the sum of all the numbers α_k that correspond to elements e_k belonging to X. However, let $F(M) = +\infty$. Then every soma of the ring $\mathfrak{A}$, M included, is F-measurable; we have $F(X) = F'(X)$ without exception; and $F(X)$ is a soma function of the class $\mathfrak{C}$ that satisfies the conditions α), α') and β') of the last two theorems but does not satisfy the condition β'') nor the condition β). The soma function $F(X)$ is neither an outer measure nor an inner measure. Note that, *under the additional assumption* $F(B) < +\infty$, $F(X)$ would also satisfy condition β) of Theorem 2 of § 227; this shows that the theorem in question is not valid if the condition β) is not required to hold also in the case that $\mu^*B = +\infty$.

Note also that in the statements of the last two theorems, we have not assumed that the somas $B = \lim\limits_{n=\infty} U_n$ and $C = \lim\limits_{n=\infty} V_n$ are measurable. The measurability of these somas, however, is a consequence of the remaining assumptions of these theorems, since the ring of measurability that an outer measure and its adjoint inner measure have in common is always complete (§ 134).

§§ 230-235. Comparison of Inner and Outer Measures

230. We consider the outer measure μ^*X and its adjoint inner measure μ_*X on the complete ring $\mathfrak{A}$. By § 224, we can assign at least one soma $\bar{A}$ of the ring of measurability $\mathfrak{M}_\mu$ to each soma A of $\mathfrak{C}_\mu$ in such a way that the conditions

$$A \subseteqq \bar{A}, \quad \mu^*A = \mu\bar{A} < +\infty \tag{230.1}$$

are satisfied. By property α') of Theorem 3 of § 228, we can in the same way assign to the soma A at least one soma $\underline{A}$ of $\mathfrak{M}_\mu$ in such a way that the conditions

$$\underline{A} \subseteqq A, \quad \mu_*A = \mu\underline{A} < +\infty \tag{230.2}$$

are satisfied. It suffices, for this, to take as $\underline{A}$ the union of a countable number of measurable subsomas U_n of A that satisfy the conditions

$$\mu U_n > \mu_* A - \frac{1}{n} \qquad (n = 1, 2, \ldots).$$

Now since $\underline{A} \subseteqq \bar{A}$, it follows that $\mu\underline{A} \leqq \mu\bar{A}$; but even if $\mu^*X = +\infty$, we have $\mu_*X \leqq \mu^*X$; consequently, the following theorem holds.

THEOREM 1: *If $\mu^* X$ is an outer measure and $\mu_* X$ is its adjoint inner measure, then we have*

$$\mu_* X \leqq \mu^* X. \tag{230.3}$$

The measurable somas $\bar{A}$ that satisfy relations (230.1) are called *measurable hulls* of A; similarly, the somas $\underline{A}$ for which (230.2) holds are called *measurable kernels* of A. Measurable hulls and measurable kernels are thus defined exclusively for somas of finite measure.

For measurable somas A, we have

$$\mu_* A = \mu^* A; \tag{230.4}$$

conversely, if this equation holds and if $\mu^* A < +\infty$, then by (230.1) and (230.2) we have

$$\mu(\bar{A} - \underline{A}) = \mu \bar{A} - \mu \underline{A} = \mu^* A - \mu_* A = 0. \tag{230.5}$$

The soma $\bar{A} - \underline{A}$ and its subsoma $A - \underline{A}$ are of measure zero; hence the soma $A = \underline{A} + (A - \underline{A})$, being the sum of two measurable somas, is measurable. Thus, we obtain the following theorem.

THEOREM 2: *Measurable somas X satisfy*

$$\mu_* X = \mu^* X. \tag{230.6}$$

Somas of finite measure for which this equation holds are measurable.

231. If $\bar{A}$ and A^0 are two measurable hulls of A, then $\bar{A}A^0$ is measurable and, in addition, satisfies

$$A \subseteqq \bar{A}A^0 \subseteqq \bar{A}, \quad \mu^* A \leqq \mu \bar{A} A^0 \leqq \mu \bar{A} = \mu^* A. \tag{231.1}$$

Thus, $\bar{A}A^0$ is itself a measurable hull of A.[3]

From $\mu \bar{A} A^0 = \mu \bar{A} < +\infty$, it follows that $\mu(\bar{A} - \bar{A}A^0) = 0$; in the same way, we find that $\mu(A^0 - \bar{A}A^0) = 0$. From this, we have the two equations

$$\mu(\bar{A} \dotplus A^0) = \mu \bar{A} + \mu(A^0 \underset{\cdot}{+} \bar{A}A^0) = \mu \bar{A} = \mu^* A, \tag{231.2}$$

$$\mu(\bar{A} \underset{\cdot}{+} A^0) = \mu(\bar{A} \underset{\cdot}{+} \bar{A}A^0) + \mu(A^0 \underset{\cdot}{+} \bar{A}A^0) = 0. \tag{231.3}$$

Entirely analogous relations hold for measurable kernels, and we obtain the following theorems.

[3] The relation (231.1) is valid even under the weaker assumption that A is a measurable hull of A and $A^0 \supseteqq A$ is a measurable soma. Use is made of this in § 235. Similarly, if $\underline{A}$ is a measurable kernel of A and $A_0 \subseteqq A$ is a measurable soma, then the relations $A \supseteqq \underline{A} + A_0$ and $\mu_* A \geqq \mu(\underline{A} \dotplus A_0) \geqq \mu \underline{A} = \mu_* A$, are valid; use is made of this in § 238.

THEOREM 3: *If $\bar{A}$ and A^0 are two measurable hulls of A, then the somas $\bar{A} \dotplus A^0$ and $\bar{A}A^0$ are likewise measurable hulls of A. If $\underline{A}$ and A_0 are measurable kernels of A, then the somas $\underline{A} \dotplus A_0$ and $\underline{A}A_0$ are likewise measurable kernels of A.*

THEOREM 4: *If $\bar{A}$ is a measurable hull and $\underline{A}$ a measurable kernel of A, then A^0 is a measurable hull of A if and only if both the relations*

$$A \subseteqq A^0, \quad \mu(\bar{A} \dotplus A^0) = 0 \tag{231.4}$$

hold; and A_0 is a measurable kernel of A if and only if

$$A \supseteqq A_0, \quad \mu(\underline{A} \dotplus A_0) = 0. \tag{231.5}$$

232. Let A and B be two disjoint somas of $\mathfrak{E}_\mu$. We denote their sum by $C = A + B$, and for each of the three somas we choose measurable hulls A^0, B^0, C^0 and measurable kernels A_0, B_0, C_0.

From $A_0 + B_0 \subseteqq A + B$, it follows that $\mu(A_0 + B_0) \leqq \mu_*(A + B)$; and consequently,

$$\mu_* A + \mu_* B = \mu A_0 + \mu B_0 = \mu(A_0 + B_0) \leqq \mu_*(A + B). \tag{232.1}$$

From $C_0 \subseteqq A + B$, we obtain

$$C_0 = C_0 A \dotplus C_0 B, \quad C_0 B^0 = C_0 A B^0 \dotplus C_0 B. \tag{232.2}$$

This implies, successively,

$$C_0 \dotplus C_0 B^0 = C_0 A \dotplus C_0 A B^0 \subseteqq A, \quad \mu(C_0 \dotplus C_0 B^0) \leqq \mu_* A. \tag{232.3}$$

This last inequality, taken in conjunction with $\mu C_0 B^0 \leqq \mu B^0 = \mu^* B$, yields the relation

$$\mu_*(A + B) = \mu C_0 = \mu(C_0 \dotplus C_0 B^0) + \mu C_0 B^0 \leqq \mu_* A + \mu^* B. \tag{232.4}$$

Finally, from the relation

$$B = C \dotplus A \subseteqq C^0 \dotplus A_0 \tag{232.5}$$

we obtain the inequality $\mu^* B \leqq \mu^* C - \mu_* A$, which we write as

$$\mu_* A + \mu^* B \leqq \mu^*(A + B). \tag{232.6}$$

From all of the foregoing, we obtain the following theorem.

THEOREM 5: *For any two disjoint somas A and B we always have the relations*

$$\mu_* A + \mu_* B \leqq \mu_*(A + B) \leqq \begin{matrix} \mu_* A + \mu^* B \\ \mu^* A + \mu_* B \end{matrix} \leqq \mu^*(A + B) \leqq \mu^* A + \mu^* B. \tag{232.7}$$

These relations were proved, to be sure, only under the assumption that the two numbers μ^*A and μ^*B are finite. However, if one of these numbers is equal to $+\infty$, then the same is true of all of the expressions in (232.7), so that the relations (232.7) hold in this case as well.

We can now assert the following theorem.

THEOREM 6: *If we decompose a measurable soma S of finite measure into any two disjoint subsomas A and B, then we always have*

$$\mu S = \mu_* A + \mu^* B = \mu^* A + \mu_* B, \tag{232.8}$$

$$\mu^* A + \mu^* B - \mu S = \mu S - \mu_* A - \mu_* B = \mu^* A - \mu_* A = \mu^* B - \mu_* B, \tag{232.9}$$

$$\mu_* A + \mu_* B \leqq \mu S \leqq \mu^* A + \mu^* B. \tag{232.10}$$

Proof: The equations (232.8) are a direct consequence of (232.7) under the assumption

$$\mu_*(A + B) = \mu^*(A + B) = \mu S,$$

which holds under the hypotheses of our theorem.

The equations (232.9) are a trivial consequence of (232.8), and the relations (232.10) merely express the fact that the various terms in the equations (232.9) are greater than or equal to zero.

233. The relation (232.1) was proved under the assumption that the numbers $\mu_* A$ and $\mu_* B$ are finite. It is valid, however, without restriction and indicates that inner measures are superadditive (§ 126). Thus, by Theorem 1 of § 126, we have the following theorem.

THEOREM 7: *The sum A of an at most countable number of somas A_j always satisfies the relation*

$$\mu_* A \geqq \sum_j \mu_* A_j. \tag{233.1}$$

If we observe that a measure function must be union-bounded, then by use of Theorem 2 of § 127 and Theorem 1 of § 131, we obtain a further theorem, as follows:

THEOREM 8: *An inner measure is a measure function if and only if it is completely additive on its domain of definition.*

234. We consider a monotonically increasing sequence $A_1 \subseteqq A_2 \subseteqq A_3 \subseteqq \dots$ of somas and put

$$A = \lim_{n=\infty} A_n. \tag{234.2}$$

Let all the numbers $\mu^* A_n$ be $< +\infty$; then, if $\bar{A}_n$ is a measurable hull of A_n, $A_n^0 = \bar{A}_n \bar{A}_{n+1} \cdots$ is likewise a measurable hull of A_n. We can therefore write

$$\mu^* A_n = \mu A_n^0, \quad A_1^0 \subseteqq A_2^0 \subseteqq \ldots, \quad A^0 = \lim_{n=\infty} A_n^0. \tag{234.3}$$

Now on the one hand, it follows from $\mu A_n^0 = \mu^* A_n \leqq \mu^* A$ that

$$\lim_{n=\infty} \mu A_n^0 \leqq \mu^* A; \tag{234.4}$$

on the other hand, however, $A \subseteqq A^0$; and hence, taking Theorem 4 of § 138 into consideration, we have

$$\mu^* A \leqq \mu A^0 = \lim_{n=\infty} \mu A_n^0. \tag{234.5}$$

Thus, the last theorem has the following more general counterpart for outer measures:

Theorem 9: *The equation*

$$\mu^* \left(\lim_{n=\infty} A_n\right) = \lim_{n=\infty} \mu^* A_n \tag{234.6}$$

holds for every monotonically increasing sequence $A_1 \subseteqq A_2 \subseteqq \ldots$ of arbitrary somas.

235. Let A and B be two somas of finite measure, let A^0 and B^0 be associated measurable hulls, and let C^0 be a measurable hull of $A \dot{+} B$. Then, by footnote 3, p. 279, the somas $C^0 A^0$, $C^0 B^0$, and $C^0(A^0 \dot{+} B^0)$ are measurable hulls of A, B, and $A \dot{+} B$, respectively. Hence, by Theorem 4 of § 231, $A^0 \underset{\cdot}{+} C^0 A^0$ and $B^0 \underset{\cdot}{+} C^0 B^0$ are somas of measure zero. Thus, the left-hand side, as well as the right-hand of the identity

$$(A^0 \dot{+} B^0) \underset{\cdot}{+} C^0 (A^0 \dot{+} B^0)$$

$$= (A^0 \underset{\cdot}{+} C^0 A^0) \underset{\cdot}{+} (B^0 \underset{\cdot}{+} C^0 B^0) \underset{\cdot}{+} A^0 (B^0 \underset{\cdot}{+} C^0 B^0) \tag{235.1}$$

is of measure zero, and in view of the theorem just referred to, this means that the soma $A^0 \dot{+} B^0$ is a measurable hull of $A \dot{+} B$. This result can be extended, as follows, to unions of a countable number of somas.

Let $X_1, X_2, \ldots$ denote any somas of finite measure and let $X_1^0, X_2^0, \ldots$ be measurable hulls of these somas. Furthermore, let us introduce the notation

$$V_k = \sum_{j=1}^{k} \dot{+} X_j, \quad V_k^0 = \sum_{j=1}^{k} \dot{+} X_j^0, \tag{235.2}$$

$$V = \sum_{j=1}^{\infty} \dot{+} X_j, \quad V^0 = \sum_{j=1}^{\infty} \dot{+} X_j^0. \tag{235.3}$$

By what we have just shown, V_k^0 is a measurable hull of V_k, and we obtain

$$\mu^* V_k = \mu V_k^0. \tag{235.4}$$

On the other hand, by Theorem 9 above, we have the equations

$$\mu^* V = \lim_{k=\infty} \mu^* V_k, \quad \mu V^0 = \lim_{k=\infty} \mu V_k^0. \tag{235.5}$$

Thus, $\mu^* V = \mu V^0$; and if $\mu^* V < +\infty$, V^0 is a measurable hull of V. This yields the following theorem.

THEOREM 10: *The union V^0 of any measurable hulls X_j^0 of the somas X_j, where X_j is an at most countable sequence, is a measurable hull of the union V of these somas, provided only $\mu^* X < +\infty$.*

§§ 236-240. The Arithmetic Mean of the Inner and Outer Measures

236. In this section we shall consider the soma function

$$\varphi(X) = \frac{1}{2}(\mu^* X + \mu_* X), \tag{236.1}$$

which, as the last equation (240.6) of the section indicates, is a self-adjoint function of the class $\mathfrak{C}$ (§ 225). We show first that $\varphi(X)$ is always a measure function.

To this end, it is sufficient, by Theorem 1 of § 131, to verify that

$$\varphi(A) \leqq \sum_j \varphi(A_j), \tag{236.2}$$

where

$$A = A_1 + A_2 + \cdots \tag{236.3}$$

denotes the sum of *pairwise disjoint* somas A_j, concerning which we make the further assumption that

$$\sum_j \varphi(A_j) < +\infty. \tag{236.4}$$

It follows from (236.1) and $0 \leqq \mu_* X \leqq \mu^* X$ that we can write

$$0 \leqq \varphi(X) \leqq \mu^* X \leqq 2\,\varphi(X). \tag{236.5}$$

Thus, we need only consider those somas A_j for which

$$\sum_j \mu^* A_j < +\infty. \tag{236.6}$$

237. Let $\bar{A}_j$ denote a measurable hull of A_j, and let

$$\bar{A} = \sum_j \dot{+} \bar{A}_j. \tag{237.1}$$

By Theorem 10 of § 235, $\bar{A}$ is a measurable hull of A, and we therefore have

$$\mu \bar{A}_j = \mu^* A_j, \quad \mu \bar{A} = \mu^* A. \tag{237.2}$$

We introduce the measurable somas

$$B_1 = \bar{A}_2 \bar{A}_1, \quad B_j = \bar{A}_{j+1}(\bar{A}_1 \dotplus \bar{A}_2 \dotplus \cdots \dotplus \bar{A}_j) \quad (j = 2, 3, \ldots), \tag{237.3}$$

and

$$B = \sum_j \dotplus B_j \tag{237.4}$$

and note the equation (cf. § 22)

$$\bar{A} = \bar{A}_1 + (\bar{A}_2 - B_1) + (\bar{A}_3 - B_2) + \cdots. \tag{237.5}$$

It follows from this equation, since all the somas that occur in it are measurable, that

$$\mu B \leqq \sum_j \mu B_j = \sum_j \mu^* A_j - \mu^* A. \tag{237.6}$$

238. Next, we introduce the measurable somas

$$C_1 = \bar{A}_2 \dotplus \bar{A}_3 \dotplus \cdots, \quad C_j = \bar{A}_1 \dotplus \cdots \dotplus \bar{A}_{j-1} \dotplus * \dotplus \bar{A}_{j+1} \dotplus \cdots$$

$$(j = 2, 3, \ldots) \tag{238.1}$$

and observe that we can write

$$A_j \subseteqq A \subseteqq A_j \dotplus C_j \qquad (j = 1, 2, \ldots). \tag{238.2}$$

From this we deduce $A = A(A_j \dotplus C_j) = A_j \dotplus AC_j \dotplus A_jC_j$, and hence

$$A \dotplus AC_j \subseteqq A_j. \tag{238.3}$$

We denote a measurable kernel of A_j by A_j', and a measurable kernel of A by A'. It follows from $A' \subseteqq A$ that $A' \dotplus A'C_j \subseteqq A \dotplus AC_j \subseteqq A_j$, and hence the soma

$$\underline{A}_j = A_j' \dotplus (A' \dotplus A'C_j) \tag{238.4}$$

is also a measurable kernel of A_j and satisfies the equation (cf. footnote 3, p. 279)

$$\mu \underline{A}_j = \mu_* A_j. \tag{238.5}$$

The measurable somas $\underline{A}_j$ are pairwise disjoint since they are subsomas of the A_j. Hence if we put

$$\underline{A} = \underline{A}_1 + \underline{A}_2 + \cdots, \tag{238.6}$$

we obtain

$$\mu \underline{A} = \sum_j \mu \underline{A}_j = \sum_j \mu_* A_j. \tag{238.7}$$

We now introduce the soma

$$R = A' \dot{+} A' \underline{A}. \tag{238.8}$$

It follows from $A' \subseteqq \underline{A} + R \subseteqq A$ that $\underline{A} + R$ is a measurable kernel of A and that we have

$$\mu R = \mu(\underline{A} + R) - \mu \underline{A} = \mu_* A - \sum_j \mu_* A_j. \tag{238.9}$$

239. By (238.4) and (238.6) we have $A' \dot{+} A'C_j \subseteqq \underline{A}_j \subseteqq \underline{A}$, so that we can write

$$A' \dot{+} A'C_j = A'\underline{A} \dot{+} A'\underline{A}\, C_j \quad \text{or} \quad R = RC_j \quad (j = 1, 2, \ldots). \tag{239.1}$$

Hence, if we put

$$C = \prod_j C_j, \tag{239.2}$$

we obtain $R \subseteqq C$ and therefore we also have

$$\mu R \leqq \mu C. \tag{239.3}$$

It follows from (237.3) and (237.4) that

$$\bar{A}_j \bar{A}_{j+m} \subseteqq B_{j+m-1} \subseteqq B \tag{239.4}$$

holds for all positive integers j and m. Applying this relation to the equation

$$\bar{A}_j C_j = \bar{A}_j \bar{A}_1 \dot{+} \cdots \dot{+} \bar{A}_j \bar{A}_{j-1} \dot{+} * \dot{+} \bar{A}_j \bar{A}_{j+1} \dot{+} \cdots, \tag{239.5}$$

which is a consequence of (238.1), and taking (239.2) into account, we obtain, successively, the relations

$$\bar{A}_j C \subseteqq \bar{A}_j C_j \subseteqq B, \quad \bar{A} C = \sum_j \dot{+} (\bar{A}_j C) \subseteqq B. \tag{239.6}$$

But now $C \subseteqq C_1 \subseteqq \bar{A}$; hence $\bar{A}C = C$, and consequently $C \subseteqq B$. From this we have the relation

$$\mu C \leqq \mu B, \tag{239.7}$$

a comparison of which with (239.3), (238.9), and (237.6) demonstrates the validity of the relation

This most remarkable inequality, as we see, is rather well concealed. It is equivalent with the relation

$$\frac{1}{2}(\mu^*A + \mu_*A) \leqq \sum_j \frac{1}{2}(\mu^*A_j + \mu_*A_j), \tag{239.9}$$

which in turn is just another way of writing (236.2).

240. Let U be a soma of the ring of measurability $\mathfrak{M}_\mu$ of μ^*X and μ_*X. Then we can write

$$\left.\begin{aligned} \mu^*X &= \mu^*XU + \mu^*(X \dot{+} XU), \\ \mu_*X &= \mu_*XU + \mu_*(X \dot{+} XU), \end{aligned}\right\} \tag{240.1}$$

and we can do so even if $\mu^*X = +\infty$; hence

$$\varphi(X) = \varphi(XU) + \varphi(X \dot{+} XU). \tag{240.2}$$

The ring of measurability $\mathfrak{M}_\mu$ is thus included in the ring of measurability $\mathfrak{M}_\varphi$ of $\varphi(X)$, i.e., $\varphi(X)$ is cometric to μ^*X (§ 143).

On the other hand, we have, by Theorem 6 of § 232,

$$\left.\begin{aligned} \mu U &= \mu^*UX + \mu_*(U \dot{+} UX), \\ \mu U &= \mu_*UX + \mu^*(U \dot{+} UX), \end{aligned}\right\} \tag{240.3}$$

and from this it follows, for $\varphi(U) = +\infty$ as well, that

$$\varphi(U) = \varphi(UX) + \varphi(U \dot{+} UX). \tag{240.4}$$

Combining all these results, we have the following theorem

THEOREM 1: *If μ^*X denotes a regular measure function, then the expression*

$$\varphi(X) = \frac{1}{2}(\mu^*X + \mu_*X) \tag{240.5}$$

represents a measure function that is cometric to, and absolutely continuous with respect to μ^*X.

If U is a μ^*-measurable soma, then

$$\varphi(U) = \varphi(UX) + \varphi(U \dot{+} UX) \tag{240.6}$$

holds for all somas X of the domain of definition of $\varphi(X)$.

If $\varphi(X)$ now happens to be a *regular* measure function, in other words, an outer measure, the corresponding inner measure must take the same value as $\varphi(X)$ on each soma X, since by (240.6), $\varphi(X)$ is a self-adjoint function of the class $\mathfrak{C}$. Then every soma of finite outer measure is φ-measurable, by Theorem 2 of § 230. But, by Theorem 2 of § 132, every soma whatsoever is φ-measurable, and we have the following theorem.

THEOREM 2: *If the measure function $\varphi(X)$ defined by* (240.5) *is not completely additive on its entire domain of definition, then $\varphi(X)$ is not a regular measure function.*

CHAPTER TEN

ISOTYPIC REGULAR MEASURE FUNCTIONS

§§ 241-244. The Principal Properties of Isotypic Measure Functions

241. We make the following definition.

DEFINITION: *Regular measure functions with the same domain of definition* $\mathfrak{A}$ *and a common base* $\mathfrak{B}$ *are called isotypic.*

To begin with, we have the following theorem.

THEOREM 1: *For every soma* X *in the domain of definition common to an at most countable number of isotypic regular measure functions* $\mu_1^* X$, $\mu_2^* X, \ldots$ *having* $\mathfrak{B}$ *as a common base, we can find a corresponding soma* X^0 *in* $\mathfrak{B}_{\sigma\delta}$ *that is a measurable hull of* X *for each of the measure functions under consideration, provided all the numbers* $\mu_j^* X$ *are finite.*

Proof: By the first few lines of § 224, for each j there is at least one soma $X_j{}^0$ in the set $\mathfrak{B}_{\sigma\delta}$ that is a μ_j^*-measurable hull of X. Then, by footnote 3, p. 279, the soma

$$X^0 = \prod_j X_j^0 \tag{241.1}$$

has all the desired properties.

When dealing with regular measure functions, it is often possible to extend properties that are postulated merely for the somas of a base $\mathfrak{B}$ to larger classes of somas belonging to the domain of definition of the measure function in question. Thus, for example, we have the following important theorem.

THEOREM 2: *We assume that the isotypic outer measures* $\mu_1^* X$, $\mu_2^* X, \ldots$ *have in common the subtractive base* $\mathfrak{B}$ *and an isotypic majorant* $\psi^* X$ *with the same base* $\mathfrak{B}$. *We also assume that for each soma* U *in* $\mathfrak{B}$, *the limit*

$$\lim_{j=\infty} \mu_j U \tag{241.2}$$

exists. Then the limit

$$\lim_{j=\infty} \mu_j^* A \tag{241.3}$$

exists for all somas A *in the common domain of definition* $\mathfrak{A}$ *for which* $\psi^* A < +\infty$. *In addition, there is a regular measure function* $\mu^* X$ *with* *base $\mathfrak{B}$ such that, for all the above-mentioned somas A, we have*

$$\mu^* A = \lim_{j=\infty} \mu_j^* A. \tag{241.4}$$

Proof: We put

$$p(U) = \lim_{j=\infty} \mu_j U \qquad (U \in \mathfrak{B}), \tag{241.5}$$

and we intend to show that $p(U)$ is a completely additive function on its domain of definition $\mathfrak{B}$.

Indeed, it follows from

$$U = U_1 + U_2 + U_3 + \cdots \qquad (U \in \mathfrak{B},\ U_k \in \mathfrak{B}) \tag{241.6}$$

since, by § 211, ψU must be finite on the base $\mathfrak{B}$, that

$$\sum_k \psi U_k = \psi U < +\infty. \tag{241.7}$$

Thus, we can assign a positive integer m_0 to each positive number ε in such a way that

$$\sum_{k=m+1}^{\infty} \psi U_k < \varepsilon \tag{241.8}$$

whenever $m > m_0$. Then from

$$\mu_j U = \sum_k \mu_j U_k \tag{241.9}$$

and $\mu_j U_k \leqq \psi U_k$ there follow the relations

$$\sum_{k=1}^{m} \mu_j U_k \leqq \mu_j U \leqq \sum_{k=1}^{m} \mu_j U_k + \varepsilon. \tag{241.10}$$

By passage to the limit, this yields

$$\sum_{k=1}^{m} p(U_k) \leqq p(U) \leqq \sum_{k=1}^{m} p(U_k) + \varepsilon. \tag{241.11}$$

The last relations hold for all $m > m_0$; hence

$$\sum_{k=1}^{\infty} p(U_k) \leqq p(U) \leqq \sum_{k=1}^{\infty} p(U_k) + \varepsilon$$

holds for every $\varepsilon > 0$, and we finally obtain the equation

$$p(U) = \sum_k p(U_k), \tag{241.12}$$

which was to be proved.

242. We now determine the maximal measure function μ^*X subordinate to the weight function $p(U)$ with base $\mathfrak{B}$. By Theorem 5 of § 210 and the definition in § 222, μ^*X is a regular measure function for which

$$\mu U = p(U) \qquad (U \in \mathfrak{B}).$$

Consequently, by (241.5), we also have

$$\mu U = \lim_{j \to \infty} \mu_j U \qquad (U \in \mathfrak{B}). \quad (242.1)$$

Every soma V in $\mathfrak{B}_\sigma$ can be represented as a sum

$$V = U_1 + U_2 + \cdots \quad (242.2)$$

of somas of the base $\mathfrak{B}$. We then have the equations

$$\psi V = \sum_k \psi U_k, \quad \mu V = \sum_k \mu U_k, \quad \mu_j V = \sum_k \mu_j U_k; \quad (242.3)$$

in addition, we have the relations

$$\left. \begin{aligned} &\mu_j U_k \leqq \psi U_k, \quad \mu U_k \leqq \psi U_k, \\ &\mu U_k = \lim_{j=\infty} \mu_j U_k. \end{aligned} \right\} \quad (242.4)$$

Now, if $\psi(V) < +\infty$, we deduce, as in § 241, that we must have

$$\mu V = \lim_{j=\infty} \mu_j V. \quad (242.5)$$

Finally, let A^0 be a soma of $\mathfrak{B}_{\sigma\delta}$ for which $\psi(A^0) < +\infty$. Then $\mathfrak{B}_\sigma$ contains a monotonically decreasing sequence of somas

$$V_1 \supseteqq V_2 \supseteqq \cdots \quad (242.6)$$

that converges to A^0 and that satisfies $\psi(V_1) < +\infty$. Then, by Theorem 5 of § 138, we have

$$\lim_{k=\infty} \psi(V_k) = \psi(A^0),$$

and therefore, given a positive number ε, we can choose a positive integer k in such a way that

$$\psi(V_k - A^0) = \psi(V_k) - \psi(A^0) < \frac{\varepsilon}{2}. \tag{242.7}$$

Then we also have

$$\left.\begin{aligned} \mu_j V_k - \mu_j A^0 &= \mu_j(V_k - A^0) < \frac{\varepsilon}{2} \quad (j = 1, 2, \ldots), \\ \mu V_k - \mu A^0 &= \mu(V_k - A^0) < \frac{\varepsilon}{2}. \end{aligned}\right\} \tag{242.8}$$

From these relations and from

$$\lim_{j=\infty} \mu_j V_k = \mu V_k \tag{242.9}$$

it follows, using

$$|\mu A^0 - \mu_j A^0| \leqq |\mu A^0 - \mu V_k| + |\mu V_k - \mu_j V_k| + |\mu_j V_k - \mu_j A^0|, \tag{242.10}$$

that we can write

$$\overline{\lim_{j=\infty}} |\mu A^0 - \mu_j A^0| \leqq \varepsilon. \tag{242.11}$$

From this, letting ε tend to zero, we obtain the equation

$$\mu A^0 = \lim_{j=\infty} \mu_j A^0. \tag{242.12}$$

This equation holds for all the somas A^0 in $\mathfrak{B}_{\sigma\delta}$ for which $\psi(A^0) < +\infty$. But if A is any soma for which $\psi^* A < +\infty$, then by Theorem 1 of § 241, for each of the measure functions $\mu_j^* X$ as well as the functions $\mu^* X$ and $\psi^* X$ there is a common measurable hull A^0 of A that belongs to $\mathfrak{B}_{\sigma\delta}$. Thus, we obtain the equations

$$\mu^* A = \mu A^0, \quad \mu_j^* A = \mu_j A^0, \tag{242.13}$$

and we also have

$$\psi A^0 = \psi^* A < +\infty. \tag{242.14}$$

Equation (242.12) can therefore also be written as

$$\mu^* A = \lim_{j=\infty} \mu_j^* A, \tag{242.15}$$

which completes the proof of the theorem.

243. Observe that the requirement $\psi^* A < +\infty$ is essential for the validity of the last theorem. However, for monotonically increasing sequences of isotypic outer measures the following analogous theorem holds under much simpler hypotheses.

THEOREM 3: *A monotonically increasing sequence*

$$\mu_1^* X \leqq \mu_2^* X \leqq \ldots \tag{243.1}$$

of outer measures, all of which admit the same subtractive base $\mathfrak{B}$, *converges to a regular measure function* $\mu^* X$ *with the same base* $\mathfrak{B}$, *provided that the limit* $\lim\limits_{j=\infty} \mu_j U$ *is finite for every soma* U *in* $\mathfrak{B}$.

Proof: By Theorem 1 of § 141, the limit function $\mu^* X$ is a measure function whose ring of measurability contains the complete ring $\overline{\mathfrak{B}}$ generated by $\mathfrak{B}$. Let X^0 be a measurable hull of X for every $\mu_j{}^* X$, and let it belong to the set of somas $\mathfrak{B}_{\sigma\delta}$ (Theorem 1 of § 241).

Then it follows from

$$\mu_j^* X = \mu_j X^0 \qquad (j = 1, 2, \ldots)$$

that

$$\mu^* X = \mu X^0. \tag{243.2}$$

Under the assumption that $\mu U < +\infty$ for every soma U in $\mathfrak{B}$, we can apply Theorem 3 of § 224, and our theorem follows immediately.

244. The following theorem deals with addition of isotypic measure functions.

THEOREM 4: *For every sequence of isotypic regular measure functions* $\mu_j^* X$ *with base* $\mathfrak{B}$, *and for every sequence of positive numbers* a_j, *the soma function*

$$\mu^* X = \sum_j a_j \mu_j^* X \tag{244.1}$$

is a regular measure function with the same base $\mathfrak{B}$, *provided that the numbers* μU *are finite for all somas* U *in* $\mathfrak{B}$.

Proof: For every positive number a, the two measure functions $\mu^* X$ and $a \cdot \mu^* X$ are isotypic measure functions as soon as one of them is regular. The theorem to be proved is thus a direct consequence of Theorem 3 of § 243; for it can be shown that for any two isotypic outer measures $\lambda^* X$ and $\mu^* X$, their sum

$$\nu^* X = \lambda^* X + \mu^* X \tag{244.2}$$

is also a regular measure function isotypic with the first two. Indeed, every λ^*-measurable and μ^*-measurable hull A^0 of A is also ν^*-measurable, and we have $\nu A^0 = \nu^* A$. Since A^0 can always be chosen from the set of somas $\mathfrak{B}_{\sigma\delta}$, it follows from Theorem 3 of § 224 that $\mathfrak{B}$ must be a base of $\nu^* X$. The somas in $\mathfrak{B}$ are ν^*-measurable, and hence it follows that $\nu^* X$ is an outer measure that is isotypic with $\lambda^* X$ and $\mu^* X$.

In conclusion, we prove one further theorem.

THEOREM 5: *Let K be any soma in the domain of definition of a regular measure function μ^*X. Then the soma function*

$$\nu^*X = \mu^*KX \tag{244.3}$$

is a regular measure function isotypic with μ^*X.

Proof: By Theorem 3 of § 145, ν^*X is cometric to μ^*X. Letting X^0 denote a μ^*-measurable hull of KX that belongs to the set of somas $\mathfrak{B}_{\sigma\delta}$, it follows from

$$KX \subseteqq X^0, \quad \mu^*KX = \mu X^0 \tag{244.4}$$

that we also have

$$KX \subseteqq KX^0 \subseteqq X^0, \quad \mu^*KX = \mu^*KX^0. \tag{244.5}$$

But the last equation can be written as

$$\nu^*X = \nu X^0, \tag{244.6}$$

and, once again, the theorem to be proved is a consequence of Theorem 3 of § 224.

§§ 245-248. The Jordan Decomposition of Completely Additive Soma Functions

245. Let $\mathfrak{A}$ be a subtractive set of somas on which there are defined two *finite, completely additive, non-negative* functions λX and μX. We shall investigate the function

$$F(X) = \lambda X - \mu X, \tag{245.1}$$

which is defined for every soma of $\mathfrak{A}$ and is itself, of course, completely additive on $\mathfrak{A}$.

The soma functions λX and μX are monotonically increasing. Thus, if Y is a subsoma of X belonging to $\mathfrak{A}$, we have

$$|F(Y)| = |\lambda Y - \mu Y| \leqq \lambda Y + \mu Y \leqq \lambda X + \mu X, \tag{245.2}$$

and therefore the function $\chi(X)$ defined by the equation

$$\chi(X) = \sup\big(|F(Y)|;\ Y \subseteqq X\big) \tag{245.3}$$

is finite for every soma of $\mathfrak{A}$.

We shall now show that, conversely, under the assumption that $\chi(X)$ is finite, a completely additive function $F(X)$ can always be represented as the difference of two completely additive non-negative functions.

To this end, we define on $\mathfrak{A}$ the monotonically increasing functions

$$\varphi(X) = \sup(F(Y);\ Y \subseteqq X), \tag{245.4}$$

$$\psi(X) = \sup(-F(Y);\ Y \subseteqq X), \tag{245.5}$$

whose difference we shall prove is equal to $F(X)$.

Since $F(X)$ is assumed to be completely additive, and therefore, certainly, additive and since $\mathfrak{A}$, being a subtractive set of somas, must contain the empty soma O, we can write

$$F(X) = F(X + O) = F(X) + F(O);$$

from this it follows that $F(O) = 0$. Thus, by (245.4) and (245.5), we must have

$$\varphi(X) \geqq 0, \quad \psi(X) \geqq 0. \tag{245.6}$$

Next, by comparing the relations (245.4) and (245.5) with (245.3) and taking into account the inequalities

$$F(Y) \leqq |F(Y)|, \quad -F(Y) \leqq |F(Y)|,$$

we obtain the relations

$$\varphi(X) \leqq \chi(X), \quad \psi(X) \leqq \chi(X). \tag{245.7}$$

Thus, by the assumption that $\chi(X)$ is finite, the non-negative numbers $\varphi(X)$ and $\psi(X)$ must likewise be finite, for every X in $\mathfrak{A}$.

Since the soma X itself is among the subsomas of X, it follows from the defining equations (245.4) and (245.5) that

$$F(X) \leqq \varphi(X), \quad -F(X) \leqq \psi(X). \tag{245.8}$$

Now let Y be any subsoma of X belonging to $\mathfrak{A}$. Then $Y' = X \dotplus Y$ also belongs to $\mathfrak{A}$; and since $X = Y + Y'$, we now have

$$F(X) = F(Y) + F(Y'). \tag{245.9}$$

But from this it follows that

$$F(X) - F(Y) = F(Y') \leqq \varphi(X), \tag{245.10}$$

and therefore we must have

$$-F(Y) \leqq \varphi(X) - F(X) \tag{245.11}$$

for every subsoma Y of X that belongs to $\mathfrak{A}$. From this and from (245.5), we obtain

$$\psi(X) \leqq \varphi(X) - F(X),$$

or

$$F(X) \leqq \varphi(X) - \psi(X). \tag{245.12}$$

If we replace $F(X)$ by $-F(X)$, however, the functions $\varphi(X)$ and $\psi(X)$ are interchanged, so that we also have

$$-F(X) \leqq \psi(X) - \varphi(X). \tag{245.13}$$

Hence we have, finally,

$$F(X) = \varphi(X) - \psi(X). \tag{245.14}$$

In deriving the representation of $F(X)$ as the difference of the two functions (245.4) and (245.5), we used the fact that $F(X)$ is additive, but not the fact that it is completely additive. We shall need this latter property to show that $\varphi(X)$ and $\psi(X)$ are themselves completely additive.

246. Let X_1 and X_2 be two disjoint somas which, together with their sum

$$X = X_1 + X_2 \tag{246.1}$$

belong to the domain of definition $\mathfrak{A}$ of $F(X)$. In addition, let Y_1 and Y_2 be subsomas of X_1 and X_2, respectively, that belong to $\mathfrak{A}$. Since the set $\mathfrak{A}$ is assumed to be subtractive, it follows from $Y_1 \subseteqq X$ and $Y_2 \subseteqq X$, by Theorem 4 of § 34, that $Y_1 + Y_2$ also belongs to $\mathfrak{A}$. Thus, by virtue of the additivity of $F(X)$, we can write

$$F(Y_1) + F(Y_2) = F(Y_1 + Y_2) \leqq \varphi(X_1 + X_2). \tag{246.2}$$

Because of the fact that this relation holds for all the subsomas Y_1 of X_1 and all the subsomas Y_2 of X_2 that belong to $\mathfrak{A}$, (245.4) enables us to obtain the relation

$$\varphi(X_1) + \varphi(X_2) \leqq \varphi(X_1 + X_2), \tag{246.3}$$

which indicates that the soma function $\varphi(X)$ is superadditive (§ 126).

Now let $X_1, X_2, \ldots$ be an at most countable number of somas of $\mathfrak{A}$, and let Z be another soma of $\mathfrak{A}$ for which

$$Z \subseteqq \sum_j \dot{+} X_j. \tag{246.4}$$

Let Z' be any subsoma of Z that belongs to $\mathfrak{A}$. Then the somas $Z'X_j$ also belong to $\mathfrak{A}$, and we have the equation

$$Z' = \sum_j \dot{+} Z'X_j.$$

But since $\mathfrak{A}$ is a subtractive set of somas, there is a sequence $\{Z_j'\}$ of pairwise disjoint somas of $\mathfrak{A}$ for which we have the relations

$$Z' = Z_1' + Z_2' + \cdots, \quad Z_j' \subseteqq X_j \quad (j = 1, 2, \ldots). \quad (246.5)$$

Now, by the complete additivity of $F(X)$, we have

$$F(Z') = F(Z_1') + F(Z_2') + \cdots, \quad (246.6)$$

and from the relation (245.4) we obtain, in addition,

$$F(Z_j') \leqq \varphi(X_j).$$

Hence, for every subsoma Z' of Z belonging to $\mathfrak{A}$, we have

$$F(Z') \leqq \sum_j \varphi(X_j);$$

and, finally, we have

$$\varphi(Z) \leqq \sum_j \varphi(X_j). \quad (246.7)$$

Accordingly, the function $\varphi(X)$ is cover-bounded (§ 126). By Theorem 2 of § 127, however, a non-negative cover-bounded soma function that is superadditive must be completely additive. In exactly the same way, we see that $\psi(X)$ must be completely additive, and we can enunciate the following theorem.

THEOREM 1: *Let a finite, completely additive soma function $F(X)$ of arbitrary sign be defined on a subtractive set of somas $\mathfrak{A}$. We assume that the function*

$$\chi(X) = \sup(|F(Y)|;\ Y \subseteqq X) \quad (246.8)$$

is finite throughout. Then, if we put

$$\left.\begin{aligned} \varphi(X) &= \sup(F(Y);\ Y \subseteqq X), \\ \psi(X) &= \sup(-F(Y);\ Y \subseteqq X), \end{aligned}\right\} \quad (246.9)$$

the functions $\varphi(X)$ and $\psi(X)$ are themselves completely additive on $\mathfrak{A}$. In addition, they are finite, monotonically increasing, and non-negative, and for every soma X in $\mathfrak{A}$, we have the equation

$$F(X) = \varphi(X) - \psi(X). \quad (246.10)$$

For every completely additive function $F(X)$, the condition $\chi(X) < +\infty$ is automatically satisfied if $F(X)$ can be represented in any way as the difference of two finite, non-negative, monotonically increasing soma functions.

The assertions of the theorem we have just proved can be interpreted as the natural extension to soma functions of the analogous result discovered by Camille Jordan (1838-1922) for functions $f(x)$ of one variable that can be represented as the difference of monotonically increasing functions.[1] We further intend to prove that each of the functions $\varphi(X)$ and $\psi(X)$ defined by (246.9) is singular (§ 143) with respect to the other; it is to Hans Hahn (1879-1934) that we are indebted for this latter result.[2]

247. In order to derive the Theorem of Hahn in complete generality for completely additive soma functions, we must require that the set of somas $\mathfrak{A}$ on which $F(X)$ is defined be not only subtractive but also *countably multiplicative.* Then, by Theorem 2 of § 43, if the soma A belongs to $\mathfrak{A}$, the totality of subsomas of A belonging to $\mathfrak{A}$ is a complete ring.

We choose a positive number ε and, taking (246.9) into account, determine a subsoma A_1 of A for which

$$\varphi(A) - \frac{\varepsilon}{2} < F(A_1) = \varphi(A_1) - \psi(A_1). \tag{247.1}$$

By the additivity of $\varphi(X)$, this can be written as

$$\varphi(A \dotplus A_1) + \psi(A_1) < \frac{\varepsilon}{2},$$

and consequently we also have

$$\varphi(A \dotplus A_1) < \frac{\varepsilon}{2}, \quad \psi(A_1) < \frac{\varepsilon}{2}. \tag{247.2}$$

We replace A by A_1 and ε by $\varepsilon/2$ in this calculation. We thereby determine a soma $A_2 \subseteqq A_1$ for which we have

$$\varphi(A_1 \dotplus A_2) < \frac{\varepsilon}{2^2}, \quad \psi(A_2) < \frac{\varepsilon}{2^2}.$$

Iteration of this process yields an infinite, monotonically decreasing sequence of somas

$$A_1 \supseteqq A_2 \supseteqq \cdots \tag{247.3}$$

that satisfy the conditions

$$\varphi(A_{k-1} \dotplus A_k) < \frac{\varepsilon}{2^k}, \quad \psi(A_k) < \frac{\varepsilon}{2^k}. \tag{247.4}$$

We now put

$$A_1' = \prod_j A_j, \tag{247.5}$$

[1] C. Jordan, *C. R. Acad. Sci. Paris,* Vol. 92 (1881), pp. 228-230; *Cours d'Analyse,* Vol. I, 2nd ed. (Paris, 1893), pp. 54-61.

[2] H. Hahn, *Theorie der reellen Funktionen,* Vol. I (Berlin, 1921), p. 404.

and from (247.4) we obtain

$$\psi(A_1') \leqq \psi(A_j) \leqq \frac{\varepsilon}{2^j} \qquad (j = 1, 2, \ldots);$$

from this it follows that

$$\psi(A_1') = 0. \tag{247.6}$$

On the other hand, Theorem 1 of § 23, applied to (247.5), yields the relation

$$A \dotplus A_1' = \sum_j \dotplus (A - A_j) = (A \dotplus A_1) + (A_1 \dotplus A_2) + \cdots, \tag{247.7}$$

and consequently we also have

$$\varphi(A \dotplus A_1') = \varphi(A \dotplus A_1) + \varphi(A_1 \dotplus A_2) + \cdots;$$

by (247.2) and (247.4), it follows from this that

$$\varphi(A \dotplus A_1') < \frac{\varepsilon}{2} + \frac{\varepsilon}{2^2} + \cdots = \varepsilon. \tag{247.8}$$

Now, if $\varphi(A) > 0$, we can choose

$$\varepsilon = \frac{\varphi(A)}{2},$$

and we have established the existence of a soma $A_1' \subseteqq A$ which, aside from equation (247.6), also satisfies the condition

$$\varphi(A \dotplus A_1') \leqq \frac{\varphi(A)}{2}. \tag{247.9}$$

If, on the other hand, $\varphi(A) = 0$, the relations (247.6) and (247.9) can again be verified by setting $A_1' = O$.

248. Writing $A_1'' = A \dotplus A_1'$, we can express the last result as follows: There is at least one decomposition

$$A = A_1' + A_1'' \tag{248.1}$$

of any given soma A of $\mathfrak{A}$ that satisfies

$$\psi(A_1') = 0, \quad \varphi(A_1'') \leqq \frac{\varphi(A)}{2}. \tag{248.2}$$

We can now apply this result to A_1'' and determine two disjoint somas A_2' and A_2'' that satisfy

$$A_1'' = A_2' + A_2'', \quad \psi(A_2') = 0, \quad \varphi(A_2'') \leqq \frac{\varphi(A_1'')}{2} \leqq \frac{\varphi(A)}{2^2}. \tag{248.3}$$

By repeating this process, we obtain a monotonically decreasing sequence of somas A''_k and, writing $A = A''_0$, a sequence of pairwise disjoint somas $A'_k = A''_{k-1} \dot{+} A''_k$, for which the relations

$$\psi(A'_k) = 0, \quad \varphi(A''_k) \leqq \frac{\varphi(A)}{2^k} \quad (k = 1, 2, \ldots) \qquad (248.4)$$

hold. Thus, if we put

$$A' = A'_1 + A'_2 + A'_3 + \cdots, \quad A'' = A''_1 A''_2 A''_3 \ldots = \lim_{k=\infty} A''_k, \qquad (248.5)$$

from (248.4) we obtain

$$\psi(A') = 0, \quad \varphi(A'') = 0. \qquad (248.6)$$

On the other hand, there follow successively from $A'_k \circ A''_k$ the relations

$$A'' \circ A'_k \quad (k = 1, 2, \ldots), \quad A'' \circ A', \qquad (248.7)$$

while the first of the equations (248.5) can also be written as

$$A' = (A \dot{+} A''_1) + (A''_1 \dot{+} A''_2) + \cdots = A \dot{+} \lim_{k=\infty} A''_k. \qquad (248.8)$$

Thus we obtain, finally,

$$A = A' + A'', \quad \varphi(A) = \varphi(A'), \quad \psi(A) = \psi(A''). \qquad (248.9)$$

The definition of a *Jordan decomposition,* which we gave in § 165, is thus applicable to our completely additive soma functions; in other words, we have the following theorem.

THEOREM 2: *If the domain of definition $\mathfrak{A}$ of a completely additive soma function $F(X)$ that satisfies Theorem* 1 *of* § 246 *is not only subtractive but also countably multiplicative, then every soma A in $\mathfrak{A}$ can be considered as the sum of two somas A' and A'' for which we have*

$$\left.\begin{aligned} F(AX) &= F(A'X) + F(A''X), \\ F(A'X) = \varphi(AX) \geqq 0, &\quad F(A''X) = -\psi(AX) \leqq 0. \end{aligned}\right\} \qquad (248.10)$$

§§ 249-255. The Difference of Two Isotypic Regular Measure Functions

249. We now intend to examine in all generality the difference

$$F(X) = \lambda^* X - \mu^* X \qquad (249.1)$$

of two isotypic regular measure functions both of which have domain of definition $\mathfrak{A}$ and base $\mathfrak{B}$. We can always choose $\mathfrak{B}$ in this case to be a subtractive set of somas, and we shall in fact always suppose this done. The domain of definition of $F(X)$ consists, in the first instance, of those somas X in $\mathfrak{A}$ for which the numbers λ^*X and μ^*X are not both infinite. We shall see, however, that under certain circumstances this domain of definition can be extended (§ 252).

$F(X)$ is in any event defined on all the somas of the base $\mathfrak{B}$. We again let $\overline{\mathfrak{B}}$ denote the complete ring generated by $\mathfrak{B}$, and in addition, we let $\mathfrak{B}^f$ denote the set of somas X in $\overline{\mathfrak{B}}$ for which the two numbers λX and μX are *both* infinite. In the sequel, we shall let U denote an arbitrary soma of $\mathfrak{B}$ and V, an arbitrary soma of $\mathfrak{B}^f$.

The set of somas $\mathfrak{B}^f$ is subtractive and countably multiplicative; moreover, each of the functions λ^*X, μ^*X, and $F(X)$ is completely additive on $\mathfrak{B}^f$. We can therefore apply Theorems 1 and 2 of the preceding section and, using equations (246.9), calculate two completely additive, non-negative functions $\varphi(V)$ and $\psi(V)$ that are defined on all the somas V of $\mathfrak{B}^f$ and satisfy the equation

$$\lambda V - \mu V = \varphi(V) - \psi(V). \tag{249.2}$$

The maximal measure function with base $\mathfrak{B}$ subordinate to the weight function $\varphi(U)$ will now be denoted by π^*X, and that subordinate to $\psi(U)$, by ν^*X. These functions are of course outer measures (cf. Theorem 5 of § 210 and the definition of § 222), which are isotypic with the functions λ^*X and μ^*X, respectively, and thus have the same domain of definition $\mathfrak{A}$. By Theorem 1 of § 223, moreover, the equations

$$\pi V = \varphi(V), \quad \nu V = \psi(V) \tag{249.3}$$

hold for all the somas V of $\mathfrak{B}^f$.

Since $\mathfrak{B}$ is subtractive, any soma X in the domain of definition of $F(X)$ can always be covered by the sum

$$M = M_1 + M_2 + M_3 + \cdots \tag{249.4}$$

of an at most countable number of pairwise disjoint somas of $\mathfrak{B}$. Then by Theorem 2 of § 248, there are decompositions

$$M_j = M_j' + M_j'' \qquad (j = 1, 2, \ldots) \tag{249.5}$$

of the somas M_j such that the equations

$$\varphi(M_j'') = 0, \quad \psi(M_j') = 0 \tag{249.6}$$

hold, and the somas M_j' and M_j'', by construction, are all contained in $\mathfrak{B}^f$.

Hence, if we put

$$M' = M_1' + M_2' + \cdots, \quad M'' = M_1'' + M_2'' + \cdots, \tag{249.7}$$

we have, by virtue of (249.3),

$$\pi M'' = \sum_j \varphi(M_j'') = 0, \quad \nu M' = \sum_j \psi(M_j') = 0. \tag{249.8}$$

This equation and

$$X \subseteqq M = M' + M'' \tag{249.9}$$

enable us to obtain the system of equations

$$\pi^* X = \pi^* X M', \quad \nu^* X = \nu^* X M'' \quad (X \subseteqq M), \tag{249.10}$$

which mean that each of the measure functions $\pi^* X$ and $\nu^* X$ is singular with respect to the other.

250. We shall show that the equation

$$\lambda^* A - \mu^* A = \pi^* A - \nu^* A \tag{250.1}$$

is satisfied by all the somas A for which at least one of the numbers $\lambda^* A$ and $\mu^* A$ is finite.

By what we have just shown, there is in any case a soma $M \supseteqq A$ in $\overline{\mathfrak{B}}$ and a decomposition of M into $M' + M''$ for which the relations (249.10) hold. Next, we put

$$\lambda_1^* X = \lambda^*(XM'), \quad \mu_1^* X = \mu^*(XM') \quad (X \subseteqq M); \tag{250.2}$$

then, by Theorems 4 and 5 of § 244, the two functions

$$\lambda_1^* X, \quad \mu_1^* X + \pi^* X \tag{250.3}$$

are regular measure functions with base $\mathfrak{B}$. But for every soma U in $\mathfrak{B}$, UM' belongs to $\mathfrak{B}^f$. If we compare (250.2) with (249.2), (249.3), and (249.10) and take $\nu(UM') = 0$ into account, we obtain the equation

$$\lambda_1 U = \mu_1 U + \pi U \qquad (U \in \mathfrak{B}).$$

Thus, on each soma of their common base $\mathfrak{B}$, both measure functions (250.3) take the same value; they are consequently (§ 211) identical and, by (250.2), the equation

$$\lambda^*(XM') = \mu^*(XM') + \pi^* X \tag{250.4}$$

is valid in general. Thus, in particular, we also have

$$\lambda^*(AM') = \mu^*(AM') + \pi^*A. \tag{250.5}$$

In exactly the same way, we obtain the equation

$$\mu^*(AM'') = \lambda^*(AM'') + \nu^*A. \tag{250.6}$$

Now if, say, $\mu^*A < +\infty$, the left-hand side of the last equation must be finite; the same holds for ν^*A; and instead of (250.6), we can write

$$\lambda^*(AM'') = \mu^*(AM'') - \nu^*A. \tag{250.7}$$

Equation (250.1), which was to be proved, can now be obtained by termwise addition of (250.5) and (250.7).

251. Let $\varkappa(X)$, $\varrho(X)$, $\sigma(X)$, and $\tau(X)$ be any finite, monotonically increasing, non-negative soma functions that have the relation

$$\varkappa(X) - \varrho(X) = \sigma(X) - \tau(X) \tag{251.1}$$

to each other. Let each of the functions $\sigma(X)$ and $\tau(X)$, furthermore, be assumed to be singular with respect to the other. We can then assign a soma N_X to each soma X in the common domain of definition of these functions in such a way as to obtain

$$\tau(N_X) = 0, \quad \sigma(X) = \sigma(XN_X). \tag{251.2}$$

From this it follows that

$$\sigma(X) = \varkappa(XN_X) - \varrho(XN_X) \leqq \varkappa(XN_X) \leqq \varkappa(X), \tag{251.3}$$

and it is proved similarly that

$$\tau(X) \leqq \varrho(X). \tag{251.4}$$

Hence we deduce the following: If $\varkappa(X)$ and $\varrho(X)$ are given, then there is at most one pair of functions $\sigma(X)$ and $\tau(X)$ having the above-mentioned properties.

By combining this result with those of the last two sections, we obtain the following theorem.

THEOREM 1: *We consider the difference*

$$F(X) = \lambda^*X - \mu^*X \tag{251.5}$$

of two isotypic regular measure functions that do not both take the value infinity for any soma in their domain of definition. Then there exists one *and only one pair of monotonically increasing soma functions π^*X and ν^*X, each singular with respect to the other, for which*

$$F(X) = \pi^*X - \nu^*X. \tag{251.6}$$

The soma functions π^*X and ν^*X are regular measure functions, and every subtractive base $\mathfrak{B}$ common to the measure functions λ^*X and μ^*X also constitutes a base for π^*X and for ν^*X. In addition, the relations

$$\pi^*X \leqq \lambda^*X, \quad \nu^*X \leqq \mu^*X \tag{251.7}$$

hold. These outer measures π^*X and ν^*X are called the positive and negative variations, respectively, of $F(X)$.

252. If the negative variation ν^*X is not identically zero, let A be a soma for which $\nu^*A > 0$. Then we must have $F(AM'') = -\nu^*A < 0$. Thus, under the assumption $F(X) \geqq 0$, we must have $\nu^*X \equiv 0$, and thus we have the following theorem.

THEOREM 2: *The difference of two isotypic regular measure functions λ^*X and μ^*X with base $\mathfrak{B}$ is itself a regular measure function with base $\mathfrak{B}$, provided that $\lambda^*X \geqq \mu^*X$ throughout.*

It should be observed that this theorem is no longer valid when it comes to outer measures that are not isotypic. Consider three pairwise disjoint somas A, B, and C and the ring consisting of the eight somas

$$O, \ A, \ B, \ C, \ B+C, \ C+A, \ A+B, \ A+B+C.$$

The measure function μ_1^*X that is induced on this ring by the base $\mathfrak{B}_1 = \{O, A+B, C\}$ and the weight function $p_1(A+B) = 1$, $p_1(C) = 2$ is regular. The measure function μ_2^*X with base $\mathfrak{B}_2 = \{O, \ A, \ B+C\}$ and weight function $p_2(A) = 4$, $p_2(B+C) = 3$ is likewise an outer measure. It is easy to compute that the soma function $F(X) = \mu_2^*X - \mu_1^*X$ is non-negative. $F(X)$ is not, however, a measure function, since we have $F(A) = 3$, $F(B) = 2$, and $F(A+B) = 6$.

It is equally unnecessary for the theorem to hold for the difference of two measure functions that are not both regular: Let μ^*X be an outer measure and μ_*^*X, the corresponding inner measure. Then, by § 240,

$$\varphi(X) = \mu^*X + \mu_*X \tag{252.1}$$

is a measure function, and

$$F(X) = \varphi(X) - \mu^*X = \mu_*X \geqq 0. \tag{252.2}$$

But $F(X)$ need not be a measure function (Theorem 8 of § 233).

We return to the consequences of Theorem 2. If, using our old notation, we put

$$\varrho^* X = \lambda^* X - \pi^* X = \mu^* X - \nu^* X, \tag{252.3}$$

then, by (251.7), $\varrho^* X \geqq 0$, and hence, by Theorem 2, $\varrho^* X$ must be a regular measure function that admits the same base $\mathfrak{B}$ as $\lambda^* X$ and $\mu^* X$. This yields the following theorem.

Theorem 3: *If $\pi^* X$ and $\nu^* X$ are the variations of a function $F(X) = \pi^* X - \nu^* X$, then we obtain the most general representation of $F(X)$ as the difference*

$$F(X) = \lambda^* X - \mu^* X \tag{252.4}$$

of isotypic outer measures by taking an arbitrary regular measure function $\varrho^* X$ that has a base in common with $\pi^* X$ and $\nu^* X$ and putting

$$\lambda^* X = \pi^* X + \varrho^* X, \quad \mu^* X = \nu^* X + \varrho^* X. \tag{252.5}$$

If the numbers $\pi^* A$ and $\nu^* A$ are not both infinite for a soma A, but if $\varrho^* A = +\infty$, then, although the function $F(X)$ is defined for $X = A$, the representation of $F(X)$ in the form (252.4) becomes meaningless if we put $X = A$. If, on the other hand, both numbers $\pi^* A$ and $\nu^* A$ are infinite, there is no representation of $F(X)$ by means of which $F(A)$ can be computed. Thus it is natural to let the domain of definition of $F(X)$ coincide with the set of somas X for which the numbers $\pi^* X$ and $\nu^* X$ are not both infinite.

253. In most applications, it is no great loss of generality to consider $F(X)$ only on the subsomas of a fixed soma M of $\mathfrak{B}^f$ for which

$$\pi M < +\infty, \quad \nu M < +\infty. \tag{253.1}$$

If such is the case, we say that $F(X)$ is a *function of bounded variation.*

For functions of bounded variation, it is useful to consider, aside from the positive variation $\pi^* X$ and the negative variation $\nu^* X$, their *total variation*

$$\tau^* X = \pi^* X + \nu^* X \tag{253.2}$$

as well. Taking equations (249.8) and (249.10) into account, we find that

$$\left.\begin{aligned} \tau^* XM' &= \pi^* XM' + \nu^* XM' = \pi^* XM' = \pi^* X, \\ \tau^* XM'' &= \pi^* XM'' + \nu^* XM'' = \nu^* XM'' = \nu^* X. \end{aligned}\right\} \tag{253.3}$$

Therefore, by (251.6), we can also write

$$\left.\begin{aligned} &F(X) = \tau^* XM' - \tau^* XM'', \\ &F(XM') = \tau^* XM', \quad F(XM'') = -\tau^* XM''. \end{aligned}\right\} \tag{253.4}$$

254. These formulas allow us to define functions of bounded variation by prescribing their total variation and the somas M' and M''.

Let τ^*X be any measure function with base $\mathfrak{B}$ and domain of definition $\mathfrak{A}$. Moreover, let M' and M'' be two disjoint somas that belong to the ring of measurability of τ^*X. We put

$$M = M' + M'' \qquad (254.1)$$

and assume that

$$\tau M < +\infty. \qquad (254.2)$$

The function

$$F(X) = \tau^*XM' - \tau^*XM'' \qquad (254.3)$$

is of bounded variation on the complete ring $\mathfrak{A}_M$ consisting of all the somas X in $\mathfrak{A}$ that are subsomas of M; its total variation is the measure function τ^*X, and its positive and negative variations are defined by the equations

$$\pi^*X = \tau^*XM', \quad \nu^*X = \tau^*XM''. \qquad (254.4)$$

Indeed, the two functions τ^*XM' and τ^*XM'' are regular measure functions with base $\mathfrak{B}$, by Theorem 5 of § 244, and each of them is singular with respect to the other.

255. If it is known that $F(X)$ is a function of bounded variation, for which formulas (254.3) and (254.4) therefore hold, then the variations π^*X, ν^*X, and τ^*X can also be computed directly from the function $F(X)$, as follows.

Since the soma M' constructed in § 249 is τ^*-measurable, there certainly exists a soma $V^0 \supseteqq M'$ in $\mathfrak{B}_{\sigma\delta}$ for which

$$\tau^*(V^0 \dotplus M') = 0 \qquad (255.1)$$

(cf. Theorem 1 of § 213, as well as § 224). Then, for every soma $X \subseteqq M$, we have both

$$\tau^*(V^0XM'') = \tau^*\big((V^0 \dotplus M')\, X\big) = 0 \qquad (255.2)$$

and

$$F(V^0X) = \tau^*(V^0XM') = \tau^*(XM') = \pi^*X. \qquad (255.3)$$

But, for every soma V in $\mathfrak{B}_{\sigma\delta}$, we have

$$F(VX) \leqq \pi^*(VX) \leqq \pi^*X, \qquad (255.4)$$

and hence

$$\pi^*X = \sup\big(F(VX);\, V \in \mathfrak{B}_{\sigma\delta}\big). \qquad (255.5)$$

In the same way, we obtain the equation

$$\nu^*X = \sup\big(-F(VX);\, V \in \mathfrak{B}_{\sigma\delta}\big). \qquad (255.6)$$

Finally, since the somas V^0 and $M \dotplus V^0$ are both π^*-measurable and ν^*-measurable, it follows from Theorem 2 of § 136 and from (255.3) that

$$F(X \dotplus V^0X) = F(X) - F(V^0X) = -\nu^*X, \tag{255.7}$$

so that we can also write

$$\tau^*X = |F(V^0X)| + |F(X \dotplus V^0X)|. \tag{255.8}$$

On the other hand, again by Theorem 2 of § 136, we have

$$|F(VX)| + |F(X \dotplus VX)| \leqq \tau^*(VX) + \tau^*(X \dotplus VX) = \tau^*X \tag{255.9}$$

for every soma V in $\mathfrak{B}_{\sigma\delta}$, so that τ^*X can be determined by the equation

$$\tau^*X = \sup\bigl(|F(VX)| + |F(X \dotplus VX)|;\ V \in \mathfrak{B}_{\sigma\delta}\bigr). \tag{255.10}$$

§§ 256-257. Comparable Outer Measures

256. We have yet to apply the notion of comparable measure functions (§§ 167 ff.) to outer measures. As a partial result in this direction, we derive the following theorem.

THEOREM 1: *Let λ^*X be a regular measure function and let f be a non-negative place function that is λ^*-integrable on the domain of definition M of λ^*X. Then the integral*

$$\mu^*X = \int_X f\, d\lambda \tag{256.1}$$

is a regular measure function that is isotypic with λ^*X.

Proof: We must show that there is at least one common base for λ^*X and μ^*X.

If f is a bounded *finitely-valued* place function, then, by (155.6), we have

$$\mu^*X = \sum_j y_j\, \lambda^*(M_jX), \tag{256.2}$$

and the above statement is then a direct consequence of Theorems 5 and 4 of § 244.

The proof for the general case, which follows, depends upon this weaker result.

By the definition of integrability given in § 160, M must be a normal soma both of λ^*X and of μ^*X. Thus, there is, in the first instance, at least one decomposition

$$M = M_0 + M_1 + M_2 + \cdots \tag{256.3}$$

with the following properties: All the M_j are λ^*-measurable, and hence also μ^*-measurable; M_0 is the subsoma of M on which $f = +\infty$; and, with $\beta(X)$ denoting the supremum of f on the soma X, we have the inequalities

$$\lambda M_j < +\infty, \ \beta(M_j) < +\infty \quad (j = 1, 2, \ldots). \quad (256.4)$$

From these properties it follows that

$$\mu M_j < +\infty \qquad (j = 1, 2, \ldots). \quad (256.5)$$

In addition, by Theorem 3 of § 160, we have

$$\lambda M_0 = \mu M_0 = 0. \quad (256.6)$$

Now let $\mathfrak{B}_0$ be any subtractive base of $\lambda^* X$. We form the set of somas $\{U_0 M_j\}$ $(U_0 \in \mathfrak{B}_0; j = 0, 1, 2, \ldots)$ as well as its subtractive closure, which latter we denote by $\mathfrak{B}$. Since

$$U_0 = \sum_j U_0 M_j, \quad \lambda U_0 = \sum_j \lambda(U_0 M_j), \quad (256.7)$$

the numbers λU_0 $(U_0 \in \mathfrak{B}_0)$ are uniquely determined by the numbers λU $(U \in \mathfrak{B})$. Thus $\mathfrak{B}$ is, in any event, a subtractive base for $\lambda^* X$. We shall now show that it is a subtractive base for $\mu^* X$ as well.

Every non-negative place function f that is integrable on M can be represented as the limit of a monotonically increasing sequence

$$f_1 \leqq f_2 \leqq f_3 \leqq \cdots \quad (256.8)$$

of bounded, finitely-valued, non-negative place functions. Then, if we put

$$\mu_k^* X = \int_X f_k \, d\lambda, \quad (256.9)$$

we obtain

$$\mu_1^* X \leqq \mu_2^* X \leqq \mu_3^* X \leqq \cdots. \quad (256.10)$$

Moreover, by Theorem 2 of § 168, we have

$$\lim_{k=\infty} \mu_k^* X = \lim_{k=\infty} \int_X f_k \, d\lambda = \int_X f \, d\lambda = \mu^* X; \quad (256.11)$$

and finally, by (256.5), (256.6), and the definition of $\mathfrak{B}$, we have

$$\mu U < +\infty \qquad (U \in \mathfrak{B}). \quad (256.12)$$

Therefore, by Theorem 3 of § 243, $\mu^* X$ is an outer measure with base $\mathfrak{B}$. This completes the proof of our theorem.

257. We are now in a position to see that outer measures are comparable in the sense of § 167—or, what is the same, in the sense of Theorem 1 of § 171—if and only if they are isotypic.

Indeed, if $\lambda^* X$ is an outer measure with subtractive base $\mathfrak{B}$, the two integrals

$$\mu_1^* X = \int_X f_1 \, d\lambda, \quad \mu_2^* X = \int_X f_2 \, d\lambda \tag{257.1}$$

are, by the last theorem, regular measure functions that are isotypic with $\lambda^* X$. Thus, there are common bases $\mathfrak{B}_1$ and $\mathfrak{B}_2$ for the pairs $\lambda^* X$, $\mu_1^* X$ and $\lambda^* X$, $\mu_2^* X$, respectively. But then the set of somas

$$\{U_1 U_2\} \qquad (U_1 \in \mathfrak{B}_1, \ U_2 \in \mathfrak{B}_2)$$

is a common base for all three measure functions; for, every soma U_1 can be covered by the base $\mathfrak{B}_2$ and can therefore be represented in the form $\sum_j U_1 U_2^{(j)}$, and a corresponding result holds for the somas U_2. Thus $\mu_1^* X$ and $\mu_2^* X$ are isotypic with each other.

Conversely, let $\mu_1^* X$ and $\mu_2^* X$ be isotypic outer measures with base $\mathfrak{B}$. For every choice of the positive number y, the outer measures

$$y \mu_1^* X, \quad \mu_2^* X \tag{257.2}$$

also have the same base $\mathfrak{B}$. Let M be a soma belonging to the complete ring $\overline{\mathfrak{B}}$ generated by $\mathfrak{B}$ for which the numbers $\mu_1^* M$ and $\mu_2^* M$ are not both infinite. Then, by §§ 249 and 250, there is a decomposition of M

$$M = M_y' + M_y'' \tag{257.3}$$

such that the subsomas M_y' and M_y'' also belong to $\overline{\mathfrak{B}}$, and moreover, such that for all somas $X \subseteq M$, the relations

$$y \mu_1^*(X M_y') - \mu_2^*(X M_y') \geqq 0, \quad y \mu_1^*(X M_y'') - \mu_2^*(X M_y'') \leqq 0 \tag{257.4}$$

are all satisfied (cf. (248.10)).

Then, by the definition given in § 167, the measure functions $\mu_1^* X$ and $\mu_2^* X$ are comparable, and we have the following theorem.

THEOREM 2: *Two outer measures $\mu_1^* X$ and $\mu_2^* X$ are comparable if and only if they are isotypic.*

Thus, by Theorem 1 of § 171, each of two isotypic outer measures admits a Lebesgue decomposition with respect to the other and, in accordance with the definition given in § 170, we can also enunciate the following theorem.

THEOREM 3: *If* $\mu_1^* X$ *and* $\mu_2^* X$ *are isotypic outer measures, then for each normal soma* M *in their domain of definition, there is a soma* N *and a place function* f *defined on* M *such that the equations*

$$\mu_2^* X = \int_X f \, d\mu_1 + \mu_2^*(XN), \quad \mu_1^* N = 0 \tag{257.5}$$

hold, provided $X \subseteqq M$.

CHAPTER ELEVEN

CONTENT FUNCTIONS

§§ 258-259. The Definition of Content Functions

258. In §§ 148 ff. we defined and investigated the *Borel-Lebesgue content* of a subset of Euclidean space $\mathfrak{R}_q$. The subject matter of those sections is, in our present terminology, a regular measure function a base for which is the totality of all intervals. Hans Hahn has generalized this notion: he calls any regular measure function μ^*X that is defined on subsets of $\mathfrak{R}_q$ and contains the Borel sets in its ring of measurability, a *content function*, provided every subset A of $\mathfrak{R}_q$ for which μ^*A is finite has at least one measurable hull $\bar{A}$ that is representable as an intersection of a countable number of open sets.[1]

Now let μ^*X be a content function in the sense of Hans Hahn, let A be a point set with $\mu^*A < +\infty$, and let A be a measurable hull of A that is the intersection of a countable number of open neighborhoods

$$U_1, U_2, \ldots \tag{258.1}$$

of A. We consider the countable number of q-dimensional open intervals with rational end-points

$$I_1, I_2, I_3, \ldots \tag{258.2}$$

that have points in common with A, and we shall show that the measurable point sets

$$B_n = \bar{A} I_n \qquad (n = 1, 2, \ldots) \tag{258.3}$$

form a base for the restriction of μ^*X to the subsets X of A. That is, it must be possible to cover each subset X of A by certain of the point sets (258.3), say $B_{n_1}, B_{n_2}, \ldots$, such that

$$\sum_j \mu B_{n_j} < \mu^*X + \varepsilon \tag{258.4}$$

holds, where ε denotes a positive number specified in advance.

---

[1] H. Hahn, *Theorie der reellen Funktionen* (Berlin, 1921), p. 444. (Content functions are defined here, by the way, for more general spaces than $\mathfrak{R}_q$.)

259. We take the following remark as our starting point: By assumption, there is a monotonically decreasing sequence $V_1 \supseteqq V_2 \supseteqq \ldots$ of open neighborhoods of X whose intersection $\overline{X}$ is a measurable hull of X. It is no loss of generality to require in addition that V_n be a subset of U_n, where U_n belongs to the sequence (258.1).

But then we have

$$\lim_{n=\infty} V_n = \overline{X} \subseteqq \bar{A}, \tag{259.1}$$

and consequently also

$$\lim_{n=\infty} V_n \bar{A} = \overline{X}.$$

Furthermore, since $\mu V_1 \bar{A} < +\infty$, we have

$$\lim_{n=\infty} \mu(V_n \bar{A} - \overline{X}) = 0 \tag{259.2}$$

by Theorem 5 of § 138. In other words, a positive number ε being given, there are open neighborhoods V of X that satisfy the condition

$$\mu V \bar{A} < \mu^* X + \frac{\varepsilon}{2}. \tag{259.3}$$

We choose such a V and cover X with a sequence

$$I_{\nu_1}, I_{\nu_2}, \ldots$$

of intervals taken from (258.2) all of which are contained in V. Next, we decompose each of the point sets

$$I_{\nu k} \dotplus I_{\nu k}\left(I_{\nu_1} \dotplus I_{\nu_2} \dotplus \cdots \dotplus I_{\nu k-1}\right) \quad (k = 2, 3, \ldots)$$

one after the other, into a sum of a finite number of intervals I_j, where we retain only those that have points in common with $\bar{A}$. In this way we obtain (if we include I_{ν_1}) a sequence of *disjoint* intervals

$$I_{m_1}, I_{m_2}, \ldots.$$

We denote the sum of the pairwise disjoint intervals $B_{m_j} = I_{m_j} \bar{A}$ by B^0 and put

$$X - B^0 X = X^1.$$

It should be observed that the point set X^1 is distributed over an at most countable number of $(q - 1)$-dimensional hyperplanes, and that, because

$$(B^0 - B^0 \overline{X}) \subseteqq (V - V\overline{X})\, \bar{A}$$

and because of the fact that $B^0\overline{X}$ is a measurable hull of B^0X, we have

$$\mu B^0 < \mu^* B^0 X + \frac{\varepsilon}{2}.$$

We can obtain, similarly, a sum B^1 of pairwise disjoint somas taken from the sequence (258.3) such that the point set

$$X^1 - B^1 X^1 = X^2$$

is contained in an at most countable number of $(q - 2)$-dimensional hyperplanes and such that we have, in addition, the inequality

$$\mu B^1 < \mu^* B^1 X^1 + \frac{\varepsilon}{4}.$$

By repeating this process $(q + 1)$ times, and writing $X^0 = X$, $X^{q+1} = O$, we obtain the relations

$$X^i - B^i X^i = X^{i+1}, \quad \mu B^i < \mu^* B^i X^i + \frac{\varepsilon}{2^{i+1}} \quad (i = 0, 1, \ldots, q).$$

From this, it follows for the point sets B_{n_j}, of which the B^i are composed and whose union, therefore, covers X, that

$$\sum_j \mu B_{n_j} < \sum_{i=0}^{q} \mu^* B^i X^i + \varepsilon. \tag{259.4}$$

If we now put $C^0 = B^0$ and $C^k = B^k \dotplus B^k(B^0 \dotplus \ldots \dotplus B^{k-1})$ for $k = 1, \ldots q$, then the point sets C^i $(i = 0, 1, \ldots, q)$ are measurable and pairwise disjoint. In addition, we have

$$B^i X^i = C^i X^i, \quad \sum_{i=0}^{q} C^i X^i = X,$$

so that by Theorem 2 of § 136,

$$\sum_{i=0}^{q} \mu^* B^i X^i = \sum_{i=0}^{q} \mu^* C^i X^i = \mu^* X.$$

If we substitute this into (259.4), we obtain (258.4).

The last result allows us to generalize the notion of content function in such a way that it can be applied to arbitrary rings of somas.

DEFINITION: *An outer measure $\mu^* X$ defined on a complete ring of somas $\mathfrak{A}$ is called a content function if to each normal soma A in $\mathfrak{A}$ there can be assigned an (at most) countable number of somas $U_1, U_2, \ldots$ of the ring of measurability $\mathfrak{M}_\mu$ of $\mu^* X$ that can be used as a base for all the subsomas of A.*

This definition is more general than that of Hahn, even for point sets on the real line. For example, if we put $\mu x_n = 0$ for every point x_n of a countable dense subset of the interval $0 < x < 1$, and $\mu x = +\infty$ for all the remaining points of this interval and if we recall[2] that the intersection D of an infinite number of neighborhoods of all the x_n can never be countable, so that $\mu D = +\infty$, we obtain a measure function that is not a content function in the sense of Hahn. According to our definition, however, it is a content function with base $\{x_n\}$.

§§ 260-267. Reduced Content Functions and their Homomorphisms

260. By § 212, in particular because of equation (212.3), arbitrary homomorphisms transform content functions into content functions. In particular, in accordance with § 147, every content function can be transformed by a measure-preserving homomorphism into a *reduced content* function, i.e., one for which every non-empty soma has a non-zero content.

Let

$$U_1, U_2, U_3, \dots \tag{260.1}$$

be the somas in a base for the reduced content function $\mu^* X$. We extend this base to a *canonical base* for $\mu^* X$ by successively computing somas

$$U_{k1}, U_{k2}, \dots, U_{kn_k} \qquad (k = 1, 2, \dots) \tag{260.2}$$

and writing these sequences one after the other. Each of the sequences (260.2) is assumed here to be related to the one following it by the formulas

$$\left.\begin{aligned} U_{(k+1)(2m-1)} &= U_{k+1} U_{km} \\ U_{(k+1)2m} &= U_{km} \dotplus U_{k+1} U_{km} \end{aligned}\right\} \quad (m = 1, 2, \dots, n_k), \tag{260.3}$$

$$U_{(k+1)n_{k+1}} = U_{k+1} \dotplus (U_{k1} + U_{k2} + \cdots + U_{kn_k}) U_{k+1}. \tag{260.4}$$

The somas U_{km} are uniquely determined if, in addition, we put

$$U_{11} = U_1, \quad n_1 = 1. \tag{260.5}$$

By (260.3) and (260.4), we have the recursion formula

$$n_{k+1} = 2 n_k + 1, \tag{260.6}$$

---

[2] See, for example, C. Carathéodory, *Reelle Funktionen*, Vol. I (Leipzig and Berlin, 1939; repr., New York, 1946), Theorem 1 of § 114, p. 95.

and, since $n_1 = 2 - 1$, we have in general

$$n_k = 2^k - 1 \qquad (k = 1, 2, \ldots). \qquad (260.7)$$

The $2^k - 1$ somas in (260.2) are precisely those that we denoted in § 19 by S_j and computed in a different way. It should be noted that the equation

$$U_{k1} + U_{k2} + \cdots + U_{kn_k} = U_1 \dot{+} U_2 \dot{+} \cdots \dot{+} U_k \qquad (260.8)$$

holds for every k, so that there is at least one non-empty soma in each of the sequences (260.2). If all the somas (260.1) happen to be pairwise disjoint, we have

$$U_{k(2^k - 2^{k-l})} = U_l \qquad (l = 1, 2, \ldots, k),$$

and all the other U_{kj} are empty.

If U_{pq} and U_{rs} are any two of the somas (260.2), then either

$$U_{rs} \circ U_{pq}, \qquad (260.9)$$

or else if, say, $r < p$,

$$U_{rs} \supseteqq U_{pq}. \qquad (260.10)$$

In the second case, the difference $U_{rs} - U_{pq}$ can always be represented as the sum of a finite number of U_{kj}.

261. By (260.3), the equations

$$\left.\begin{array}{l} \mu U_{km} = \mu U_{(k+1)(2m-1)} + \mu U_{(k+1)2m} \\ (k = 1, 2, \ldots; \; m = 1, 2, \ldots, n_k) \end{array}\right\} \qquad (261.1)$$

hold among the values μU_{kj} of the given content function on the somas U_{kj} of the canonical base (260.2).

Our aim is to show that the non-negative numbers μU_{kj} can be chosen freely, subject to the restriction that the recursion formulas (261.1) hold and that the numbers μU_k, which can easily be calculated from the μU_{ij} by using (260.3) and (260.4), are all > 0.

The result that will be obtained is reminiscent of the properties of the power series that are used in the generation of analytic functions. For the countably many coefficients of a power series are used, on the one hand, to compute the values of the function within the circle of convergence, and on the other hand, to determine the Riemann surface on which the function is defined. In the present case, the numbers μU_{ij} are used not only to determine the values of the content function $\mu^* X$ on its ring of measurability $\mathfrak{M}_\mu$, but also to determine the structure of $\mathfrak{M}_\mu$ itself.

262. Let $\mathfrak{B}$ denote the canonical base consisting of the U_{ij} and let us first examine the somas V of the countably additive closure $\mathfrak{B}_\sigma$ of $\mathfrak{B}$. Every soma V in $\mathfrak{B}_\sigma$ can be written as

$$V = W_1 \dotplus W_2 \dotplus \cdots \dotplus W_p \dotplus \cdots, \tag{262.1}$$

where the W_p denote certain of the somas U_{ij}, written in any order and not necessarily without repetitions. Observe that to each soma U_{pq} of $\mathfrak{B}$ there can be assigned only a *finite number* of somas U_{rs} for which $U_{pq} \subseteqq U_{rs}$. Hence, in each of the sequences

$$W_p, W_{p+1}, W_{p+2}, \ldots \qquad (p = 1, 2, \ldots) \tag{262.2}$$

there is a first soma

$$W_{p+k_p} \supseteqq W_p \qquad (k_p \geqq 0) \tag{262.3}$$

of such a kind that, for every soma W_{p+m} of the sequence (262.2), $W_p \subseteqq W_{p+m}$ implies $W_{p+m} \subseteqq W_{p+k_p}$.

Then, if we write

$$W_{p+k_p} = W_p \tag{262.4}$$

we obtain

$$V = W_1' \dotplus W_2' \dotplus \cdots. \tag{262.5}$$

If we now compare an arbitrary soma W_p' with a preceding soma W_k' $(k < p)$, then either $W_p' \circ W_k'$ or else $W_p' \subseteqq W_k'$. Hence we also always have either

$$W_p' \circ (W_1' \dotplus W_2' \dotplus \cdots \dotplus W_{p-1}')$$

or

$$W_p' \subseteqq (W_1' \dotplus W_2' \dotplus \cdots \dotplus W_{p-1}'). \tag{262.6}$$

We delete from (262.5) all those W_p' for which the second is the case and reintroduce the earlier (unprimed) notation for the remaining W_k'. In this way, each soma V in $\mathfrak{B}_\sigma$ is represented as the sum

$$V = W_{m_1} + W_{m_2} + \cdots \tag{262.7}$$

of an at most countable number of pairwise disjoint somas U_{ij} of $\mathfrak{B}$. The value of the content function $\mu^* X$ for $X = V$ is then given by the equation

$$\mu V = \sum_j \mu W_{m_j}. \tag{262.8}$$

The set of somas $\mathfrak{B}_\sigma$ is of course countably additive. At the same time, it is also multiplicative. For if we put

$$V' = \sum_j U_{p_j q_j}, \quad V'' = \sum_k U_{r_k s_k}, \tag{262.9}$$

we can write

$$V'V'' = \sum_{j\,k} U_{p_j q_j} U_{r_k s_k}. \tag{262.10}$$

But now, every non-empty term on the right-hand side of (262.10) is equal to one of its two factors, so that, again, the soma $V'V''$ can be written in the form (262.7) and hence belongs to $\mathfrak{B}_\sigma$.

It can be verified that we always have

$$\mu V'V'' \leqq \mu V'' \tag{262.11}$$

and that equality holds in this last relation if and only if

$$V'' \subseteqq V'. \tag{262.12}$$

263. We are now in a position to consider monotonically decreasing sequences of somas of $\mathfrak{B}_\sigma$,

$$V_1 \supseteqq V_2 \supseteqq V_3 \supseteqq \cdots, \tag{263.1}$$

and indeed, we shall consider each such sequence as a representation of a soma X of the ring of measurability $\mathfrak{M}_\mu$ of μX, where we define

$$\mu X = \lim_{n=\infty} \mu V_n. \tag{263.2}$$

Since $\mu^* X$ is assumed to be a reduced measure, we put $X = O$ if $\mu X = 0$ in (263.2). In the general case $\mu X > 0$, we must fix conditions for two sequences of type (263.1) to be assigned the same soma. To this end, we consider a second sequence

$$W_1 \supseteqq W_2 \supseteqq W_3 \supseteqq \cdots \tag{263.3}$$

of somas of $\mathfrak{B}_\sigma$, to which is assigned the soma Y and we postulate that the intersection XY belongs to the sequence

$$V_1 W_1 \supseteqq V_2 W_2 \supseteqq V_3 W_3 \supseteqq \cdots. \tag{263.4}$$

We now set up the following definition.

DEFINITION: *Two monotonically decreasing sequences* (263.1) *and* (263.3) *of somas of $\mathfrak{B}_\sigma$ are to be taken as representing the same soma X of the ring of measurability $\mathfrak{M}_\mu$ of the reduced content function under consideration if and only if we have the equations*

$$\lim_{n=\infty} \mu V_n = \lim_{n=\infty} \mu W_n = \lim_{n=\infty} \mu (V_n W_n). \tag{263.5}$$

It must now be shown that this definition does not lead to a contradiction and that the set of somas generated in this way is a complete ring on which μX is completely additive.

264. The easiest way to verify all these statements is to map the somas of the ring of measurability of the content function $\mu^* X$ onto certain point sets on the real line. We again consider the canonical base (260.2) of the content function, and assign to each soma U_{ij} an interval u_{ij} on the half-line $x \geqq 0$ whose length $m u_{ij}$ is defined by the equation

$$m\, u_{ij} = \mu\, U_{ij}\,. \tag{264.1}$$

Intervals of length zero are taken here to mean individual points. For each k, the intervals

$$u_{k1}, u_{k2}, \ldots, u_{k n_k} \qquad (k = 1, 2, 3, \ldots) \tag{264.2}$$

are lined up from left to right: for every k the left-hand end-point of the first non-vanishing interval (264.2) is the point $x = 0$, and all succeeding intervals have as their left-hand end-points the right-hand end-point of the preceding interval.

Let e denote the countable set consisting of the end-points of all the intervals u_{ij} thus constructed, and let $\bar{e}$ denote the closure of e. Moreover, let ω denote the least upper bound of the points of $\bar{e}$. If $\omega = +\infty$, let Ω denote the totality of all points $x \geqq 0$, and let it denote the closed interval $0 \leqq x \leqq \omega$ if ω is finite. Now it can happen that the point set e is everywhere-dense on Ω, in which case $\Omega = \bar{e}$. In general, however, the point set

$$\Omega - \bar{e} = \delta_1 + \delta_2 + \delta_3 + \cdots \tag{264.3}$$

is made up of pairwise disjoint intervals δ_k which contain none of the end-points of the intervals u_{ij}. We say that these δ_k correspond to *indecomposable somas* D_k in the ring of measurability $\mathfrak{M}_\mu$ of $\mu^* X$.

265. We begin by remarking, first, that every interval η on the positive real axis whose end-points ξ' and ξ'' belong to e can be split into subintervals that coincide with certain of the u_{ij}.

Second, if ξ' or ξ'' is a point of accumulation of ηe, we can find at least countably many $u_{i_k j_k}$ that fill out the interval η (except for their end-points) and that cluster at most about the end-points of η, so that we can still write

$$\sum_k m\, u_{i_k j_k} = \xi'' - \xi'. \tag{265.1}$$

If we let $\mathfrak{b}$ denote the canonical base (264.2) and $\mathfrak{b}_\sigma$, the countably additive closure of $\mathfrak{b}$, then in both these cases the interval η includes at least one soma of $\mathfrak{b}_\sigma$ that differs from η by at most a null set.

Third, we consider an interval η whose end-points, if they are not points of e nor accumulation points of ηe, are at least accumulation points of $e - \eta e$. Then if ε is any positive number, we can find an interval $\eta^* \supseteqq \eta$ that differs from a soma of $\mathfrak{b}_\sigma$ only by a null set and that satisfies

$$m\,\eta^* < m\,\eta + \varepsilon\,. \tag{265.2}$$

This result can immediately be generalized. Let

$$\varDelta = \eta_1 + \eta_2 + \cdots \tag{265.3}$$

denote an arbitrary open subset of Ω, no boundary point of which lies in the point set (264.3) and for which $m\varDelta < +\infty$. Then, given any number ε, we can assign to each subinterval η_k of $\varDelta$ an interval $\eta_k{}^* \supseteqq \eta_k$ that is equivalent to a point set of $\mathfrak{b}_\sigma$, i.e., differs from such a set by at most a null set, and for which

$$m\,\eta_k^* < m\,\eta_k + \frac{\varepsilon}{2k} \qquad (k = 1, 2, \ldots). \tag{265.4}$$

If we then put

$$\varDelta^* = \eta_1^* \dotplus \eta_2^* \dotplus \cdots, \tag{265.5}$$

then, in the first place, $\varDelta^* \supseteqq \varDelta$, second, $\varDelta^*$ is equivalent to a point set of $\mathfrak{b}_\sigma$, and third,

$$m\,\varDelta^* < m\varDelta + \varepsilon. \tag{265.6}$$

266. We now consider subsets of Ω (§ 264) constructed as follows: they should be either Lebesgue-measurable subsets of $\bar{e}$ or else the sum of such a point set with an at most countable number of intervals δ_k belonging to the sequence (264.3). The totality of point sets of this sort forms a complete ring $\mathfrak{a}^*$.

Now it should be observed that every point set a^* in $\mathfrak{a}^*$ for which $ma^* < +\infty$, can be covered, to within a null set, by an open point set v^* in $\mathfrak{b}_\sigma$ for which

$$m\,v^* < m\,a^* + \varepsilon$$

holds, where ε denotes an arbitrary positive number.

267. After these preliminaries, we consider the homomorphism of the positive real line $x \geqq 0$ that carries the subsets a^* of this half-line onto the somas a of the reduced Lebesgue content. By § 212, the complete ring $\mathfrak{a}^*$ considered just above is transformed into a complete ring $\mathfrak{a}$ of somas a. Then not only are the somas U_{ij} of the canonical base $\mathfrak{B}$ of § 260 mapped one-to-one onto the reduced intervals u_{ij} of the base $\mathfrak{b}$, but the same holds true, in view of the exposition of § 262, for the countably additive closure $\mathfrak{B}_\sigma$, when we compare its somas with those of $\mathfrak{b}_\sigma$.

Thus, to every monotonically decreasing sequence (263.1) of somas V_n of $\mathfrak{B}_\sigma$ there corresponds one-to-one a like sequence

$$v_1 \supseteqq v_2 \supseteqq v_3 \supseteqq \cdots \tag{267.1}$$

of (reduced) somas of $\mathfrak{b}_\sigma$, and similarly, to the sequence (263.3) there corresponds a sequence

$$w_1 \supseteqq w_2 \supseteqq w_3 \supseteqq \cdots. \tag{267.2}$$

Since the sequences v_n and w_n of somas converge, we can write

$$\lim_{n=\infty} v_n = x, \quad \lim_{n=\infty} w_n = y, \quad \lim_{n=\infty} v_n\, w_n = x\, y. \tag{267.3}$$

Moreover, since the content function presently being considered is reduced, $x = y$ if and only if

$$\lim_{n=\infty} m\, v_n = \lim_{n=\infty} m\, w_n = \lim_{n=\infty} m\,(v_n\, w_n). \tag{267.4}$$

But these conditions correspond precisely to those of equations (263.5).

Thus, to each soma X that satisfies the definition of § 263 there corresponds exactly one class of equivalent subsets of the real line or, what amounts to the same thing, exactly one soma x in $\mathfrak{a}$.

If, conversely, a is a soma in $\mathfrak{a}$, we choose on the real line any representative a^* of a contained in $\mathfrak{a}^*$. Then there is at least one sequence (267.1) of point sets in $\mathfrak{b}_\sigma$ that converges to a measurable hull of a^*. The corresponding sequence (263.1) then defines a soma A that is mapped onto a. It is easy to satisfy oneself that the relations (263.5) always hold between any two sequences obtained in this way. For this one-to-one correspondence, we always have

$$\mu\, A = m\, a.$$

We can now define the operations of union, conjunction, and intersection on the somas $A, B, \ldots,$ by letting them be induced from the corresponding operations on the somas $a, b, \ldots$; and finally, we obtain the following two theorems.

Theorem 1: *If the values assumed by a reduced content function $\mu^* X$ on one of its canonical bases are given, then the ring of measurability $\mathfrak{M}_\mu$ of this function, as well as the values of the function μX on the somas X of $\mathfrak{M}_\mu$, are uniquely determined. In addition, the values on the canonical base can be prescribed arbitrarily, provided they satisfy the conditions of* § 261.

THEOREM 2: *The ring of measurability $\mathfrak{M}_\mu$ of a reduced content function can be mapped isomorphically, and with preservation of measure, onto a complete ring of subsets of the positive real line that are measured by means of the reduced Lebesgue content.*

Most of the content functions that are used in the applications of our theory do not have any indecomposable somas (cf. § 264). Then the somas of $\mathfrak{M}_\mu$ are mapped homomorphically and with preservation of measure onto the measurable subsets of Ω. Such content functions are called *ordinary content functions.* If two somas M and M' are assigned the same content by two ordinary reduced content functions μ^*X and μ'^*X', respectively, then the subsomas of M can be mapped isomorphically and with preservation of measure onto the subsomas of M'.

§§ 268-271. The Jessen Infinite-dimensional Torus

268. The application of the last result even to the ordinary Lebesgue content in $\mathfrak{R}_n$ yields remarkable results. For, disregarding sets of measure zero, the measurable subsets of $\mathfrak{R}_n$ can be mapped by a one-to-one measure-preserving mapping onto linear point sets. From this it follows that it suffices, in principle, to develop the notion of place function and Lebesgue integral for functions of one variable. Jessen[3] has shown that a very similar state of affairs exists in certain infinite-dimensional spaces.

The ordinary torus $\mathfrak{T}_2$ can be looked upon as the topological product of two circles c_1 and c_2. We shall consider the topological product of two arcs δ_1 and δ_2 on these circles to be an interval. Moreover, we shall assume that the length of each of the circles c_i is unity; to each of the intervals, as just defined, we assign a weight equal to the product of the lengths of the arcs δ_i. From this weight function, we can obtain the measure of an arbitrary point set just as in Euclidean space (§§ 148 ff.). We obtain the same numerical results if we replace the totality of all possible intervals $\{\delta_1, \delta_2\}$ by the countable number of intervals for which the end-points of the δ_i have rational ordinates. By the definition given in § 259, this defines a content function on the torus, for which all our earlier theorems are valid.

We now consider, with Jessen, an infinite number of circles $c_1, c_2, \ldots$ of unit length, and their topological product. The points of each one of these circles c_i are determined by numbers x_i that lie in the interval $0 \leqq x < 1$. It is occasionally more convenient to allow the x_i to vary arbitrarily over the interval $-\infty < x < +\infty$, and then to reduce them modulo one. In this way, we obtain a torus-like space $\mathfrak{T}_\infty$ of an infinite number of dimensions.

[3] B. Jessen, *Acta. Math.*, Vol. 63 (1934), pp. 249-323.

269. We shall say of an infinite sequence of points P_j in the Jessen torus with coordinates $x_{j\nu}$ that it converges to a point P_0 with coordinates ξ_ν, if the limits

$$\lim_{j=\infty} x_{j\nu} \equiv \xi_\nu \pmod 1 \tag{269.1}$$

exist. We say of a point set that it has P_0 as a point of accumulation, if it contains a sequence of points converging to P_0. A subset of this torus that contains all of its points of accumulation is said, as usual, to be closed.

We also wish to introduce infinite-dimensional intervals in the torus space, by use of which the interior of a point set can be defined. These intervals are to be determined in such a way that any sequence of points that converges to a point of an interval itself lies in that interval, with the exception perhaps of an at most finite number of points. From this alone it follows that the notion of the interval that we introduced for the n-dimensional torus $\mathfrak{T}_n$ (that is, the topological product of n circular arcs $\delta_1, \ldots, \delta_n$) cannot be carried over unchanged to the Jessen torus $\mathfrak{T}_\infty$. For if $\delta_1, \delta_2, \ldots$ are an infinite number of arcs and P_0 is a point whose coordinate $x_{0\nu}$ lies in δ_ν, let us consider points Q_j whose coordinates $y_{j\nu}$ are given by

$$y_{j\nu} = x_{0\nu} \quad \text{for} \quad \nu = 1, 2, \ldots, j,$$

while $y_{j\nu}$ lies outside the arc δ_j for $\nu > j$. By the above definition, the points Q_j converge to P_0; yet none of these points belongs to the topological product of the δ_k.

But Jessen has found that the topological product of an infinite number of arcs or full circles of the first N circles $c_1, \ldots, c_N$ with the full circles $c_{N+1}, c_{N+2}, \ldots$ gives rise to a good definition of an interval in $\mathfrak{T}_\infty$. In the first place, it is obvious that the complement of such a Jessen interval is a closed set in the sense of our definition above. Second, if A is a proper closed subset of $\mathfrak{T}_\infty$ and P is a point in the complement of A, we can find Jessen intervals that contain the point P and are disjoint from A. We can even require that the vertices of these intervals have rational coordinates on the δ_k-axes. Since every Jessen interval has only a finite number of vertices, there are only a countable number of intervals with this property. From this it follows that the complement of A can be covered by an at most countable number of intervals each of which is disjoint from A.

Finally, we can take as open point sets the complements of any closed point sets or the unions of any finite or countable number of intervals, for these two notions prove to be equivalent. A great many of the theorems about subsets of $\mathfrak{R}_n$ can be extended to the space $\mathfrak{T}_\infty$ by means of these concepts. For example, the Heine-Borel Covering Theorem is also valid in this space.

270. The point sets of $\mathfrak{T}_\infty$ form a ring of somas to which we can apply the results of Chapter Eight (§§ 206 ff.). To this end, we assign to each interval U the weight function $p(U)$ whose value is the product of the lengths of the arcs δ_i. From this weight function we obtain a measure function m^*A that is defined for every point set A of $\mathfrak{T}_\infty$. Just as in the theory of the Lebesgue measure (§ 148 ff.), this proves to be a regular measure function.

Every interval obtained by the above construction has only a finite number of vertices. Among these intervals, as we have already remarked, there are a countably infinite number whose vertices have rational coordinates. Now, we obtain the same measure function m^*A if we define the weight function only on such intervals, so that, by § 259, m^*A must be a *content function*.

271. All the results of the present chapter are thus valid also for the Jessen torus. As Jessen himself did, we can partition the point sets of this space into classes each of which consists of equivalent point sets, i.e., sets that differ only by sets of measure zero. Moreover, all of these classes can be mapped by a one-to-one measure-preserving mapping onto linear point sets. Every measurable place function in the torus space then corresponds to a measurable place function $f(x)$ on the x-axis, and the integrals of such functions are left invariant by this homomorphism. Jessen used this mapping to extend the theory of the Lebesgue integral to the torus space. For us, such a theory is already at hand, since the point sets of $\mathfrak{T}_\infty$ can be looked upon as somas. Thus, the Jessen torus is a non-trivial example that extends beyond the theory of Lebesgue measure.

§§ 272-278. The Vitali Covering Theorem

272. The Vitali Covering Theorem[4] is one of the oldest theorems of the Borel-Lebesgue theory. It gives a criterion, applicable to very general systems of somas, for recognizing when they can be used as bases for reduced ordinary content functions.

We begin with the following definition.

DEFINITION: *A normal covering system of cubes in q-dimensional Euclidean space $\mathfrak{R}_q$ is a set $\{W\}$ of (open) cubes of this space satisfying the following conditions:*

To every bounded subset A of $\mathfrak{R}_q$ and to every neighborhood U of A there can be assigned an at most countable sequence of cubes of the set $\{W\}$,

[4] G. Vitali, *Atti Accad. Sci. Torino,* Vol. 43 (1907/08), pp. 75-82; generalized to q-dimensional space by H. Lebesgue, *Ann. Sci. Ecole Norm.* (3), Vol. 27 (1910), pp. 365, 390-395.

$$W_1, W_2, \ldots$$

ordered in accordance with decreasing edge-length, whose union covers A and is contained in U.

A sequence of cubes in $\mathfrak{R}_q$

$$W_1, W_2, W_3, \ldots \tag{272.1}$$

whose edge-length decreases with increasing index constitutes a normal covering system if to every point P of $\mathfrak{R}_q$ and to every neighborhood U_P of P there can be assigned at least one cube from among (272.1) that contains P in its interior and is contained in U_P; sequences (272.1) of this kind are quite easy to produce.[5]

Then if A is any point set and U is a neighborhood of A, let us assign to every point P in A the *first* cube $W_{n(P)}$ that is contained in U and contains P in its interior. In this way, we obtain a function

$$n(P) = f(P) \qquad (P \in A)$$

that takes only integer values. Let A_n be the subset of A on which $f(P) = n$; some of these point sets A_n may be empty, and the rest

$$A_{n_1}, A_{n_2}, \ldots \qquad (n_1 < n_2 < \ldots) \tag{272.2}$$

are pairwise disjoint. But now we have the two relations

$$A = A_{n_1} + A_{n_2} + \cdots, \quad A_{n_j} \subseteqq W_{n_j} \subseteqq U \quad (j = 1, 2, \ldots), \tag{272.3}$$

and from this it follows that

$$A \subseteqq W_{n_1} \dotplus W_{n_2} \dotplus \cdots \subseteqq U.$$

---

[5] To each positive integer p let us assign all possible systems $k_1, k_2, \ldots, k_q$ of positive integers that satisfy the conditions

$$|k_j| \leqq p^2+1 \qquad (j = 1, 2, \ldots, q).$$

For each of these systems we consider the q-dimensional cube

$$\frac{k_j - 1}{p} < x_j < \frac{k_j + 1}{p} \qquad (j = 1, 2, \ldots, q).$$

For a proof of the fact that the conditions of the text are satisfied in this case, see C. Carathéodory, *Reelle Funktionen*, Vol. I (Leipzig and Berlin, 1939; repr., New York, 1946), p. 71.

273. We obtain another normal covering system of cubes as follows:

To each point P in $\mathfrak{R}_q$ assign a cube $W(P, a_P)$ with center P and length of edge a_P. Then if A is any bounded subset of $\mathfrak{R}_q$, let us put

$$A = A_0 + A_1 + A_2 + \cdots, \tag{273.1}$$

where A_0 denotes the set consisting of all the points P_0 of A for which $A_{P_0} > 1$; in general, let A_n consist of all the points P_n of A for which

$$\frac{1}{2^{n-1}} \geqq a_{P_n} > \frac{1}{2^n} \qquad (n = 1, 2, \ldots). \tag{273.2}$$

Now let us cover the space with a lattice of cubes

$$w_1, w_2, \ldots, \tag{273.3}$$

with length of edge $(1/2^n)/3$. Since A_n is bounded, there is but a *finite* number of cubes in the sequence (273.3), say the cubes

$$w_{m_1}, w_{m_2}, \ldots, w_{m_r}, \tag{273.4}$$

whose closures $\overline{w}_{m_j}$ $(j = 1, 2, \ldots, r)$ have a point Q_j in common with A_n. Then the cube $W(Q_j, a_{Q_j})$ includes the closed cube $\overline{w}_{m_j}$ in its interior, and the set of points

$$W(Q_1, a_{Q_1}) \dotplus \cdots \dotplus W(Q_r, a_{Q_r}), \tag{273.5}$$

which consists of the union of a finite number of cubes $W(P, a_P)$, covers A_n. The cubes that successively cover the point sets $A_0, A_1, A_2, \ldots$ in this way can be put into sequence in order of decreasing length of edge, and they cover A itself.

Now to each point P of $\mathfrak{R}_q$ let us assign not just one cube $W(P, a_P)$, but a sequence of concentric cubes

$$\left.\begin{array}{l} W(P, a_P^{(1)}), \quad W(P, a_P^{(2)}), \ldots \\ a_P^{(1)} > a_P^{(2)} > \ldots, \quad \lim\limits_{n=\infty} a_P^{(n)} = 0. \end{array}\right\} \tag{273.6}$$

Let A be any bounded point set, and let U be any neighborhood of A. To each point P of A let us assign the first cube of the sequence (273.6) that is contained in U, and let us proceed as above with these new cubes. Just as in § 22, we obtain a sequence of cubes that are ordered according to size, that are contained in U, and whose union covers A.

274. We shall next prove the following theorem.

THEOREM 1: *Let every cube W of a normal covering system contain a closed point set S whose Borel-Lebesgue content satisfies the condition*

$$m\, S > \alpha\, m\, W \qquad (0 < \alpha < 1), \quad (274.1)$$

where α denotes the same number for each and every cube of the system. Then if A is a bounded subset of $\Re_q$ whose Borel-Lebesgue content m^*A is > 0, if U is a neighborhood of A, and if ϑ is any fixed number for which $0 < \vartheta < 1$, then there is a finite number of the above-mentioned point sets S, say

$$S_1, S_2, \ldots, S_p, \quad (274.2)$$

that are pairwise disjoint and whose sum

$$T = S_1 + S_2 + \cdots + S_p \quad (274.3)$$

satisfies the pair of conditions

$$m^*(A - AT) < \vartheta\, m^*A\,, \quad T \subseteqq U. \quad (274.4)$$

Note: Observe that because of the measurability of T, we must also have the inequality

$$m^*AT > (1 - \vartheta)\, m^*A\,. \quad (274.5)$$

Proof: We let

$$\eta = \frac{\alpha}{4 \cdot 3^q} \quad (274.6)$$

(the justification for this choice of η will become apparent later), and we determine an open subset U_1 of U that contains A and satisfies

$$m\, U_1 < (1 + \eta)\, m^* A\,. \quad (274.7)$$

Next, we cover A with a countable number of our (open) cubes

$$W_1', W_2', W_3', \ldots; \quad (274.8)$$

these are all assumed to be contained in U_1 and arranged in decreasing order of size. We now delete from the sequence (274.8) all those cubes that have an (interior) point in common with W_1'; let W_{n_2} be the first remaining cube. We now delete all those cubes that have a point in common with W_{n_2}; let W_{n_3} be the first remaining cube. Continuing in this way, we obtain a sequence of pairwise disjoint cubes

$$W_1' = W_{n_1}', W_{n_2}', \ldots, W_{nk}', \ldots. \quad (274.9)$$

But since the edge of each deleted cube is shorter than the edge of the cube with which it had points in common, every point of A lies in at least one cube W''_{n_j} that is concentric with W'_{n_j} and has an edge three times as long. Thus, the union of the W''_{n_j} covers A, and we can write

$$m^* A \leq \sum_j m W''_{n_j} = 3^q \sum_j m W'_{n_j}. \tag{274.10}$$

Now, letting S_j denote the closed point set that lies in W'_{n_j} and using (274.1), we obtain the inequality

$$m^* A < \frac{3^q}{\alpha} \sum_j m S_j. \tag{274.11}$$

We can therefore choose the positive integer p_1 so large as to satisfy the inequality

$$\sum_{j=1}^{p_1} m S_j > \frac{\alpha}{2 \cdot 3^q} m^* A. \tag{274.12}$$

The closed point sets S_j, just like the W'_{n_j}, are pairwise disjoint. Hence with the notation

$$T_1 = S_1 + S_2 + \cdots + S_{p_1}, \tag{274.13}$$

we have

$$m T_1 > \frac{\alpha}{2 \cdot 3^q} m^* A. \tag{274.14}$$

Now, all the W'_{n_j}, and therefore all the S_j, and finally T_1 as well, are contained in U_1. Hence a comparison of (274.7) with (274.14) yields

$$m (U_1 - T_1) < \left(1 + \eta - \frac{\alpha}{2 \cdot 3^q}\right) m^* A. \tag{274.15}$$

Therefore, if we introduce the notation

$$\vartheta_1 = 1 - \frac{\alpha}{4 \cdot 3^q} \qquad (0 < \vartheta_1 < 1), \tag{274.16}$$

in view of (274.6), we can write

$$m (U_1 - T_1) < \vartheta_1 m^* A \tag{274.17}$$

instead of (274.15).

275. We let

$$A_1 = A - A T_1 \tag{275.1}$$

denote the subset of A that is not a subset of T_1. The point set A_1 is a subset of the open set $U_1 - T_1$, which is therefore a neighborhood of A_1; moreover, it follows from (274.17) and (275.1) that

$$m^* A_1 < \vartheta_1 m^* A. \tag{275.2}$$

We repeat our construction after replacing A by A_1, and U_1 by an open subset U_2 of $U_1 - T_1$ which contains A_1 and for which

$$m\,U_2 < \left(1 + \frac{\alpha}{4 \cdot 3^q}\right) m^* A_1. \tag{275.3}$$

Furthermore, we fix a system

$$S_{p_1+1}, S_{p_1+2}, \ldots, S_{p_2} \qquad (p_2 > p_1) \tag{275.4}$$

of closed point sets S that are disjoint from all the earlier ones as well as among themselves, and for which, if we write

$$A_2 = A_1 - A_1\,(S_{p_1+1} + \cdots + S_{p_2}), \tag{275.5}$$

the relation

$$m^* A_2 < \vartheta_1\, m^* A_1 < \vartheta_1^2\, m^* A, \tag{275.6}$$

analogous to (275.2), holds.

If we now write

$$T_2 = S_1 + S_2 + \cdots + S_{p_1} + \cdots + S_{p_2}$$

and take note of the equation

$$A - AT_2 = (A - AT_1) - A\,(T_2 - T_1) = A_1 - A_1\,(T_2 - T_1) = A_2,$$

we finally obtain from (275.6) the inequality

$$m^*\,(A - AT_2) < \vartheta_1^2\, m^* A.$$

Continuing in this way, with the use of the notation

$$T_n = S_1 + \cdots + S_{p_1} + \cdots + S_{p_2} + \cdots + S_{p_n},$$

we have, in general, the relation

$$m^*\,(A - AT_n) < \vartheta_1^n\, m^* A.$$

But n can be chosen so large that

$$\vartheta_1^n < \vartheta,$$

where ϑ denotes the number that occurs in Theorem 1 of § 274, so that the proof of this theorem is now complete.

276. The above theorem can be generalized and supplemented, as follows:

THEOREM 2: *Let*

$$\alpha_1 > \alpha_2 > \ldots, \quad \lim_{n=\infty} \alpha_n = 0$$

be a monotonically decreasing sequence of positive integers that converges to zero; moreover, let

$$R_1 + R_2 + \cdots + R_n + \cdots$$

be a decomposition of the space $\mathfrak{R}_q$. *We assume that the closed point sets* S_j *are so chosen that Theorem* 1 *can be applied to every subset of* R_n *under the hypothesis* $\alpha = \alpha_n$.

Then every point set A *can be covered, to within a set of measure zero, by an at most countable number of* S_j *that are pairwise disjoint and are all contained in a pre-assigned neighborhood* U *of* A.

Proof: We consider a sequence $\{W_n\}$ of concentric cubes the length of whose edges is 1, 2, 3, ... and we put

$$A_n = A W_n (R_1 + R_2 + \cdots + R_n). \tag{276.1}$$

Then the sequence of bounded point sets A_n is monotonically increasing, and we have

$$A = \lim_{n=\infty} A_n. \tag{276.2}$$

By hypothesis, Theorem 1 can be applied to each of the point sets A_n, with $\alpha = \alpha_n$. Our goal is to determine systems of pairwise disjoint S_j all contained in U and whose successive sums we shall denote by $T_1, T_2, \ldots$, which are such that, on the one hand,

$$T_1 \subseteqq T_2 \subseteqq T_3 \subseteqq \ldots, \tag{276.3}$$

while on the other hand, the inequalities

$$m^* (A_n - T_n A_n) < \frac{1}{2^n} \qquad (n = 1, 2, \ldots) \tag{276.4}$$

all hold. In order to obtain T_{n+1} from T_n, we apply Theorem 1 to the point set

$$B_{n+1} = A_{n+1} - T_n A_{n+1} \tag{276.5}$$

by choosing a finite number of pairwise disjoint S_j all of which lie in the neighborhood $U - T_n$ of B_{n+1}, and by requiring, in addition, that

$$m^* (B_{n+1} - (T_{n+1} - T_n) B_{n+1}) < \vartheta\, m^* B_{n+1} < \frac{1}{2^{n+1}}. \tag{276.6}$$

Here $T_{n+1} - T_n$ denotes the sum of the S_j in question. By virtue of the identity

$$B_{n+1} - (T_{n+1} - T_n) B_{n+1} = A_{n+1} - T_{n+1} A_{n+1},$$

we also have

$$m^*(A_{n+1} - T_{n+1}A_{n+1}) < \frac{1}{2^{n+1}}.$$

Next, we put

$$T = \lim_{n=\infty} T_n = S_1 + S_2 + \cdots$$

and obtain

$$A_n - TA_n \subseteqq A_n - T_nA_n, \quad m^*(A_n - TA_n) < \frac{1}{2^n}.$$

Hence, since $A_n - TA_n \subseteqq A_{n+m} - TA_{n+m}$, we also have

$$m^*(A_n - TA_n) < \frac{1}{2^{n+m}} \qquad (m = 1, 2, \ldots),$$

so that

$$m^*(A_n - TA_n) = 0 \qquad (n = 1, 2, \ldots).$$

By a final passage to the limit, we obtain

$$m^*(A - TA) = \lim_{n=\infty} m^*(A_n - TA_n) = 0,$$

which proves Theorem 2.

277. As our first application of the Vitali Theorem, we prove the following theorem.

THEOREM 3: *The outer Borel-Lebesgue content m^*A of a point set A remains invariant under any Euclidean motion.*

Proof: It is a direct consequence of the definition of the Borel-Lebesgue content that m^*A remains invariant under translation within $\mathfrak{R}_q$.

We now consider a point set A for which $m^*A < +\infty$, and, given any positive number ε, a neighborhood U of A for which the relation

$$m\,U < m^*A + \varepsilon \tag{277.1}$$

holds. An arbitrary Euclidean motion transforms A into A' and U into U'; then U' is a neighborhood of A'. In every cube W of a normal covering system, we imbed a concentric closed sphere (i.e., the set of points whose distance from a fixed point is less than or equal to a fixed number ϱ) whose diameter is equal to one-third the length of an edge of W. Theorem 2 of § 276 can be applied to this system of spheres. Thus, there are at most a countable number of pairwise disjoint spheres S_j' that all lie in U' and whose sum T' covers A' except for a (possibly empty) set of measure zero. The inverse Euclidean motion transforms every sphere S_j' into a sphere S_j that lies in U and can be superimposed upon S_j' by means of a translation. Letting T denote the sum of the pairwise disjoint spheres S_j, we have the relations

$$m^* A' \leqq m T', \quad m T' = m T, \quad m T \leqq m U, \tag{277.2}$$

which, if we take (277.1) into account, yield the inequality

$$m^* A' < m^* A + \varepsilon. \tag{277.3}$$

In consequence, since ε was arbitrary, we have

$$m^* A' \leqq m^* A. \tag{277.4}$$

If A is a null set, (277.4) is equivalent with

$$m^* A' = m^* A. \tag{277.5}$$

In the general case $m^*A > 0$, we repeat the above argument, interchanging A and A'; (277.5) then follows from a comparison of (277.4) with

$$m^* A \leqq m^* A'.$$

278. We now turn our attention once again to the most general reduced content functions μ^*X, which we have already examined in §§ 260 ff., but this time with special emphasis on the isomorphic measure-preserving mappings of these content functions onto the Borel-Lebesgue content on a subset of the real line.

To each of the intervals u_{ij} of § 264, provided it is not of length zero, we assign a subset s_{ij} of u_{ij}, which, upon adjunction of the end-points of u_{ij}, is closed. Then there is at least one open subset v_{ij} of the real line such that

$$s_{ij} = u_{ij} \dot{+} u_{ij} v_{ij}. \tag{278.1}$$

Now let a be any point set lying on the previously considered interval $0 < x < \omega$ on the real line and having no point in common with the "indecomposable" intervals δ_k of § 264. If we make the assumption, say, that there exists a fixed number α $(0 < \alpha < 1)$ for which

$$m\, s_{ij} > \alpha\, m\, u_{ij} \tag{278.2}$$

always holds, then, according to Theorem 2 of § 276 (which is still valid if the cubes of the covering system are replaced by their closures; cf. C. Carathéodory, *Reelle Funktionen,* Volume I, Theorem 1 of § 87), we can cover the point set a to within a set of measure zero by an at most countable number of point sets s_{ij} that lie in a prescribed neighborhood of a and are pairwise disjoint.

This construction can be extended without any difficulty to the somas on which the content function μ^*X is defined. Indeed, if $\{U_{ij}\}$ is a canonical base of μ^*X, we merely assign to each U_{ij} the soma

$$S_{ij} = U_{ij} \dotplus U_{ij} V_{ij}, \tag{278.3}$$

where V_{ij} designates a soma in $\mathfrak{B}_\sigma$. Then we have the following theorem.

THEOREM 4: *To each soma U_{ij} in a canonical base of the reduced content function μ^*X let there be assigned a soma S_{ij} defined by* (278.3). *If there is a number α $(0 < \alpha < 1)$ for which*

$$\mu\, S_{ij} > \alpha\, \mu\, U_{ij}$$

holds throughout, then the S_{ij}, together with the indecomposable somas D_k of μ^*X, if any such exist, form a base of the content function μ^*X.

§§ 279-282. The Lebesgue Integral

279. The totality of subsets X of $\mathfrak{R}_q$ can be looked upon as a ring of somas. Since the *Borel-Lebesgue* content m^*X is a measure function, we can define integrals

$$n^*X = \int_X f\, dm \tag{279.1}$$

in accordance with Chapter Six; such integrals are called *Lebesgue* integrals. Here the place function f, which is now just an ordinary point function $f(P)$, must be m^*-measurable. This is the case, in particular, when the point sets $S(y)$ of a nest of somas of $f(P)$ are Borel sets, and therefore also when $f(P)$ is obtainable from sequences of continuous functions by a finite number of successive limit processes.

By Theorem 1 of § 256 and Theorem 2 of § 257, the measure function n^*X is comparable (§§ 167 ff.) with m^*X, provided f is assumed to be $\geqq 0$ and integrable on the domain under consideration; in addition, n^*X is absolutely continuous with respect to m^*X, and the arguments of § 176 are applicable.

280. Conversely, let n^*X be a content function that is comparable with the Borel-Lebesgue content m^*X as well as absolutely continuous with respect to m^*X. Then, by Theorem 2 of § 171, equation (279.1) holds, and $f(P)$ can be calculated by the method of §§ 168 ff.

In this instance, however, we can also recover $f(P)$ by means of limit processes that are modeled after those of the ordinary differential calculus.

We let $W(P, a)$ denote the cube in $\mathfrak{R}_q$ with center P and edge of length a, and we observe that for any two points P_1 and P_2 of the space, the expression

$$m\left(W(P_1, a) \dotplus W(P_2, a)\right)$$

tends to zero with the distance $P_1 P_2$.

Since n^*X is assumed to be absolutely continuous, $n(W(P, a))$ is an everywhere-continuous function of P. It can be proved, likewise, that $m(W(P, a))$ and $n(W(P, a))$ are continuous functions of a for each fixed P. Then if we choose a point P of the space and a sequence

$$a_1 > a_2 > \dots, \quad \lim_{j=\infty} a_j = 0 \tag{280.1}$$

that converges monotonically to zero and yet is such that the right-hand side of the equation

$$D_n(P) = \lim_{j=\infty} \frac{n(W(P, a_j))}{m(W(P, a_j))} \tag{280.2}$$

converges, we call $D_n(P)$ a *mean derivate* of the content function n^*X at the point P.

Among the mean derivates there is a largest

$$\overline{D}_n(P) = \overline{\lim_{a=0}} \frac{n(W(P, a))}{m(W(P, a))} \tag{280.3}$$

and a smallest

$$\underline{D}_n(P) = \underline{\lim_{a=0}} \frac{n(W(P, a))}{m(W(P, a))}, \tag{280.4}$$

which are called the *upper mean derivate* and the *lower mean derivate*, respectively. They are m^*-measurable point functions: indeed, for each fixed $a > 0$, by the reasoning above, the function

$$\varphi(P, a) = \frac{n(W(P, a))}{m(W(P, a))}$$

is an everywhere-continuous function of P. Hence, if we put

$$\psi(P, a) = \sup \varphi(P, a_k),$$

where $\{a_k\}$ denotes a countable everywhere-dense subset of the interval $0 < x < a$, we have

$$\overline{D}_n(P) = \lim_{a=0} \psi(P, a).$$

Thus $\bar{D}_n(P)$ can be generated from $\varphi(P, a)$ by limit processes, and the same is true of $\underline{D}_n(P)$.

It is our aim to show that all mean derivates (280.2) are equivalent functions in the sense of Theorem 2 of § 180 and consequently are all m^*-measurable and that all these $D_n(P)$ can be inserted for f in the right-hand side of (279.1).

281. Let $D_n(P)$ now be any m^*-measurable mean derivate of n^*X. We let $\alpha(A)$ and $\beta(A)$ denote the infimum and supremum of the point function $D_n(P)$ on the point set A, and we assume, in addition, that the two numbers m^*A and n^*A are finite and that $m^*A > 0$.

Then if δ is any positive number and $\bar{A}$ is a common measurable hull of A for both the measure functions under consideration, a neighborhood U of A can be found that satisfies

$$mU < m^*A + \delta. \tag{281.1}$$

But then $m(U - \bar{A}) < \delta$, and by § 177, $n(U - \bar{A}) \leqq \varepsilon(\delta)$, so that we can also write

$$nU \leqq n^*A + \varepsilon(\delta). \tag{281.2}$$

Next, we assume that $\alpha(A) > 0$ and that $\beta(A) < +\infty$, and we choose any two positive numbers α' and β' that satisfy the conditions

$$\alpha' < \alpha(A), \quad \beta' > \beta(A); \tag{281.3}$$

with these assumptions, we can construct a countable number of cubes

$$W_1'(P),\ W_2'(P), \ldots \tag{281.4}$$

about each point P of A as center, whose sides tend to zero, so that on the one hand, the inequalities

$$\alpha' < \frac{n(W_k'(P))}{m(W_k'(P))}, \quad \beta' > \frac{n(W_k'(P))}{m(W_k'(P))} \quad (k = 1, 2, \ldots) \tag{281.5}$$

hold, and on the other hand, all the $W_k'(P)$ lie in U.

By the Vitali Covering Theorem (Theorem 2 of § 276), we can now choose a countable number of points $P_1, P_2, \ldots$ in A and for each of these points P_i find a cube W_i having P_i as center, such that the cubes

$$W_1,\ W_2, \ldots$$

are pairwise disjoint and such that their union T covers the point set A to within a null set. Then, by (281.5), we have

$$\alpha' m W_k < n W_k < \beta' m W_k \qquad (k = 1, 2, \ldots).$$

Summing over k, we obtain

$$\alpha' m T < n T < \beta' m T. \tag{281.6}$$

But by our construction, we have

$$m(A - AT) = 0, \quad n(A - AT) = 0,$$

and so, taking (281.1), (281.2), and $T \subseteq U$ into account, we also have

$$m^*A = m^*AT \leqq mT < m^*A + \delta,\ n^*A = n^*AT \leqq nT \leqq n^*A + \varepsilon(\delta). \tag{281.7}$$

A comparison of (281.6) with (281.7) now yields

$$\left.\begin{aligned} \alpha' m^* A \leqq \alpha' m T < n T \leqq n^* A + \varepsilon(\delta), \\ n^* A \leqq n T < \beta' m T < \beta'(m^* A + \delta). \end{aligned}\right\} \tag{281.8}$$

If we let δ tend to zero, α' tend to $\alpha(A)$, and β' tend to $\beta(A)$ in this relation, we finally obtain

$$\alpha(A)\, m^* A \leqq n^* A \leqq \beta(A)\, m^* A, \tag{281.9}$$

a relation that is valid even in the excluded cases $\alpha(A) = 0$ and $\beta(A) = +\infty$.

By Theorem 2 of § 159, we can therefore write

$$n^* A = \int_A D_n(P)\, dm. \tag{281.10}$$

Since this last equation holds for all point sets A as well as for all measurable mean derivates of n^*X, any two of these mean derivates must be equivalent functions in the sense of Theorem 2 of § 180. This holds true, in particular, of the extremal mean derivates $\underline{D}_n(P)$ and $\overline{D}_n(P)$, which we have already found to be measurable. Consequently, we can deduce from the relation

$$\underline{D}_n(P) \leqq D_n(P) \leqq \overline{D}_n(P) \tag{281.11}$$

that any $D_n(P)$ is equivalent to $\overline{D}_n(P)$ and hence must be measurable.

THEOREM 1: *Every mean derivate $D_n(P)$ of a content function n^*X that is comparable with the Borel-Lebesgue content m^*X and absolutely continuous with respect to it, is an m^*-measurable function that satisfies the equation*

$$n^* X = \int_X D_n(P)\, dm. \tag{281.12}$$

Thus, all these mean derivates are equivalent with respect to the homomorphism that carries the null ring of m^*X into the empty soma. The content function n^*X is a Lebesgue integral.

If $\underline{D}_n(P) = \overline{D}_n(P)$, we say that n^*X is *differentiable in the mean* at the point P. It then follows from

$$\int\limits_X \left(\overline{D}_n(\mathrm{P}) - \underline{D}_n(\mathrm{P})\right) dm = 0$$

that the points with this property fill out $\mathfrak{R}_q$ to within a set of measure zero.

282. Lebesgue has generalized the notion of a derivate.[6] To each point P of the space, we assign a positive number $\vartheta(P) < 1$ as well as a nested sequence of cubes $W(P, a_k)$ with P as center and the length of edge a_k tending to zero. Let us also choose a measurable subset σ_k of each of these cubes in such a way that, on the one hand,

$$m\,\sigma_k > \vartheta(P)\, m\, W(P, a_k) \qquad (k = 1, 2, \ldots), \quad (282.1)$$

but that, on the other hand, the right-hand side of the equation

$$\Delta_n(P) = \lim_{k=\infty} \frac{n(\sigma_k)}{m(\sigma_k)} \qquad (282.2)$$

exists. Then $\Delta_n(P)$ is called a *generalized derivate* of the absolutely continuous content function n^*X. We intend to show that all generalized derivatives $\Delta_n(P)$ agree at every point P of the space except on a set of measure zero.

Let E be the subset of the entire space $\mathfrak{R}_q$ at each point of which n^*X is differentiable in the mean, and let $[S(y)]$ be the lower nest of somas of $D_n(P)$ on E. We choose a fixed $y > 0$ that is to remain fixed throughout this discussion, and we put

$$\varphi(A) = \int\limits_A \left(D_n(P) + 1 - y\right) dm = n^*A + (1 - y)\, m^*A \qquad (282.3)$$

for each subset A of the space. At every point P of $AS(y)$ we have $D_n(P) \leqq y$, hence $D_n(P) + 1 - y \leqq 1$, and thus, by the Mean-Value Theorem (159.1), we have

$$\varphi\left(A\, S(y)\right) \leqq m^* A\,.$$

On the other hand, the measurability of $S(y)$ implies

[6] H. Lebesgue, *Ann. Sci. Ecole Norm.* (3) Vol. 27 (1910), pp. 387-391, 395-396.

$$\varphi(A) = \varphi(A\,S(y)) + \varphi(A - A\,S(y)),$$

and a comparison of the last three relations yields

$$n^* A \leqq y\, m^* A + \varphi(A - A\,S(y)). \tag{282.4}$$

Next, we introduce the content function

$$\psi(A) = \int_{A - A\,S(y)} |D_n(P) + (1 - y)|\, dm. \tag{282.5}$$

But by (282.3) and (166.5), we have

$$|\varphi(A - A\,S(y))| \leqq \psi(A), \tag{282.6}$$

so that the relation (282.4) implies

$$n^* A \leqq y\, m^* A + \psi(A). \tag{282.7}$$

By (282.5), the content function $\psi(A)$, which is absolutely continuous with respect to m^*A, vanishes on the point set $S(y)$. Hence there is a subset $T(y)$ of $S(y)$ such that the mean derivate of $\psi(A)$ exists and is zero at each point of $T(y)$ and such that $S(y) - T(y)$ is a null set.

Let us consider the formulas (282.1) and (282.2) for a point P in $T(y)$. We have, first, by (282.7),

$$n\,\sigma_k \leqq y\, m\,\sigma_k + \psi(\sigma_k) \leqq y\, m\,\sigma_k + \psi(W(P; a_k)), \tag{282.8}$$

from which, by use of (282.1), we obtain

$$\frac{n(\sigma_k)}{m(\sigma_k)} \leqq y + \frac{1}{\vartheta(P)}\,\frac{\psi(W(P, a_k))}{m(W(P, a_k))}. \tag{282.9}$$

Next, however, since P belongs to $T(y)$,

$$\lim_{k=\infty} \frac{\psi(W(P, a_k))}{m(W(P, a_k))} = 0;$$

and hence, by (282.2),

$$\Delta_n(P) \leqq y. \tag{282.10}$$

The only points of the space that can possibly satisfy the two conditions

$$D_n(P) \leqq y \quad \text{and} \quad \Delta_n(P) > y \tag{282.11}$$

thus lie either in the point set $S(y) - T(y)$ or else in the complement E' of E. Thus, there is a null set

$$N'(y) = (S(y) - T(y)) \dotplus E' \tag{282.12}$$

that contains all the points for which the pair of relations (282.11) are valid. In the same way, there is a null set $N''(y)$ that contains all those points for which both

$$D_n(P) \geqq y \quad \text{and} \quad \Delta_n(P) < y$$

hold. We let

$$N(y) = N'(y) \dotplus N''(y), \tag{282.13}$$

and consider $N(y_k)$ for a countable set of positive values $y_1, y_2, \ldots$ that are everywhere dense on the half-line $y > 0$. Then, if P is a point for which $D_n(P) \neq \Delta_n(P)$, there is at least one number y_k lying between $D_n(P)$ and $\Delta_n(P)$, and P must belong to the set

$$N^* = N(y_1) \dotplus N(y_2) \dotplus \cdots, \tag{282.14}$$

which is of measure zero. Consequently, we have proved the following theorem.

THEOREM 2: *Each of the content functions n^*X that were considered in Theorem 1 is differentiable at every point of the space that does not lie on a certain null set N^*, i.e., the generalized derivates $\Delta_n(P)$ all have the same value at each of these points. Each of the functions $\Delta_n(P)$ is thus measurable and satisfies the equation*

$$n^*X = \int_X \Delta_n(P)\, dm. \tag{282.15}$$

§§ 283-284. Comparable Content Functions

283. We consider two reduced content functions, μ^*X and ν^*X, and assume that they have the same canonical base $\{U_{ij}\}$. We assume in addition that no indecomposable somas (§ 264) appear either in connection with μ^*X or with ν^*X.

We cannot simply apply Theorem 2 of § 257 forthwith to such a pair of content functions; for, two somas A and B that are distinct in the sense of the definition of § 263 for one of our functions may very well coincide for the other of them. Nonetheless, there is even here a Lebesgue decomposition of the one content function with respect to the other.

We consider rectangular coordinate axes in a plane and we assign an interval u_{ij}, or a point, on the positive x-axis to each of the somas U_{ij}, in the way described in § 264; similarly, we assign to each U_{ij} an interval (or a point) u'_{ij} on the y-axis, whose length is given by $\nu U_{ij} = m u'_{ij}$. Finally, whenever u_{ij} and u'_{ij} both have finite length for the same values of i and j, let us mark two points in the plane, the first of which has the left-hand end-points of these two intervals as abscissa and ordinate, respectively, and the other of which has the right-hand end-points of these intervals as its coordinates. In this way we obtain a monotone function

$$y = f(x),$$

which may even be discontinuous; such discontinuities occur whenever u_{ij} is reduced to a single point and u'_{ij} is of non-zero length.

284. We apply a famous theorem of Lebesgue[7] to this function $f(x)$; this theorem, which can be proved by the methods of the preceding section, states that every monotone function, continuous or not, is differentiable on a measurable kernel of each interval of definition. The derivative $f'(x)$ is measurable for the content function m^*a (§ 267) and integrable on every closed subinterval of Ω. Hence, there exists a content function

$$m'_1\, a = \int_a f'(x)\, dm, \tag{284.1}$$

which is less than or equal to $m'a$, where m'^*a signifies the content function defined on Ω by means of the weight function $m'u_{ij} = \nu U_{ij}$ on the canonical base $\{u_{ij}\}$. Lebesgue proved,[8] moreover, that the difference

$$m'_2\, a = m'\, a - m'_1\, a \tag{284.2}$$

is a content function that is singular with respect to m^*a. This theorem contains the first example of a *Lebesgue decomposition* that occurs in the literature.

We can now define two abstract reduced content functions $\nu_1{}^*X$ and $\nu_2{}^*X$ by means of the equations

$$\nu_1\, U_{ij} = m'_1\, u_{ij}, \quad \nu_2\, U_{ij} = m'_2\, u_{ij}.,$$

where $\nu_1{}^*X$ is absolutely continuous with respect to μ^*X and $\nu_2{}^*X$ is singular with respect to μ^*X and where the equation

$$\nu^* X = \nu_1^* X + \nu_2^* X$$

holds for all the somas X in the domain of definition of ν^*X.

In this context, the definitions of singularity and absolute continuity (§ 143; cf. also § 176) are to be replaced by the following:

1. There is a monotonically increasing function $\varepsilon(\delta)$, defined for every positive number δ, such that

---

[7] H. Lebesgue, *Leçons sur l'Intégration* 2nd ed. (Paris, 1928), p. 185.

[8] H. Lebesgue, *Ann. Sci. Ecole Norm.* (3) Vol. 27 (1910), p. 419.

$$\lim_{\delta=0} \varepsilon(\delta) = 0$$

and such that, for every soma

$$V = \sum_k U_{i_k j_k}$$

in $\mathfrak{B}_\sigma$ (§ 262) that satisfies the condition

$$\mu V < \delta ,$$

we have the relation

$$\nu_1 V < \varepsilon(\delta) .$$

2. To each positive number ε and to each soma A in the domain of definition of $\nu_2{}^*X$ there can be assigned a soma V in $\mathfrak{B}_\sigma$ that satisfies the two relations

$$\nu_2^* VA = \nu_2^* A , \quad \mu V < \varepsilon .$$

By these means, we are assured that the theorem concerning the existence of Lebesgue decompositions is valid also for pairs of reduced content functions that have the same canonical base $\{U_{ij}\}$.

§§ 285-289. Linear Measure

285. The simplest example of a measure function that must be computed by the method of § 215 is obtained through a generalization of the notion of length.

We take arbitrary subsets A of q-dimensional Euclidean space as the sets whose linear measure we wish. For the time being, we choose all bounded subsets of the space as a base for our measure function. The weight we shall assign to each point set U in this base is its *diameter,* i.e., the least upper bound of the Euclidean distances between any two of its points.

If A is any point set whose linear measure is to be determined, we choose any number $\varrho > 0$, cover A in all possible ways with a countable number of point sets U_k whose diameters d_k are all less than or equal to the number ϱ, and find the greatest lower bound $\mathfrak{L}_\varrho A$ of the sums

$$d_1 + d_2 + d_3 + \cdots$$

that we obtain by each such covering.

As ϱ decreases, the base becomes smaller, as was postulated in § 215, and the number $\mathfrak{L}_\varrho A$ therefore cannot decrease. Hence, the limit

$$\mathfrak{L}^* A = \lim_{\varrho=0} \mathfrak{L}_\varrho A ,$$

which we shall call the *linear measure* of A, always exists. By § 215, the function $\mathfrak{L}^*A$ is a measure function.

If A and B are two disjoint point sets whose distance is $\delta > 0$, then the family of U_k, for $\varrho < \delta/2$, that have points in common with and cover $A + B$ splits into two disjoint classes. One class comprises all the U_k that contain points of A but no points of B, while the other comprises those U_k that contain points of B but no points of A. Thus, we have

$$\mathfrak{L}_\varrho (A + B) = \mathfrak{L}_\varrho A + \mathfrak{L}_\varrho B \qquad \left(\varrho < \frac{\delta}{2}\right).$$

Then by Theorem 3 of § 220, *the Borel sets belong to the ring of measurability of* $\mathfrak{L}^*A$.

286. The base that we have used up to now can be specialized considerably. Note first of all that the diameter d of any bounded point set is equal to the diameter of its *convex hull,* that is, of the smallest closed convex point set that includes the given set. Thus we can require from the outset that the covering sets U_k be closed and convex, without altering the numbers $\mathfrak{L}_\varrho A$ and $\mathfrak{L}^*A$.

We can also require, at the same time, that the U_k be *open* convex sets, that is, *convex domains.* In order to show that $\mathfrak{L}^*A$ remains unchanged in this case as well, we consider a covering sequence $U_1, U_2, \ldots$ of closed, convex point sets; we enclose each point of U_k in a q-dimensional open sphere (i.e., the set of points whose distance from a fixed point is less than a fixed number r) of radius $\varrho/2^{k+1}$ having that point as center; and for each k, we let C_k denote the union of these spheres, so that C_k is a convex domain. Moreover, we let $\Lambda_\varrho A$ designate the number corresponding to the number $\mathfrak{L}_\varrho A$ that is obtained when the covering sequences consist of convex domains.

To begin with, we have, by § 285,

$$\mathfrak{L}_\varrho A \leqq \Lambda_\varrho A. \tag{286.1}$$

Second, we have the following estimate on the diameter δ_k of the convex domain C_k just considered:

$$\delta_k \leqq d_k + \frac{\varrho}{2^k} < 2\,\varrho,$$

from which it follows that

$$\Lambda_{2\varrho} A \leqq \sum_{k=1}^{\infty} \delta_k \leqq \sum_{k=1}^{\infty} \left(d_k + \frac{\varrho}{2^k}\right) = \sum_{k=1}^{\infty} d_k + \varrho.$$

Consequently, we also have

$$\Lambda_{2\varrho} A \leqq \mathfrak{L}_{\varrho} A + \varrho , \tag{286.2}$$

and, in conjunction with (286.1), we obtain

$$\mathfrak{L}^* A = \lim_{\varrho=0} \mathfrak{L}_{\varrho} A \leqq \lim_{\varrho=0} \Lambda_{\varrho} A = \lim_{\varrho=0} \Lambda_{2\varrho} A \leqq \lim_{\varrho=0} (\mathfrak{L}_{\varrho} A + \varrho) = \mathfrak{L}^* A .$$

Thus, in conclusion, we can write

$$\lim_{\varrho=0} \Lambda_{\varrho} A = \mathfrak{L}^* A , \tag{286.3}$$

from which we deduce that the convex domains form an adequate base for the measure function $\mathfrak{L}^*A$.

We now cover the point set A with an infinite number of successive sequences of convex domains U_{kj} such that, first, the diameters δ_{kj} of the various covering sets $U_{k1}, U_{k2}, \ldots$ are all less than $1/k$, and second,

$$\sum_j \delta_{kj} < \Lambda_{1/k} A + \frac{1}{k} \tag{286.4}$$

holds. If next we put

$$V_k = U_{k1} \dotplus U_{k2} \dotplus \cdots, \quad \bar{A} = V_1 V_2 V_3 \ldots , \tag{286.5}$$

we see that $\bar{A}$ is the intersection of a countable number of open sets, and since $\bar{A}$ contains the point set A, we have

$$\mathfrak{L}^* A \leqq \mathfrak{L} \bar{A} . \tag{286.6}$$

On the other hand, $\bar{A} \subseteqq V_k$, and consequently

$$\Lambda_{1/k} \bar{A} \leqq \Lambda_{1/k} V_k \leqq \sum_j \delta_{kj} ;$$

hence, by (286.4),

$$\Lambda_{1/k} \bar{A} < \Lambda_{1/k} A + \frac{1}{k} \qquad (k = 1, 2, \ldots) ,$$

from which it follows, by passage to the limit, that

$$\mathfrak{L} \bar{A} \leqq \mathfrak{L}^* A . \tag{286.7}$$

A comparison of (286.6) with (286.7) shows that $\bar{A}$ is a measurable hull of A.

Thus, the measure function $\mathfrak{L}^*A$ is a *content function in the sense of Hans Hahn,* and by §§ 258-259, a content function in our sense.

287. We let g be any straight line of the space; we project a point set A and the covering sets U_k, which are convex domains, orthogonally onto g. Suppose that A is projected onto the point set A' and that each U_k is projected onto an interval U'_k of length d'_k; this length d'_k is not larger than the diameter d_k of U_k.

Now the totality of intervals U'_k covers A', and if m^*A' denotes the Borel-Lebesgue content of A' on the straight line g, we have

$$m^* A' \leqq \sum_k d'_k \leqq \sum_k d_k .$$

From this we deduce further that

$$m^* A' \leqq \mathfrak{L}_\varrho A \leqq \mathfrak{L}^* A \qquad (0 < \varrho < +\infty). \quad (287.1)$$

The Borel-Lebesgue content m^*A' of the orthogonal projection of a point set A in $\mathfrak{R}_q$ onto any straight line g of the space is never greater than the linear measure of A.

288. Let γ be a non-self-intersecting curve, that is, the homeomorphic image (one-to-one continuous image) of the closed line-segment $0 \leqq t \leqq 1$; moreover, let P_1P_2 be the straight line-segment that joins the end-points P_1 and P_2 of γ. If we project γ orthogonally onto the straight line g that contains P_1 and P_2, the image of γ under this projection contains the entire segment P_1P_2. Hence it follows that $\mathfrak{L}\gamma$ is not smaller than the length of the segment P_1P_2.

Next, let $\mathfrak{P}$ denote any (open) polygon inscribed in γ whose vertices lie in sequence on γ; let $\gamma_1, \gamma_2, \ldots, \gamma_n$ denote the segments of γ whose end-points are at the vertices of $\mathfrak{P}$; and consider the equation

$$\mathfrak{L}\gamma = \mathfrak{L}\gamma_1 + \mathfrak{L}\gamma_2 + \cdots + \mathfrak{L}\gamma_n .$$

It follows that $\mathfrak{L}\gamma$ can be no smaller than the length of the polygon $\mathfrak{P}$. Hence $\mathfrak{L}\gamma$ can have a finite value only if the lengths of all possible polygons inscribed (in the above sense) in γ admit a finite least upper bound λ, i.e., only if the curve γ is rectifiable and of length λ. Moreover, the relation

$$\mathfrak{L}\gamma \geqq \lambda$$

follows from these considerations.

We now decompose γ into a finite number of successive curve-segments $\gamma_1, \gamma_2, \ldots, \gamma_n$ whose diameters are $\leqq \varrho$, in such a way that any two neighboring segments have only one point in common, and we use the γ_k in place of the U_k of § 258. On each γ_k there are two points whose distance is equal to the diameter d_k of γ_k. If we use these points as the vertices of an inscribed polygon, the length of this polygon can in no case be less than the sum of the diameters d_k; hence, for every number $\varrho > 0$, we have

$$\mathfrak{L}_\varrho \gamma \leqq \lambda;$$

consequently, we also have $\mathfrak{L}\gamma \leqq \lambda$; and the proof of the identity between the linear measure of γ and its length is thus complete.

If we introduce the arc-length s as parameter for γ, we obtain a mapping of γ onto the s-axis that is measure-preserving in the following sense: Let A' be any point set on the s-axis, and let A be the image of this point set on γ. Then, where m^*A' denotes the outer Borel-Lebesgue content of A', we always have

$$\mathfrak{L}^* A = m^* A'.$$

289. There are even totally disconnected perfect point sets whose linear measure is finite and non-zero. The simplest example of such a point set is obtained as follows:

We consider an equilateral triangle OPQ in the plane, whose sides are of length one. At every vertex of this zero-order triangle, we form a similar

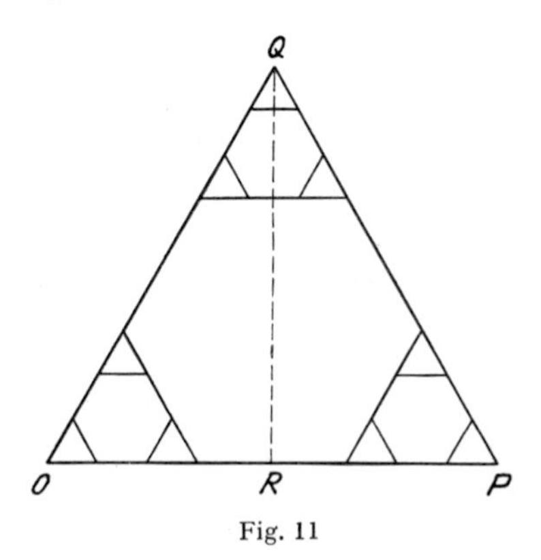

Fig. 11

triangle of first order, obtained by trisection of the sides of the large triangle. At each of the nine vertices of the first-order triangles, we form a triangle of second order, whose sides are thus of length $1/3^2$, and we continue this procedure without limit. We then consider the perfect point set A that consists of all the vertices of the various triangles of all orders, as well as all the points of accumulation of this countable point set.

Now, A is covered by the 3^p closed p-th order triangles, each of which is of diameter $d_p = 1/3^p$. The sum of these diameters is equal to one, and so we have

$$\mathfrak{L}_\varrho A \leqq 1 \qquad (289.1)$$

for $\varrho > 1/3^p$. But this inequality holds for every $\varrho > 0$, since p can be taken arbitrarily large, and thus we see that

$$\mathfrak{L} A \leqq 1. \tag{289.2}$$

Next, we project each point of A orthogonally onto the base OP of the zero-order triangle. On every ordinate line passing through a point of OP that has abscissa

$$\xi_{pq} = \frac{p}{3^q} \quad (p = 1, 2, \ldots, 3^q - 1; \; q = 1, 2, \ldots), \tag{289.3}$$

there are two vertices of our triangular partition; every ordinate line that passes through one of the remaining points of OP cuts an infinite number of nested triangles of the triangular partition and meets the point set A in precisely one point. Thus, the projection A' of A on OP completely fills out the side OP. Therefore, by the result of § 287, we have

$$\mathfrak{L} A \geqq 1; \tag{289.4}$$

finally, by comparison of (289.2) with (289.4) we obtain

$$\mathfrak{L} A = 1. \tag{289.5}$$

It is a consequence of the above that the subset of A that lies in one of the p-th order triangles has linear measure $1/3^p$. Hence, the linear measure of the subset of A that lies in a strip whose edges are parallel to the altitude QR and have the abscissas ξ_{pq} and ξ_{rs} is always equal to the width of the strip. For every subset B of A mapped onto the point set B' by the orthogonal projection onto OP, we then find

$$\mathfrak{L}^* B = m^* B',$$

where $m^* B'$ denotes the Borel-Lebesgue content of B'.

On the other hand, if we project the point set A orthogonally onto the altitude QR of the triangle OPQ, the image under the projection is a Cantor discontinuum of content zero.

The point set A has triaxial symmetry. For three directions of the straight line g onto which A is orthogonally projected, we have $mA' = 1$; for three other directions, that come exactly half-way between the first three, we have $mA' = 0$; and for all other directions, mA' lies between these two numbers.

A. S. Besicovitch, in a marvelous work[9] that should be read by everyone interested in the theory of linear measure, has constructed a much more remarkable example, in which for every possible direction of the straight line g, the number mA' is zero.

[9] A. S. Besicovitch, "On the fundamental geometrical properties of linearly measurable plane sets of points," *Math. Ann.*, Vol. 98 (1927), pp. 422-464.

APPENDIX

SOMAS AS ELEMENTS OF PARTIALLY ORDERED SETS

§§ 290-297. A New Axiom System for Somas

290. We should now like to make certain additional axiomatic investigations that are of fundamental significance to the theory of somas.

Up to now, we have taken somas to be elements of a Boolean ring (cf. §§ 8-13), since calculation with such elements takes the simplest and most elegant form. It is more natural in many instances, however, to give the primary rôle to the operation $A \dotplus B$ of union rather than to the operation $A \dotplus B$ of conjunction. This is done, for example, in Volume I of *Reelle Funktionen* (Leipzig, 1939; repr., New York, 1946), where the issue is that of the development of the theory of point sets, which are, after all, just a special case of somas.

Now it is quite remarkable that an *independent* theory of somas can be obtained by taking these mathematical objects to be elements of a partially ordered set that satisfies a few additional requirements.

In order to show this, we define somas and also the relations between them by means of the following new system of axioms and definitions.

AXIOM 1*a: *Every system of somas $A, B, \ldots$ forms a partially ordered set $\mathfrak{M}_0$. That is, a relation $A \subseteqq B$ holds for certain pairs of elements of $\mathfrak{M}_0$, in such a way that the following two conditions are satisfied:*

1. *$X \subseteqq X$ for all $X \in \mathfrak{M}_0$;*
2. *If $A \subseteqq B$ and $B \subseteqq C$, then $A \subseteqq C$.*

If $A \subseteqq B$, A is called a subsoma of B, and B is called a containing soma of A.

AXIOM 1*b: *The relation $A \subseteqq B$ is also to satisfy the following requirements:*

3. *If $A \subseteqq B$ and $B \subseteqq A$, then $A = B$, i.e., A is identical with B;*
4. *There is a soma O that satisfies $O \subseteqq X$ for all $X \in \mathfrak{M}_0$. This soma O is called the empty soma.*

At most one soma O can exist that has the properties mentioned above, for if $O' \subseteqq O$ and $O \subseteqq O'$, then by 3., it follows that $O = O'$.

DEFINITION 1*: *Two somas are said to be disjoint if they have no subsoma in common other than O, or in other words, if* $X \subseteqq A$ *and* $X \subseteqq B$ *implies* $X = O$. *The fact that A and B are disjoint is indicated by the symbol* $A \circ B$.

An immediate consequence of this is the following theorem.

THEOREM 1: $O \circ X$ *for all* $X \in \mathfrak{M}_0$.

AXIOM 2*a: *For every two somas A and B, there is a smallest common containing soma, i.e., there is at least one soma V that satisfies* $A \subseteqq V$ *and* $B \subseteqq V$ *and for which we have* $V \subseteqq W$ *for all somas W that satisfy both* $A \subseteqq W$ *and* $B \subseteqq W$.

DEFINITION 2*: *The smallest common containing soma of A and B, which, by 3. of Axiom 1*b, is uniquely determined, is called the union of A and B and is denoted by* $A \dotplus B$.

The following theorem is an immediate consequence of the foregoing.

THEOREM 2: *The following rules hold for the operation of union:*

$$A \dotplus O = A, \quad A \dotplus A = A. \tag{290.1}$$

$$A \dotplus B = B \dotplus A, \quad A \dotplus (B \dotplus C) = (A \dotplus B) \dotplus C. \tag{290.2}$$

By mathematical induction, it follows that every finite number of somas $A_1, A_2, \ldots, A_n$ admits a smallest common containing soma, which is called their union and is written $\sum_{j=1}^{n} \dotplus A_j$.

AXIOM 2*b: *For every countably infinite sequence of somas* $A_1, A_2, \ldots$ *there is a smallest common containing soma, which is called their union and is denoted by* $\sum_j \dotplus A_j$.

AXIOM 3*: *For any three somas A, B, and C, the relations*

$$C \circ A \text{ and } C \circ B \tag{290.3}$$

together imply the further relation

$$C \circ (A \dotplus B). \tag{290.4}$$

AXIOM 4*: *Among the solutions X of the equation*

$$X \dotplus A = A \dotplus B \tag{290.5}$$

there is at least one that satisfies

$$X \circ A \tag{290.6}$$

The somas that we defined in Chapter One by means of Axioms 1-4 of §§ 8-13 must also, of course, satisfy the present axioms and definitions: this is clear for Axioms 1* and 2*; Axiom 3* is a special case of Theorem 1 of § 17; Axiom 4* is verified by putting

$$X = B \dotplus AB.$$

We now deal with the converse problem of showing that every mathematical object that satisfies our new axioms, Axioms 1* through 4*, is a soma in the earlier sense also. To this end, we shall show at considerable length that every object that satisfies Axioms 1*, 2*a, 3*, and 4* is an element of a Boolean ring, i.e., satisfies Axioms 1-3 of §§ 8-10. Under these circumstances, Axiom 2*b is no whit different from Axiom 4 of § 13. Thus, the mathematical objects defined by our new axioms are the same as those we considered earlier.

291. We must still set up a few theorems that follow almost from the very wording of Axioms 1*a, 1*b, and 2*a.

THEOREM 3: *Each of the relations*

$$A \subseteqq B, \quad A \dotplus B = B \tag{291.1}$$

implies the other.

Proof: We put

$$V = A \dotplus B \tag{291.2}$$

and note the relations

$$A \subseteqq V, \quad B \subseteqq V. \tag{291.3}$$

First, if $V = B$, we must have $A \subseteqq B$. Second, if $A \subseteqq B$, it follows from $A \subseteqq B$ and $B \subseteqq B$ that $V \subseteqq B$; hence we must have $V = B$.

THEOREM 4: *If* $X \circ A$ *and* $X \subseteqq A$, *then* $X = O$.

Proof: X must be a subsoma common to both X and A, and since $X \circ A$, it must coincide with the empty soma.

THEOREM 5: *If* $X \circ B$ *and* $A \subseteqq B$, *then* $X \circ A$.

Proof: *Since* $A \subseteqq B$, every subsoma of A is a subsoma of B, and every subsoma common to X and A is also a common subsoma of X and B. Since $X \circ B$, such a common subsoma of X and B must be the empty soma, and so we have shown that $X \circ A$.

292. If A and B are any two somas, then by Axiom 4*, there is at least one soma X for which the two relations

$$X \dotplus A = A \dotplus B, \quad X \circ A \tag{292.1}$$

both hold. In the same way, there is a soma X' satisfying

$$X' \dotplus B = B \dotplus X, \quad X' \circ B. \tag{292.2}$$

We let X'' denote a subsoma common to X' and A. From

$$X'' \subseteqq A, \quad A \circ X$$

it follows, by Theorem 5 of § 291, that

$$X'' \circ X.$$

Likewise, it follows from $X'' \subseteqq X'$ and $X' \circ B$ that

$$X'' \circ B,$$

and therefore, by Axiom 3*, we can write

$$X'' \circ (B \dotplus X). \tag{292.3}$$

On the other hand, however, we have the relations

$$X'' \subseteqq X' \subseteqq X' \dotplus B = B \dotplus X. \tag{292.4}$$

By Theorem 4 of § 291, it follows from (292.3) and (292.4) that

$$X'' = O. \tag{292.5}$$

But this means that X' and A are disjoint; hence, since $X' \circ B$, we have

$$X' \circ (A \dotplus B). \tag{292.6}$$

On the other hand, however, we have

$$X' \subseteqq B \dotplus X \subseteqq B \dotplus X \dotplus A$$

and

$$B \dotplus (X \dotplus A) = B \dotplus (A \dotplus B) = A \dotplus B,$$

so that we can write

$$X' \subseteqq A \dotplus B. \tag{292.7}$$

A comparison of (292.6) with (292.7) now yields $X' = O$, and from (292.2) we deduce the relation

$$X \dotplus B = B \quad \text{i.e.,} \quad X \subseteqq B. \tag{292.8}$$

Next, let C be any soma for which we have

$$C \subseteqq A \dotplus B, \quad C \circ A. \tag{292.9}$$

By comparison of (292.1) with the first of these relations, we obtain

$$(C \dotplus X) \dotplus A = C \dotplus (A \dotplus B) = A \dotplus B. \tag{292.10}$$

On the other hand, it follows from $C \circ A$ and $X \circ A$, by Axiom 3*, that

$$(C \dotplus X) \circ A. \tag{292.11}$$

Thus the soma $C \dotplus X$ satisfies the assumptions that were made for the soma X, and therefore, by (292.8), we have

$$C \dotplus X \subseteqq B.$$

It follows from this last relation that $C \subseteqq B$, and consequently we have the following theorem.

THEOREM 6: *If $C \subseteqq A \dotplus B$ and $C \circ A$, then $C \subseteqq B$.*

293. Let X again be a soma for which the relations (292.1) hold; moreover, let Y be a soma that satisfies

$$Y \dotplus X = X \dotplus B, \quad Y \circ X. \tag{293.1}$$

Then (292.8) implies the relations

$$Y \dotplus X = B, \quad Y \subseteqq B. \tag{293.2}$$

Next, we consider another soma Z for which

$$Z \dotplus A = A \dotplus Y, \quad Z \circ A. \tag{293.3}$$

Then $Z \subseteqq Y$, by Theorem 6; and by Theorem 5, $Z \subseteqq Y$ and $Y \circ X$ imply

$$Z \circ X.$$

Now $Z \circ X$ and $Z \circ A$ imply $Z \circ (A \dotplus X)$, and by (292.1) this can be written as

$$Z \circ (A \dotplus B). \tag{293.4}$$

But now we have

$$Z \subseteqq A \dotplus Y \subseteqq A \dotplus (Y \dotplus X) = A \dotplus B; \tag{293.5}$$

hence, by Theorem 4, $Z = O$. Hence we can write

$$A \dotplus Y = A, \quad Y \subseteqq A \tag{293.6}$$

in place of (293.3).

294. By means of the considerations above, we have assigned to every pair of somas A and B a pair of somas X and Y that satisfy the conditions

$$X \circ A, \quad X \subseteqq B, \quad Y \subseteqq A, \quad Y \subseteqq B, \tag{294.1}$$

$$X \dotplus Y = B. \tag{294.2}$$

Let X_1 and Y_1 be two additional somas for which we have, similarly,

$$X_1 \circ A, \quad X_1 \subseteqq B, \quad Y_1 \subseteqq A, \quad Y_1 \subseteqq B. \tag{294.3}$$

The relations

$$X_1 \circ Y, \quad Y_1 \circ X \tag{294.4}$$

follow respectively from $Y \subseteqq A$ and $A \circ X_1$, on the one hand, and from $Y_1 \subseteqq A$ and $A \circ X$ on the other. But we also have the relations

$$X_1 \subseteqq B = X \dotplus Y, \quad Y_1 \subseteqq B = X \dotplus Y, \tag{294.5}$$

and by Theorem 6 above, we must then have

$$X_1 \subseteqq X, \quad Y_1 \subseteqq Y. \tag{294.6}$$

From this it follows that there can be only one pair of somas X and Y for which the formulas (294.1) and (294.2) both hold. In summary, we have the following theorem.

THEOREM 7: *To every pair of somas A and B, we can assign in one and only one way a pair of somas X and Y satisfying all the relations*

$$X \circ A, \quad Y \subseteqq A, \quad X \dotplus Y = B. \tag{294.7}$$

Here X is the largest soma for which both $X \circ A$ and $X \subseteqq B$ hold, and Y is the largest soma for which both $Y \subseteqq A$ and $Y \subseteqq B$ hold.

295. We now change notation. If A and B are any two somas, let T_1, T_2, and T_3 denote the largest somas (which, by the preceding theorem, always exist) satisfying

$$\left.\begin{array}{ll} T_1 \subseteqq A, & T_1 \subseteqq B; \\ T_2 \circ A, & T_2 \subseteqq B; \\ T_3 \subseteqq A, & T_3 \circ B. \end{array}\right\} \tag{295.1}$$

The somas T_1, T_2, and T_3 are pairwise disjoint: indeed, the relation $T_2 \circ T_3$ follows from the relations $T_2 \circ A$ and $T_3 \subseteqq A$, and the other two relations $T_1 \circ T_3$ and $T_1 \circ T_2$ can be verified in a similar way.

Finally, the equations

$$A = T_1 \dotplus T_3, \quad B = T_1 \dotplus T_2 \tag{295.2}$$

follow from the last theorem. If, conversely, T_1', T_2', and T_3' are three pairwise disjoint somas that satisfy

$$A = T_1' \dotplus T_3', \quad B = T_1' \dotplus T_2', \tag{295.3}$$

then we have the relations

$$T_2' \circ A, \quad T_1' \subseteqq A, \quad T_1' \dotplus T_2' = B, \tag{295.4}$$

and consequently $T_1' = T_1$ and $T_2' = T_2$. The equation $T_3' = T_3$ is verified in exactly the same way, and consequently we have the following theorem.

THEOREM 8: *If A and B are any somas, then three pairwise disjoint somas T_1, T_2, and T_3 can be found that satisfy the equations*

$$A = T_1 \dotplus T_3, \quad B = T_1 \dotplus T_2, \tag{295.5}$$

and these three somas are uniquely determined by (295.5).

296. In addition to the somas A and B, we now consider a third soma C, as well as the somas T_1, T_2, and T_3 that are uniquely determined by (295.5). By repeated application of Theorem 8, we obtain nine somas S_1 through S_7, R_1, and R_2 that are uniquely determined by the equations

$$\left.\begin{array}{ll} T_1 = S_1 \dotplus S_4, & C = S_1 \dotplus R_1, \\ T_2 = S_2 \dotplus S_6, & R_1 = S_2 \dotplus R_2, \\ T_3 = S_3 \dotplus S_5, & R_2 = S_3 \dotplus S_7, \end{array}\right\} \tag{296.1}$$

provided we require that each of the triples of somas

$$(S_1, S_4, R_1), \ (S_2, S_6, R_2), \ (S_3, S_5, S_7) \tag{296.2}$$

as well as (T_1, T_2, T_3) shall consist of pairwise disjoint somas. Next, it follows from equation (296.1) that the somas $S_1, \ldots, S_7$ are pairwise disjoint. Finally, from (295.5) and (296.1), we obtain the equations

$$\left.\begin{array}{l} A = S_1 \dotplus S_3 \dotplus S_4 \dotplus S_5, \\ B = S_1 \dotplus S_2 \dotplus S_4 \dotplus S_6, \\ C = S_1 \dotplus S_2 \dotplus S_3 \dotplus S_7, \end{array}\right\} \tag{296.3}$$

and we have recovered the situation depicted in Fig. 7 of § 21.

297. Following the prescription of § 4, we form the matrix (cf. (4.4))

	T_1	T_2	T_3
A	1	0	1
B	1	1	0

that corresponds to the equations (295.5). In the same way, we let the matrix

	S_1	S_2	S_3	S_4	S_5	S_6	S_7
A	1	0	1	1	1	0	0
B	1	1	0	1	0	1	0
C	1	1	1	0	0	0	1

correspond to the equations (295.5). Using the first of these matrices, we must then write, by § 5,

$$A \dotplus B = T_2 \dotplus T_3, \quad AB = T_1. \tag{297.1}$$

These equations uniquely define the *conjunction* and the *intersection* of the two somas A and B. In the case that $B = A$, equations (295.5) are satisfied when we put $T_1 = A$ and $T_2 = T_3 = O$, and consequently we have

$$A \dotplus A = O, \quad AA = A. \tag{297.2}$$

From the second matrix, by the same rule, we deduce the formulas

$$A \dotplus B = (S_2 \dotplus S_6) \dotplus (S_3 \dotplus S_5) = S_2 \dotplus S_3 \dotplus S_5 \dotplus S_6, \tag{297.3}$$

$$AB = S_1 \dotplus S_4, \tag{297.4}$$

which, except for the notation, coincide with (297.1).

It is now easy to verify that we must also have

$$(A \dotplus B) \dotplus C = A \dotplus (B \dotplus C) = S_1 \dotplus S_5 \dotplus S_6 \dotplus S_7, \tag{297.5}$$

$$(AB)C = A(BC) = S_1, \tag{297.6}$$

$$C(A \dotplus B) = CA \dotplus CB = S_2 \dotplus S_3. \tag{297.7}$$

Furthermore, the equations

$$A \dotplus B = B \dotplus A, \quad AB = BA, \quad A \dotplus O = A \tag{297.8}$$

are of course satisfied here. Finally, the equation

$$A \dotplus X = B \tag{297.9}$$

always has a solution, since it follows from the above that

$$A \dotplus B = A \dotplus (A \dotplus X) = (A \dotplus A) \dotplus X = O \dotplus X = X. \tag{297.10}$$

Thus, mathematical objects that satisfy Axioms 1*, 2*a, 3*, and 4* of § 290 also satisfy Axioms 1-3 of §§ 8-10. By the remark at the end of § 290, this completes the proof of the equivalence between our new axiom system and the old.

§§ 298-302. The Partitioning of a Set into Classes

298. Somas can always be viewed as *classes* of a fixed set, and it is often convenient to make use of such a representation for somas. For this reason, we shall now consider the most general partitioning of a set into classes.

Let $\mathfrak{m}_0$ be a non-empty set whose elements are denoted by lower case italic letters $a, b, c, \ldots$. We shall designate subsets of $\mathfrak{m}_0$ by lower case German letters $\mathfrak{a}, \mathfrak{b}, \ldots$, and we shall use the symbol

$$a \in \mathfrak{a} \tag{298.1}$$

to express the fact that a is an element of $\mathfrak{a}$. We shall express the statement that $\mathfrak{b}$ is a subset of $\mathfrak{a}$, i.e., that

$$\text{if} \quad a \in \mathfrak{b} \quad \text{then} \quad a \in \mathfrak{a} \tag{298.2}$$

by writing

$$\mathfrak{b} \prec \mathfrak{a} \quad \text{or} \quad \mathfrak{a} \succ \mathfrak{b}, \tag{298.3}$$

while, to avoid confusion, the notation $B \subseteqq A$ will be reserved exclusively for somas.

We shall denote the union and the intersection of a finite or infinite number of sets, $\mathfrak{a}, \mathfrak{b}, \ldots$ however, just as for somas, by $\mathfrak{a} \dotplus \mathfrak{b} \dotplus \ldots$ and $\mathfrak{a}\mathfrak{b} \ldots$; likewise, $\mathfrak{a} \circ \mathfrak{b}$ shall express that the two sets have no element in common.

299. DEFINITION 1: *A collection of pairwise disjoint, non-empty subsets of* $\mathfrak{m}_0$ *is called a partition of* $\mathfrak{m}_0$ *into classes, and the subsets themselves are called classes, if each element of* $\mathfrak{m}_0$ *belongs to one of these subsets. The partition may consist of the single class* $\mathfrak{m}_0$.

The number of classes need not be either finite or countable.

We let $\mathfrak{c}(a)$ denote the class which contains the element a of $\mathfrak{m}_0$. If b is any element of $\mathfrak{c}(a)$, we must have $\mathfrak{c}(a) = \mathfrak{c}(b)$; for, the two classes $\mathfrak{c}(a)$ and $\mathfrak{c}(b)$ have the element b in common and hence cannot be disjoint. The following relations are thus valid for the symbol $\mathfrak{c}(a)$:

$$a \in \mathfrak{c}(a). \tag{299.1}$$

$$\text{if} \quad b \in \mathfrak{c}(a) \quad \text{then} \quad \mathfrak{c}(b) = \mathfrak{c}(a). \tag{299.2}$$

In this notation, one and the same class is represented by several different symbols whenever this class has more than one element; but this is precisely where the convenience lies, for we have the following theorem.

THEOREM 1: *If a subset* $\mathfrak{c}(a)$ *of* $\mathfrak{m}_0$ *is assigned to each element* a *of* $\mathfrak{m}_0$ *in such a way that* (299.1) *and* (299.2) *hold, then the sets* $\mathfrak{c}(a)$ *constitute a partition of* $\mathfrak{m}_0$ *into classes.*

Proof: By (299.1), each element a of $\mathfrak{m}_0$ belongs to one of the classes, namely, to $\mathfrak{c}(a)$. If two of the classes, $\mathfrak{c}(a)$ and $\mathfrak{c}(b)$, have an element e in common, then, by (299.2), we have

$$\mathfrak{c}(e) = \mathfrak{c}(a), \quad \mathfrak{c}(e) = \mathfrak{c}(b) \tag{299.3}$$

and hence $\mathfrak{c}(a) = \mathfrak{c}(b)$. Thus, two classes that are not identical must be disjoint.

In the same way we prove the following more general theorem.

THEOREM 2: *Let* $\mathfrak{m}_0$ *and* $\mathfrak{m}_0'$ *be any two sets of elements* a *and* a', *respectively, where the sets* $\mathfrak{m}_0$ *and* $\mathfrak{m}_0'$ *may coincide. To each element* a *in* $\mathfrak{m}_0$ *let there correspond a subset* $\mathfrak{p}'(a)$ *of* $\mathfrak{m}_0'$. *If* $\mathfrak{c}(a)$ *denotes the totality of elements* b *in* $\mathfrak{m}_0$ *for which*

$$\mathfrak{p}'(b) = \mathfrak{p}'(a) \tag{299.4}$$

then the sets $\mathfrak{c}(a)$ *constitute a partition of* $\mathfrak{m}_0$ *into classes.*

300. We consider a partition of $\mathfrak{m}_0$ into classes $\mathfrak{c}(a)$, and a non-empty subset $\mathfrak{n}$ of $\mathfrak{m}_0$. If, for each element $a \in \mathfrak{n}$, we let the subset

$$\mathfrak{c}_1(a) = \mathfrak{n}\,\mathfrak{c}(a) \tag{300.1}$$

correspond to the element a, we thereby partition the subset $\mathfrak{n}$ into classes. Each of these classes $\mathfrak{c}_1(a)$ is a subset of the class $\mathfrak{c}(a)$; it is conceivable, however, that $\mathfrak{c}_1(a) = \mathfrak{c}(a)$ for each a in $\mathfrak{n}$. If this is indeed the case, then $\mathfrak{n}$ is a *union of classes* $\mathfrak{c}(a)$.

We let $\mathfrak{m}$ denote the totality of elements a in $\mathfrak{m}_0$ for which the intersection $\mathfrak{n}\mathfrak{c}(a)$ is non-empty. If $a \in \mathfrak{n}$, then $a \in \mathfrak{n}\mathfrak{c}(a)$, and consequently

$$\mathfrak{n} \prec \mathfrak{m}. \tag{300.2}$$

In addition, we have the relation

$$\text{if} \quad a \in \mathfrak{m} \quad \text{then} \quad \mathfrak{c}(a) \prec \mathfrak{m}; \tag{300.3}$$

indeed, if b is an element of $\mathfrak{c}(a)$, then $\mathfrak{c}(a) = \mathfrak{c}(b)$ and $\mathfrak{n}\mathfrak{c}(b)$ is non-empty, since the same is true of $\mathfrak{n}\mathfrak{c}(a)$. Consequently, $b \in \mathfrak{m}$, so that (300.3) is verified. The statement (300.3) expresses the fact that the set $\mathfrak{m}$ is a union of classes $\mathfrak{c}(a)$.

Let $\mathfrak{p}$ be any union of classes $\mathfrak{c}(a)$ that contains $\mathfrak{n}$ as a subset. To each element a of $\mathfrak{m}$ we can assign an element b of $\mathfrak{n}\mathfrak{c}(a)$. Then b, and consequently $\mathfrak{c}(b)$ as well, is contained in $\mathfrak{p}$. Then, since $a \in \mathfrak{c}(b)$, we also have $a \in \mathfrak{p}$, and finally, $\mathfrak{m} \prec \mathfrak{p}$. In consequence, we have the following theorem.

THEOREM 3: *To every subset* $\mathfrak{n}$ *of* $\mathfrak{m}_0$ *there can be assigned a smallest union* $\mathfrak{m}$ *of classes* $\mathfrak{c}(a)$ *that contains* $\mathfrak{n}$ *as a subset. The set* $\mathfrak{m}$ *consists of all the elements* a *of* $\mathfrak{m}_0$ *for which* $\mathfrak{n}\mathfrak{c}(a)$ *is non-empty.*

301. The partition of a set $\mathfrak{m}_0$ into classes can also be brought into correspondence with the so-called normal congruences, or equivalence relations, defined as follows:

DEFINITION 2: *A normal congruence (or, an equivalence relation) is given on a set* $\mathfrak{m}_0$ *if a relation* $a \equiv b$ *holds for certain pairs,* a, b *of elements of* $\mathfrak{m}_0$ *such that the following conditions are satisfied:*

$$a \equiv a \text{ for all } a \in \mathfrak{m}_0; \tag{301.1}$$

$$\text{if } \quad a \equiv b \quad \text{and} \quad b \equiv c \quad \text{then} \quad a \equiv c; \tag{301.2}$$

$$\text{if } \quad a \equiv b \quad \text{then} \quad b \equiv a. \tag{301.3}$$

A relation for which (301.1) holds is called *reflexive*; one for which (301.2) holds is called *transitive*; and finally, a relation is called *symmetric* if (301.3) holds.

If a is any element of $\mathfrak{m}_0$, let $\mathfrak{c}(a)$ be the totality of elements b in $\mathfrak{m}_0$ for which $a \equiv b$. Then, by (301.1), we have

$$a \in \mathfrak{c}(a), \tag{301.4}$$

so that the set $\mathfrak{c}(a)$ can never be empty. The relation (301.2) can be written as

$$\text{if } \quad b \in \mathfrak{c}(a) \quad \text{and} \quad c \in \mathfrak{c}(b) \quad \text{then} \quad c \in \mathfrak{c}(a). \tag{301.5}$$

This last relation states that every element of $\mathfrak{c}(b)$ is also an element of $\mathfrak{c}(a)$, provided b belongs to $\mathfrak{c}(a)$; consequently, we may write it as

$$\text{if } \quad b \in \mathfrak{c}(a) \quad \text{then} \quad \mathfrak{c}(b) \prec \mathfrak{c}(a) \tag{301.6}$$

or as

$$\text{if } \quad a \equiv b \quad \text{then} \quad \mathfrak{c}(b) \prec \mathfrak{c}(a). \tag{301.7}$$

We see from this by the symmetry property (301.3) that whenever $a \equiv b$ it always follows that $\mathfrak{c}(a) = \mathfrak{c}(b)$, and this is equivalent with the condition (299.2).

Thus, $\mathfrak{m}_0$ is partitioned into classes by means of a normal congruence. Conversely, given a partition of $\mathfrak{m}_0$ into classes $\mathfrak{c}(a)$, we obtain a normal congruence by writing $a \equiv b$ for two elements a and b if and only if they belong to the same class, i.e., if and only if $\mathfrak{c}(a) = \mathfrak{c}(b)$.

302. We shall now consider each of the classes $\mathfrak{c}(a)$, $\mathfrak{c}(b)$, ... as a single mathematical object, and we shall denote these new objects by capital italic letters $A, B, \ldots$. Thus, we may write

$$A = \mathfrak{c}(a). \tag{302.1}$$

The various elements $a, a', \ldots$ in $\mathfrak{c}(a)$ are called the *representatives* of A. We choose one fixed representative a_0 from each of the classes $\mathfrak{c}(a)$. The set $\mathfrak{n}_0$ of all such elements a_0 is then in a one-to-one correspondence with the set $\mathfrak{M}_0$ of all elements A. Every subset $\mathfrak{n}$ of $\mathfrak{n}_0$ corresponds to a subset $\mathfrak{M}$ of $\mathfrak{M}_0$, and conversely.

If the subset $\mathfrak{n}$ of $\mathfrak{n}_0$ is enlarged into a union $\mathfrak{m}$ of classes $\mathfrak{c}(a)$, by the construction given in § 300, we shall write

$$\mathfrak{M} \sim \mathfrak{m}. \tag{302.2}$$

If we consider a finite or a countable number of sets $\mathfrak{M}_j$ of elements A and if, as in (302.2), we write

$$\mathfrak{M}_j \sim \mathfrak{m}_j \qquad (j = 1, 2, \ldots), \tag{302.3}$$

then the propositions

$$\sum_j \dotplus \mathfrak{M}_j \sim \sum_j \dotplus \mathfrak{m}_j, \tag{302.4}$$

$$\mathfrak{M}_1 \circ \mathfrak{M}_2 \quad \text{if and only if} \quad \mathfrak{m}_1 \circ \mathfrak{m}_2 \tag{302.5}$$

hold.

It can also be verified that the following relations hold:

$$\mathfrak{M}_1 \prec \mathfrak{M}_2 \quad \text{if and only if} \quad \mathfrak{m}_1 \prec \mathfrak{m}_2, \tag{302.6}$$

$$\prod_j \mathfrak{M}_j \sim \prod_j \mathfrak{m}_j, \tag{302.7}$$

$$\mathfrak{M}_1 - \mathfrak{M}_1\mathfrak{M}_2 \sim \mathfrak{m}_1 - \mathfrak{m}_1\mathfrak{m}_2. \tag{302.8}$$

§§ 303-304. Partially Ordered Sets

303. From now on, we assume that the non-empty set $\mathfrak{m}_0$ is partially ordered in the sense of Definition 2 of § 11. If we compare this definition with the definition of a normal congruence in § 301, we see that the relation $a \subseteqq b$, which is read "a precedes b," is reflexive and transitive, but not symmetric. Partially ordered sets can be obtained by means of the following theorem.

THEOREM 1: *Let $\mathfrak{m}_0$ and $\mathfrak{m}_0'$ be two non-empty sets of elements a and a' respectively. Let a subset $\mathfrak{p}'(a)$ of $\mathfrak{m}_0'$ be assigned to each of the elements a in $\mathfrak{m}_0$. Define the relation $a \subseteqq b$ to hold between a pair of elements a and b of $\mathfrak{m}_0$ if and only if*

$$\mathfrak{p}'(b) \prec \mathfrak{p}'(a). \tag{303.1}$$

Then $\mathfrak{m}_0$ is partially ordered.

Proof: The relation

$$a \subseteqq a \tag{303.2}$$

is a consequence of the relation

$$\mathfrak{p}'(a) \prec \mathfrak{p}'(a), \tag{303.3}$$

and the assertion

$$\text{if} \quad a \subseteqq b \quad \text{and} \quad b \subseteqq c \quad \text{then} \quad a \subseteqq c \tag{303.4}$$

is equivalent with

$$\text{if} \quad \mathfrak{p}'(b) \prec \mathfrak{p}'(a) \quad \text{and} \quad \mathfrak{p}'(c) \prec \mathfrak{p}'(b) \quad \text{then} \quad \mathfrak{p}'(c) \prec \mathfrak{p}'(a). \tag{303.5}$$

A remarkable special case of the above theorem is obtained by first putting $\mathfrak{m}_0' = \mathfrak{m}_0$ and $\mathfrak{p}'(a) = \mathfrak{m}(a)$ and then assuming that the subsets $\mathfrak{m}(a)$ satisfy the two relations

$$a \in \mathfrak{m}(a), \tag{303.6}$$

$$\text{if} \quad b \in \mathfrak{m}(a) \quad \text{then} \quad \mathfrak{m}(b) \prec \mathfrak{m}(a). \tag{303.7}$$

In the first place, then, it follows by hypothesis from $b \in \mathfrak{m}(a)$ that $a \subseteqq b$. And it follows from $a \subseteqq b$ not only that $\mathfrak{m}(b) \prec \mathfrak{m}(a)$, but also, since by (303.6) we must have $b \in \mathfrak{m}(b)$, that $b \in \mathfrak{m}(a)$.

Thus, the set $\mathfrak{m}(a)$ consists precisely of all those elements b for which $a \subseteqq b$.

Conversely, if $\mathfrak{m}_0$ is a partially ordered set and we let $\mathfrak{m}(a)$ denote the totality of elements b that satisfy $a \subseteqq b$, the two relations (303.6) and (303.7) must hold.

Thus, we see that for a partially ordered set $\mathfrak{m}_0$ that is defined quite abstractly, a suitable mapping reduces the relation $a \subseteqq b$ between its elements to the canonical relation (303.1), which is reflexive and transitive by its very nature. We can enunciate the following theorem.

THEOREM 2: *If $\mathfrak{m}_0$ is any partially ordered set, the ordering of its elements can always be obtained by an application of Theorem* 1. *If we replace the sets $\mathfrak{p}'(a)$ used in that theorem by subsets $\mathfrak{m}(a)$ of $\mathfrak{m}_0$ that consist of the totality of elements b in $\mathfrak{m}_0$ for which we have $a \subseteqq b$, then the relations* (303.6) *and* (303.7) *hold. Conversely, the latter two relations indicate that $\mathfrak{m}(a)$ has the above-mentioned property.*

304. It does not necessarily follow for an arbitrary partially ordered set $\mathfrak{m}_0$ that $a = b$ if both $a \subseteqq b$ and $b \subseteqq a$ hold (cf. § 11). But it is easy to partition $\mathfrak{m}_0$ into classes that do have this property.

To each element a of $\mathfrak{m}_0$ we assign the subset $\mathfrak{c}(a)$ consisting of all the elements b for which $\mathfrak{m}(a) = \mathfrak{m}(b)$. In this way, we obtain, by Theorem 2 of § 299, a partition of $\mathfrak{m}_0$ into classes $\mathfrak{c}(a)$.

Let

$$b \in \mathfrak{m}(a) \quad \text{and} \quad e \in \mathfrak{c}(b); \tag{304.1}$$

by assumption, we have

$$\mathfrak{m}(b) \prec \mathfrak{m}(a), \quad \mathfrak{m}(e) = \mathfrak{m}(b), \quad e \in \mathfrak{m}(e), \tag{304.2}$$

and consequently e belongs to $\mathfrak{m}(a)$. But this can be written as

$$\text{if} \quad b \in \mathfrak{m}(a) \quad \text{then} \quad \mathfrak{c}(b) \prec \mathfrak{m}(a), \tag{304.3}$$

i.e., *each of the sets* $\mathfrak{m}(a)$ *is a union of classes* $\mathfrak{c}(a)$. As in § 302, we introduce new elements $A, B, \ldots$ by means of the equation

$$A = \mathfrak{c}(a). \tag{304.4}$$

In this way, using the notation of § 302, we obtain a set $\mathfrak{M}_0$ of elements A; moreover, just as we did there, we can define the sets

$$\mathfrak{M}(A) \sim \mathfrak{m}(a), \tag{304.5}$$

where a denotes any representative of A. It follows from $a \in \mathfrak{m}(a)$ that

$$A \in \mathfrak{M}(A). \tag{304.6}$$

If b is a representative of an element B for which $B \in \mathfrak{M}(A)$, we have $b \in \mathfrak{m}(a)$. Then, by (303.7), we have $\mathfrak{m}(b) \prec \mathfrak{m}(a)$, and consequently, by (302.6), we also have $\mathfrak{M}(B) \prec \mathfrak{M}(A)$; thus, we have

$$\text{if} \quad B \in \mathfrak{M}(A) \quad \text{then} \quad \mathfrak{M}(B) \prec \mathfrak{M}(A). \tag{304.7}$$

The relations (304.6) *and* (304.7) *indicate that the set* $\mathfrak{M}_0$ *of elements* A *is itself partially ordered if we make the following definition:* $A \subseteqq B$ *if and only if* $\mathfrak{M}(B) \prec \mathfrak{M}(A)$.

If we now have $A \subseteqq B$ and $B \subseteqq A$ simultaneously, we must have

$$\mathfrak{m}(b) \prec \mathfrak{m}(a) \quad \text{and} \quad \mathfrak{m}(a) \prec \mathfrak{m}(b)$$

for any two representatives a and b of A and B, respectively; but then $\mathfrak{m}(a) = \mathfrak{m}(b)$, and this is precisely the condition under which $A = B$. Hence we have the following theorem.

THEOREM 3: *Every partially ordered set* $\mathfrak{m}_0$ *of elements* $a, b, \ldots$ *can be partitioned into classes* $A = \mathfrak{c}(a)$ *that themselves constitute a partially ordered set* $\mathfrak{M}_0$ *of elements* $A, B, \ldots$ *having the following additional property: If* a *and* b *are representatives of* $A = \mathfrak{c}(a)$ *and* $B = \mathfrak{c}(b)$, *then* $A \subseteqq B$ *and* $a \subseteqq b$

are equivalent; furthermore, if the two relations $A \subseteqq B$ and $B \subseteqq A$ both hold, it follows that $A = B$.

§§ 305-308. Applications to the Theory of Somas

305. The last theorem permits us to start with arbitrary partially ordered sets and construct sets that satisfy Axiom 1*b of § 290. To this end, we partition the given partially ordered set $\mathfrak{m}_0$ into classes $A = \mathfrak{c}(a)$ that satisfy condition 3. of that axiom. If there is an element O in $\mathfrak{M}_0$ for which condition 4. holds, let o be a representative of O. Then for every element a in $\mathfrak{m}_0$, we must have

$$\mathfrak{m}(a) \prec \mathfrak{m}(o) \prec \mathfrak{m}_0.$$

But since $a \in \mathfrak{m}(a)$, we must also have $\mathfrak{m}_0 \prec \mathfrak{m}(o)$, and consequently,

$$\mathfrak{m}(o) = \mathfrak{m}_0. \tag{305.1}$$

If there is no element o in $\mathfrak{m}_0$ for which (305.1) holds, let us adjoin to $\mathfrak{m}_0$ a new element, which we shall denote by o and let us then determine a partial ordering of

$$\overline{\mathfrak{m}}_0 = \mathfrak{m}_0 + o$$

by means of the relations

$$\left.\begin{aligned} \overline{\mathfrak{m}}(a) &= \mathfrak{m}(a) \quad \text{for} \quad a \in \mathfrak{m}_0, \\ \overline{\mathfrak{m}}(o) &= \mathfrak{m}_0 + o. \end{aligned}\right\} \tag{305.2}$$

In this way, we always obtain a set of elements

$$A = \mathfrak{c}(a), \quad O = \mathfrak{c}(o) \tag{305.3}$$

that satisfy Axiom 1* of § 290.

306. Next, we assume that the set of elements $A, B, \ldots$ that we have just constructed, which from now on we shall call somas, satisfies not only Axiom 1* but also Axiom 2*, which postulates the existence of the smallest common containing soma

$$V = \sum_j \dotplus A_j \tag{306.1}$$

of the finite or countable number of somas A_j. Let a_j and v be representatives of the somas A_j and V, respectively. Since $A_j \subseteqq V$, we must have

$$\mathfrak{m}(v) \prec \mathfrak{m}(a_j) \qquad (j = 1, 2, \ldots). \tag{306.2}$$

If we next consider the intersection of all the sets $\mathfrak{m}(a_j)$ and put

$$\mathfrak{d} = \mathfrak{m}(a_1)\ \mathfrak{m}(a_2)\ \ldots, \tag{306.3}$$

then by (306.2), we have

$$\mathfrak{m}(v) \prec \mathfrak{d}. \tag{306.4}$$

Now let b be any element of $\mathfrak{d}$, and let $B = \mathfrak{c}(b)$ be the soma whose representative is b. Then $b \in \mathfrak{m}(a_j)$ for every $j = 1, 2, \ldots$, and consequently, by (303.7), we also have $\mathfrak{m}(b) \prec \mathfrak{m}(a_j)$. The soma B then satisfies the relations $A_j \subseteqq B$, and by assumption, we have $V \subseteqq B$, or

$$\mathfrak{m}(b) \prec \mathfrak{m}(v).$$

Consequently, $b \in \mathfrak{m}(v)$, and hence

$$\mathfrak{d} \prec \mathfrak{m}(v).$$

We can therefore write

$$\mathfrak{m}(v) = \mathfrak{m}(a_1)\ \mathfrak{m}(a_2)\ \ldots. \tag{306.5}$$

If, conversely, v is an element of the set of representatives $\mathfrak{m}_0$ that satisfies (306.5) and if b is the representative of a soma B that satisfies $A_j \subseteqq B$ for every $j = 1, 2, \ldots$, then $\mathfrak{m}(b) \prec \mathfrak{m}(v)$, and hence $V \subseteqq B$, where V denotes the soma $V = \mathfrak{c}(v)$. On the other hand, however, $A_j \subseteqq V$, since $\mathfrak{m}(v) \prec \mathfrak{m}(a_j)$, and so V is the union of the somas A_j. We thus have the following theorem.

THEOREM 1: *Axioms* 1* *and* 2* *of* § 290 *both hold simultaneously if and only if an element v in $\mathfrak{m}_0$ satisfying equation* (306.5) *can be assigned to each finite or countable sequence of elements $a_1, a_2, \ldots$ in the set $\mathfrak{m}_0$ of representatives.*

307. We shall now examine the mutual independence of the axioms of § 290.

Axioms 2*, 3*, and 4* presuppose the validity of Axiom 1*, so that the latter axiom must of necessity be postulated in any case. Now, Axiom 2*a is not a consequence of Axiom 1*, as the following example indicates:

Let the set of representatives $\mathfrak{m}_0$ consist of three elements, so that we may write

$$\mathfrak{m}_0 = \{1, 2, 3\}. \tag{307.1}$$

We then put

$$\mathfrak{m}(1) = \{1, 2, 3\}, \quad \mathfrak{m}(2) = \{2\}, \quad \mathfrak{m}(3) = \{3\} \tag{307.2}$$

and obtain three distinct pseudo-somas

$$O \sim \mathfrak{m}(1), \quad A \sim \mathfrak{m}(2), \quad B \sim \mathfrak{m}(3) \tag{307.3}$$

and the relations

$$O \subseteqq A, \quad O \subseteqq B, \quad A \circ B. \tag{307.4}$$

But there is no common containing soma of A and B: Axiom 2*a fails.

The notion of the union of two somas occurs in the wording of Axioms 3* and 4*. If either of these axioms is to hold, we must therefore assume that Axioms 1* and 2*a already both hold.

In the following example, Axioms 1*, 2*a, and 4* hold, but Axiom 3* does not. We put

$$\mathfrak{m}_0 = \{1, 2, 3, 4, 5\}, \tag{307.5}$$

$$\left.\begin{array}{l} A \sim \mathfrak{m}(2) = \{2, 5\},\ B \sim \mathfrak{m}(3) = \{3, 5\},\ C \sim \mathfrak{m}(4) = \{4, 5\}, \\ O \sim \mathfrak{m}(1) = \{1, 2, 3, 4, 5\},\ D \sim \mathfrak{m}(5) = \{5\}, \end{array}\right\} \tag{307.6}$$

where, again, these pseudo-somas are all distinct. We then have the relations

$$\left.\begin{array}{ccc} O \subseteqq A \subseteqq D, & O \subseteqq B \subseteqq D, & O \subseteqq C \subseteqq D, \\ B \circ C, & C \circ A, & A \circ B, \\ \multicolumn{3}{c}{B \dotplus C = C \dotplus A = A \dotplus B = D.} \end{array}\right\} \tag{307.7}$$

It is very easy to verify that Axiom 4* is satisfied in this example. For example, the relations

$$X \dotplus A = A \dotplus B, \quad X \circ A \tag{307.8}$$

can be satisfied both by taking $X = B$ and by taking $X = C$. And this very fact—that the relations (307.8) can be satisfied by two of our pseudo-somas —shows that Axiom 3* fails here, by contradicting Theorem 7 of § 294. We can also check the failure of Axiom 3* directly, for we have $C \circ A$ and $C \circ B$, whereas $C(A \dotplus B) = C \neq O$.

308. Finally, the closed subsets of a Euclidean space yield an example of pseudo-somas for which Axioms 1*, 2*a, 2*b, and 3* hold, but Axiom 4* does not.

The union $A \dotplus B$ of two of these pseudo-somas, the relations $A \circ B$ and $A \subseteqq B$, and the intersection $\prod_j A_j$ of an at most countable number of A_j are defined as usual in the theory of point sets. The union

$$V = \sum_j \dotplus A_j$$

of a countable number of pseudo-somas, however, is taken equal to the closure of the ordinary union of the corresponding point sets. With these stipulations, the first three axioms hold.

Now if B is a continuum consisting of more than one point and if A denotes a point of this continuum, there is no closed point set X satisfying both

$$X \dotplus A = A \dotplus B, \quad \text{and} \quad X \circ A.$$

Thus, Axiom 4* fails to hold.

We have deduced the existence of the intersection of two somas from Axiom 4* (cf. § 297). Our example shows that Axiom 4* cannot be replaced by the requirement that the intersection of even a countable number of somas exists.

The preceding discussion shows that Axioms 1*, 2*a, 3*, and 4* cannot be simplified.

The same holds for Axiom 2*b, whose independence from the other axioms we have already proved in § 13.

§§ 309-312. Systems of Somas that are not Isomorphic to Systems of Subsets of a Set

309. Complete rings of somas can be obtained also by partitioning into classes certain sets of somas *that are not rings.* We obtain in this way examples of rings of somas that enjoy highly unusual properties.

We consider the set $\mathfrak{m}_0$ of *open* subsets $a, b, c, \ldots$ of the Euclidean plane. This set $\mathfrak{m}_0$ is not subtractive, and hence is not a ring. We partition $\mathfrak{m}_0$ into classes

$$A = \{a\}, \quad B = \{b\}, \ldots, \tag{309.1}$$

by putting two open plane sets of points a_1 and a_2 into the same class if and only if their closures $\bar{a}_1$ and $\bar{a}_2$ coincide (cf. Theorem 2 of § 299).

We make the following definition: The relation $A \subseteqq B$ is to hold between two classes A and B if and only if the relation $\bar{a} \prec \bar{b}$ holds for any two representatives a and b, respectively, of A and B. With this definition, $A \subseteqq B$ and $B \subseteqq A$ together imply $A = B$. The empty plane set of points o is also to be looked upon as an open set; the soma that corresponds to it is the empty soma O. This completes the verification of Axiom 1* of § 290 for the somas (309.1).

We continue to let $\bar{a}$ denote the closure of an open point set a, and let a^0 denote the *interior* of $\bar{a}$. Then we always have $a \prec a^0$; and $a^0 \prec b^0$ whenever $\bar{a} \prec \bar{b}$. Thus, if we are to have $A \subseteqq B$, we must have $a \prec b^0$ for *every* representative a of the soma A. Conversely, if there are two representatives a and b of the somas A and B for which $a \prec b^0$, then $A \subseteqq B$.

We now denote the somas in a sequence of somas by $A_1, A_2, \ldots$, and any representatives of the various A_j by $a_1, a_2, \ldots$. Moreover, let w be a representative of a soma W for which we have

$$A_j \subseteqq W \qquad (j = 1, 2, \ldots). \tag{309.2}$$

The interior w^0 of the closure $\overline{w}$ of w must then satisfy $a_j \prec w^0$ for every j. The union

$$v = a_1 \dotplus a_2 \dotplus \dots \tag{309.3}$$

of the open point sets a_j, being itself an open point set, is a representative of some soma V. Now since $v \prec w^0$, it follows that $V \subseteqq W$; and since $a_j \prec v$, it follows that $A_j \subseteqq V$, for $j = 1, 2, \dots$. But this expresses that Axiom 2* of § 290 holds for our somas, so that we may write

$$V = \sum_j \dotplus A_j. \tag{309.4}$$

310. If two somas A and B are not disjoint, they have at least one non-empty subsoma C in common (Definition 1* of § 290). Since $C \subseteqq A$ and $C \subseteqq B$, we have $c \prec a^0$ and $c \prec b^0$ for every representative c of C. Thus the intersection $a^0 b^0$, which contains as a subset the non-empty open point set c, cannot be empty. Therefore neither can the intersection ab of two *arbitrary* representatives of A and B be empty. For since a is an open point set, it follows from $a \circ b$ that $a \circ \overline{b}$ and hence that $a \circ b^0$. From this, we deduce further that $b^0 \circ \overline{a}$, and $b^0 \circ a^0$, contradicting the assumption.

Conversely, if the open point set $c = ab$ is non-empty, the soma C with representative c is likewise non-empty, and we have $C \subseteqq A$ and $C \subseteqq B$.

Thus we see that *the relations* $a \circ b$ *and* $A \circ B$ *are equivalent.*

Let a, b, and c be any three representatives of the somas A, B, and C. We assume that $A \circ C$ and $B \circ C$; then by the above, we must have $a \circ c$ and $b \circ c$, and hence $(a \dotplus b) \circ c$. But the point set $a \dotplus b$ is a representative of $A \dotplus B$, so that we also have $(A \dotplus B) \circ C$. Thus Axiom 3* is verified for our somas.

Lastly, we consider two arbitrary somas A and B with representatives a and b, and let B_1 be the soma with representative

$$b_1 = b - b\,\overline{a}. \tag{310.1}$$

To begin with, it follows from $b_1 \circ a$ that

$$B_1 \circ A. \tag{310.2}$$

Every point of accumulation of $a \dotplus b$ that is not a point of accumulation of a, i.e., that does not belong to $\overline{a}$, is a point of accumulation of b and belongs to the open complement of $\overline{a}$. Therefore, it must be a point of accumulation of b_1. Furthermore, every point of b belongs to the closure of $a + b_1$. Thus, the two point sets $a + b_1$ and $a \dotplus b$ have identical closures, and because of this, we have

$$B_1 \dotplus A = A \dotplus B. \tag{310.3}$$

This completes the proof of the last axiom of § 290, Axiom 4*, and we have shown that the classes (309.1) can be looked upon as a complete ring of somas.

311. In the preceding sections, we assigned a soma A to each open subset of the Euclidean plane, and this assignment, as we have shown, satisfies the two conditions required of a homomorphism in the definition of § 56.

The only reason it is not a homomorphism is that the set $\mathfrak{m}_0$ of open plane sets of points does not constitute a ring of somas.

Worse than that, *the assumption that these somas A, B, ... can be mapped isomorphically onto any sets $\{\alpha\}$, $\{\beta\}$, ... of elements leads to a contradiction.*

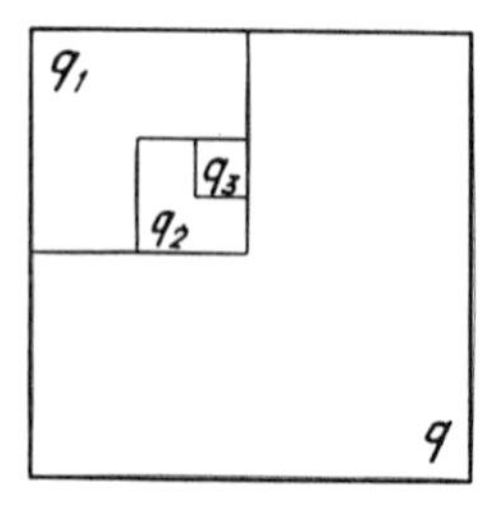

Fig. 12

For let such a mapping carry, say, the soma Q, which has the square q as representative, into the non-empty set given by the relation

$$\{\beta\} = \sigma Q\,; \tag{311.1}$$

let ω be a fixed element of this set.

We cut q up into four sub-squares that correspond, say, to the somas Q', Q'', Q''', and $Q^{(\mathrm{iv})}$. These somas are pairwise disjoint, and furthermore,

$$Q = Q' + Q'' + Q''' + Q^{(\mathrm{iv})}. \tag{311.2}$$

Under the assumed homomorphism, one of our four somas—let us denote it by Q_1—is mapped into

$$\sigma Q_1 = \{\beta\}_1, \tag{311.3}$$

with $\{\beta\}_1$ containing the element ω. Let q_1 be the sub-square that is a representative of Q_1. We cut q_1 into four congruent sub-squares and let q_2 denote the one that represents a soma Q_2 whose image

$$\{\beta\}_2 = \sigma Q_2 \tag{311.4}$$

contains the element ω (Fig. 12). We continue in this way, and obtain an infinite monotonically decreasing sequence of somas

$$Q_1 \supseteqq Q_2 \supseteqq Q_3 \supseteqq \ldots \tag{311.5}$$

such that each of the sets

$$\{\beta\}_j = \sigma Q_j \qquad (j = 1, 2, \ldots) \quad (311.6)$$

contains the element ω. Next, we consider the somas

$$A_j = Q \dotplus Q_j \qquad (j = 1, 2, \ldots). \quad (311.7)$$

Each of these somas admits as one of its representatives the open point set that is obtained when we remove from the square q those points that belong to the intersection of q with the closure $\bar{q}_j$ of q_j. Then the union

$$A = \sum_j \dotplus A_j$$

admits as one of its representatives the whole square q, with the omission of at most *one* point, and hence

$$Q = \sum_j \dotplus A_j. \quad (311.8)$$

But none of the sets

$$\{\alpha\}_j = \sigma A_j \quad (311.9)$$

contains the element ω, and consequently, the union of these sets cannot be identical with $\{\beta\}$. Thus we have the following theorem.

Theorem 1: *There are complete rings of somas that cannot be mapped isomorphically onto a system of sets.*[1]

312. The system of somas that we defined in § 309 also has many other quite remarkable properties.

We shall assume that a measure function $\varphi(X)$ defined on the complete ring of somas (309.1) is such that every non-empty soma in this ring contains at least one φ-measurable non-empty subsoma.

Now if the open plane set a is a representative of a soma A with

$$\varphi(A) < +\infty \quad (312.1)$$

---

[1] According to M. H. Stone, however, in "The theory of representations for Boolean algebras," *Trans. Amer. Math. Soc.,* Vol. 40 (1936), pp. 37-111, every ring of somas can be mapped isomorphically onto a ring of sets provided that the requirements for isomorphism are loosened just enough to allow the image set of the smallest common containing soma of an infinite number of somas to differ from—i.e., properly to contain—the union of the corresponding sets.

According to L. H. Loomis, moreover, in "On the representation of σ-complete Boolean algebras," *Bull. Amer. Math. Soc.,* Vol. 53 (1947), pp. 757-760, every complete ring of somas is isomorphic to the quotient ring $\mathfrak{M}/\mathfrak{J}$ of a complete ring $\mathfrak{M}$ of sets by a complete, $\mathfrak{M}$-hereditary subring (=complete ideal of sets) $\mathfrak{J}$ of $\mathfrak{M}$. Cf. also §§ 59-63 of the present book.

and if q is a square contained in a, let us cut q into n^2 congruent sub-squares $q_1, q_2, \ldots, q_{n^2}$.

By assumption, each of these sub-squares contains at least one open point set a_j that is a representative of a φ-measurable soma U_j.

The various somas $U_1, U_2, \ldots$ are pairwise disjoint, according to § 310, and so the relations

$$\sum_{j=1}^{n^2} \varphi(U_j) \leqq \varphi(A)$$

hold. Hence at least one of the various numbers $\varphi(U_j)$ must be less than or equal to the number $\varphi(A)/n^2$.

We deduce from this that every soma A for which $\varphi(A) < +\infty$ has φ-measurable subsomas of arbitrarily small measure.

We now consider a countable sequence of points $P_1', P_2', \ldots$ that are everywhere dense on the representative a of A. We write these points in the order

$$P_1', P_2', P_1', P_2', P_3', P_1', P_2', P_3', P_4', P_1', \ldots, \tag{312.2}$$

so that each point P_k' appears an infinite number of times in the sequence (312.2). We relabel the points of the sequence (312.2), writing in place of (312.2)

$$P_1, P_2, P_3, \ldots. \tag{312.3}$$

In other words, we mean to have

$$P_1' = P_1 = P_3 = P_6 = P_{10} = \ldots, \quad P_2' = P_2 = P_4 = P_7 \ldots, \quad \ldots$$

Next, we take each point P_j to be the center of a square q_j that is contained in a and has side of length less than or equal to $1/j$.

Now let ε be any positive number. In each square q_j we choose an open point set b_j that is a representative of a soma B_j for which

$$\varphi(B_j) \leqq \varepsilon/2^j. \tag{312.4}$$

The union b of all the point sets b_j represents a soma $B = \sum_j \dot{+} B_j$, by § 309, and by (312.4) we then have

$$\varphi(B) \leqq \sum_j \varphi(B_j) \leqq \varepsilon. \tag{312.5}$$

But now each point P in the interior of the point set a or on its boundary is, by construction, a point of accumulation of b; thus, the closures of these point sets satisfy $\bar{a} = \bar{b}$, and consequently, by the definition of our somas,

$$B = A. \tag{312.6}$$

Continuing, it follows from (312.5) that $\varphi(A) \leqq \varepsilon$, and since $\varepsilon > 0$ was chosen arbitrarily,

$$\varphi(A) = 0. \tag{312.7}$$

In conclusion, we have obtained the following result:

THEOREM 2: *There are complete rings $\mathfrak{A}$ of somas that have the following property: If $\varphi(X)$ is any measure function defined on $\mathfrak{A}$ and if A is a soma of $\mathfrak{A}$ for which*

$$0 < \varphi(A) < +\infty,$$

then there exist subsomas B of A such that they, and all their non-empty subsomas, are not φ-measurable.

EARLIER PUBLICATIONS BY CONSTANTIN CARATHÉODORY ON THE ALGEBRAIZATION OF MEASURE AND INTEGRAL

1. *Entwurf für eine Algebraisierung des Integralbegriffs,* S.-B. Math.-Nat. Kl. Bayer. Akad. Wiss., 1938, pp. 27-69.

2. *Bemerkungen zur Axiomatik der Somentheorie,* S.-B. Math.-Nat. Kl. Bayer. Akad. Wiss., 1938, pp. 175-183.

3. *Die Homomorphien von Somen und die Multiplikation von Inhaltsfunktionen,* Ann. Scuola Norm. Sup. Pisa (2), Vol. 8 (1939), pp. 105-130.

4. *Über die Differentiation von Massfunctionen,* Math. Z., Vol. 46 (1940), pp. 181-189.

5. *Bemerkungen zum Riesz-Fischerschen Satz und zur Ergodentheorie,* Abh. Math. Sem. Hansischen Universität, Vol. 14 (1941), pp. 351-389.

6. *Gepaarte Mengen, Verbände, Somenringe,* Math. Z., Vol. 48 (1942), pp. 4-26.

7. *Bemerkungen zum Ergodensatz von G. Birkhoff* S.-B. Math.-Nat. Kl. Bayer. Akad. Wiss., 1944, pp. 189-208.

LIST OF SYMBOLS

[*Selected list; In order of earliest occurrence*]

INDEX